Schizophrenia and the Family

Monograph Series on Schizophrenia No. 7

Schizophrenia and the Family

by Theodore Lidz, M.D., Stephen Fleck, M.D.,
and Alice R. Cornelison, M.S.S.

With the Collaboration of

Yrjö O. Alanen, M.D.
Dorothy Terry Carlson, Ph.D.
Dorothy D. Ciarlo, Ph.D.
Daniel X. Freedman, M.D.
Jules Holzberg, Ph.D.
Eleanor I. Kay, M.A.
Ruth W. Lidz, M.D.
Nea Norton, M.S.S.
Beulah Parker, M.D.
Judith L. Ricci, M.A.
Bernice L. Rosman, Ph.D.
Sarah Schafer, M.A.
Margaret T. Singer, Ph.D.
Ezra Vogel, Ph.D.
Cynthia Wild, Ph.D.

Department of Psychiatry
Yale University School of Medicine

INTERNATIONAL UNIVERSITIES PRESS, INC. • NEW YORK

To
Fredrick C. Redlich

Contents

PART III

Studies of Thought and Communication of Parents

Acknowledgments

We wish to thank the many persons who have helped carry out this lengthy investigation. Our collaborators are listed on the title page of the book and the participation of each in a specific aspect of the work is noted at the beginning of each chapter. The contributions of Dr. Beulah Parker who helped start the project and of Dr. Dorothy Terry Carlson and Mrs. Sarah Schafer who were members of the research team for many years extend beyond any specific chapters. The influence of our collaborator by correspondence, Dr. Margaret Thaler Singer, is apparent in several of the last chapters.

Members of the staff of the Yale Psychiatric Institute have aided our work by their cooperation, through reports provided, and by helping establish the therapeutic milieu which has been essential to the conduct of the investigation.

We are particularly grateful to Miss Hope Mag, Miss Doris Berndtson, Mrs. Catherine Molloy, and Mrs. Myrna Schwartz for patiently deciphering our handwritings, transcribing our voices, and for the many other secretarial tasks they have carried out.

Mrs. Harriette Borsuch is responsible for the preparation of the manuscript and the collation of the references. We are indebted to her not only for her careful work but also for many suggestions and corrections. We wish to express our appreciation for her devotion to the task.

The following publishers and journals permitted use of articles which were originally published by them, as noted in footnotes at the start of the chapters: American Journal of Psychiatry, American Journal of Orthopsychiatry, AMA Archives of Neurology and Psychiatry, Archives of General Psychiatry, Forest Hospital Publications, Grune & Stratton, Journal of the American Psychoanalytic

Association, Journal of Nervous and Mental Disease, Journal of Psychiatric Research, Mental Hygiene, and Psychiatry.

The investigations on which this volume is based were supported by grants from the National Institute of Mental Health, The Social Research Foundation, and the Supreme Council Thirty-Third Degree Masons, Northern Jurisdiction (Chapter I).

It follows from the nature of the facts which form the material of psycho-analysis that we are obliged to pay as much attention in our case histories to the purely human and social circumstances of our patients as to the somatic data and the symptoms of the disorder. Above all, our interest will be directed towards their family circumstances.

—FREUD (1905)

Introduction

Over the past twelve years we have been conducting an intensive study of the intrafamilial environment in which schizophrenic patients grew up. During this time we have written and usually published papers dealing with various aspects of the complex data in order to analyze the material and work through theoretical problems as well as to report our findings. Confronted by a wealth of pertinent data in an almost virgin field and lacking a conceptual framework for analyzing and describing the material, we found the discipline of condensing data and formulating hypotheses extremely useful. Now that the prolonged exploratory phase of the work has ended and it becomes possible to formulate and investigate testable hypotheses, we are publishing the significant papers in one volume. The collection contains several previously unpublished papers that round out the study.

For the most part, each paper deals with a particular aspect of the data isolated from the totality to permit scrutiny and presentation. A grasp of the interrelationships of the different segments of the picture is essential for an appreciation of the significance of these family situations as a whole and of their impacts upon the offspring who became schizophrenic. As the published papers appeared in various journals over a span of nine years, only those persons who have specifically sought them out have been able to survey and properly assess our findings. The collection offers the reader the opportunity to follow us on a quest which we—and others—have found absorbing; which has provided wealth of new insights; and which, we believe we may say, has done much to change the conceptualization of schizophrenia, its etiology, and the approaches to its treatment.

We had considered writing a book that offered a comprehensive and carefully organized expression of the end results of the study and our current views on each aspect of it. There are a number of reasons for not doing so. We have not reached closure concerning our findings and even less concerning theory. Although our formulations seem to us to gain in clarity and comprehensivity, some earlier formulations may turn out to have greater pertinence than certain current views. We wish to present what we have done and how we have thought about the data, and think that the articles contain more freshness and challenge than would a retrospective survey. We do not wish to serve up a warmed-over stew. Perhaps, even more important, writing—at least for us—consumes time and effort, and we are far from the end of the road, engaged in ongoing studies provoked by what we are herein reporting. Lastly, we are turning from the analysis of seventeen families that form the core material of our study to other related studies not because we have exhausted the data but because it has exhausted us, and it is time for us to be finished with it.

The theoretical considerations that entered into the study and which influenced our perception of the data are presented in a general way in the paper, "Schizophrenia and the Family" and are amplified and developed as pertinent in each paper, and cannot be presented more concisely in this introduction. A separate volume, *The Family and Human Adaptation* (Lidz, 1963a) contains some of the reappraisal of the functions and functioning of the family that has been essential to the comprehension of our findings. This introduction will present only the reasons for embarking on the investigation; the approach and methods used, in order to be able to delete the repetition of such statements from the individual papers; some comments upon the problems encountered in analyzing and assessing the data; and finally a few notes concerning the papers themselves.

At the outset, the investigators were venturing into an area that had remained virtually unexplored. Aside from two studies (Chapter I; Reichard and Tillman, 1950), interest in the family had been confined to genetic studies and to concerns with mothers and their personality characteristics or psychopathology. During the past decade the picture has changed profoundly. Largely due to these studies and those of Jackson and Bateson; Wynne, Bowen, and their coworkers, and colleagues in the United States; Y. O. Alanen in Finland; and

Delay, Deniker, and Green in France—but also with many others contributing—the importance of the family environment to the genesis of schizophrenia is now widely recognized, and in some settings even taken for granted. Concomitantly, recognition of the importance of the family as the primary social unit gave rise to conjoint family therapy, fostered notably by Ackerman (1958b) and the group in Palo Alto (Jackson, 1959) which has contributed to the understanding of family dynamics and communication. The publication of Parson and Bales's *Family, Socialization and Interaction Process* (1955) was of particular moment to us because its theory meshed with our findings and thinking and offered other useful guidelines. While much remains to be done in clarifying the intrafamilial factors in the etiology of schizophrenia, the extent and magnitude of the problems within these families have now been documented and the nature of the difficulties delineated.

ORIGINS OF STUDY

Observations concerning the peculiarities of the parents of psychotic patients are nothing new. Almost a hundred years ago both Griesinger and Ideler (Delay et al., 1957) had noted the frequency of eccentric and strange parental behavior and commented that aside from genetic influence, the environmental or educational influences of such parents upon their children must be taken into account. However, the dominant orientations concerning the etiology of schizophrenia directed attention away from the topic and the potential importance of the observations. Until Adolf Meyer (1906) who seriously suggested that schizophrenia could be a "habit deterioration" or a "reaction type," psychiatrists virtually without exception sought to follow the lead of the remainder of medicine in searching for a specific structural, infectious, or biochemical cause of schizophrenia —a trend fortified by the discovery of the cause of general paresis. This conviction was not even countered in any definitive manner by psychoanalysts who continued to believe in a toxic or genetic etiology of the condition. Dynamically oriented psychiatry—psychobiology as well as psychoanalysis—concentrated upon the development of the individual patient, and not upon the setting in which it occurred. Analysis directed attention to the earliest mother-child relationships following Abraham's (1908) concept that schizophrenia indicated a fixation and regression to the earliest oral phase, and also to the problem of unconscious homosexuality following Freud's (1911) analysis of the Schreber case but with the tacit implication that the homosexuality was a constitutional matter. In H. S. Sullivan's (1925-26) early writings an appreciation of the importance of the family configurations and interrelationships can be found.

Although our intensive investigation of the families of schizophrenic patients was started in 1952, one of us (T. L.) had begun studying the topic in 1940. As a resident in charge of Adolf Meyer's private male service, he had considerable contact with the relatives of the small number of patients on the unit. Still inexperienced, he did not yet know what was considered germane to the study and treatment of schizophrenic reactions. He became impressed by the personality problems of the immediate relatives of the schizophrenic patients and the extremely devastating family milieu in which these upper-class patients had been reared. Even without consideration of other factors such as genetics, metabolic disorder, brain anomaly, or, of chronic masturbation, homosexuality, etc., it seemed unlikely that these persons could have grown up without becoming seriously disturbed. The impression was heightened when the uncle of one youth declined the customary explanation that his nephew suffered from a condition of unknown origins; he had come to describe and explain why the boy was ill. He carefully depicted the serious and enduring conflict between the parents; the mother's depression and apathy following the patient's birth; her efforts to cling to this child to give some meaning to her unhappy marriage; the father's rigidities and paranoid sensitivities; the patient's feelings of being overwhelmed when his self-aggrandizing father failed in business, etc. Soon thereafter the sister of another patient spent many hours detailing how her brother had been expected to live up to the image of their father, a ruthless financier who presented a grandiose model, but at the same time had been sissified by a doting mother who sought to woo him from the father's influence and from developing into a callous person like her husband. The sister went on to explain how her childhood had been unhappy in this disturbed household, but she had not been burdened with the unrealistic expectations placed upon her brother, and as she had resented her mother's preference for her brother, she had been able to liberate herself from the family in adolescence. A paper describing the family settings of a small series of schizophrenic patients failed to elicit enthusiasm from his senior colleagues and remained unpublished because it was so removed from current concepts that the writer considered that he may have been concerned with a coincidence of unusual cases. However, to broaden the base and to learn whether such family situations might have pertinence to the etiology of schizophrenia, a more structured study was carried out with Dr. Ruth Lidz in 1941. The family histories in the charts of fifty consecutively admitted schizophrenic patients and fifty psychotically depressed patients were compared. The War and prolonged overseas service precluded completion of the analysis of the data, and the findings were not published until 1949. The paper, included as Chapter I of this volume, appears to be the first concerned with the total family setting: it drew attention to notable differences in the family backgrounds of the two groups of patients, and indicated that further attention to the area was warranted.

During the years between 1945 and 1950, the experiences of several psychiatrists in Baltimore with analytically oriented therapy of schizophrenic patients verified prior impressions, for all of these patients had disturbed parents and disorganizing family backgrounds. How such data became a central issue in treatment was indicated in a paper (Chapter II) which points out some of these implications of the mother's use of the child to complete her life and her inability to establish boundaries between herself and the child—a finding that had also been made by Reichard and Tillman (1950) in their highly significant paper on parent-child relationships in schizophrenia.

Now, other reasons also directed to a need to focus on the patient's early family environment. A series of studies[1] of patients with a wide variety of brain pathology and metabolic and toxic impairments of cerebral functioning had further demonstrated that the thought disorders of all such patients differed from those of schizo-

---

[1] Lidz (1939, 1942, 1949); Lidz, Carter, Lewis, and Surratt (1952); Lidz, Gay, and Tietze (1942); Lidz and Kahn (1946); Lidz, Miller, Padget, and Stedem (1949); Newell and Lidz (1946).

phrenic patients. Patients with known brain dysfunctions that affected their thinking suffered a degradation of intellectual potential. Both tests and psychotherapeutic work with schizophrenic patients indicated that they retained their intellectual potential but used it in distorted ways. As the child receives his basic training in the meaning of words and in ways of communicating, reasoning, and thinking within his family of origin, it seemed reasonable to believe that a study of the intrafamilial influences upon the child's development might provide a useful approach to the problem of schizophrenic thinking.

Further, the individual's reactions in all subsequent group and interpersonal situations rest upon the foundations provided within the family. Yet the family has its own needs, which may take precedence over its educational functions. It may be deviant from the remainder of society, set mutually exclusive demands upon the child, provide inconsistent emotional experiences, teach paralogical ways, and in many other areas provide faulty schooling. Although the family is not the only influence upon the developing ego, it provides the most consistent or consistently inconsistent set of influences impinging upon the child. It seemed imperative to scrutinize the family milieu for determinants of schizophrenic reactions, but an investigation of the influence of the family and its members upon the emergent generation presented very grave methodological and conceptual difficulties. Neither suitable techniques nor an adequate conceptual framework for a dynamic study of family transactions existed. Preliminary studies indicated the need to examine the entire family situation rather than some segment of it. The father appeared to be seriously disturbed just as often as the mother, and the vicissitudes of the family life as a whole appeared of potential importance. The basis for the belief that schizophrenia is determined by events in the early, oral phase of development is purely hypothetical, unsupported by evidence that the earliest mother-child relationships are more deleterious than those of certain other psychiatric patients. The cardinal symptomatology of schizophrenia would seem to indicate that later developmental periods also have critical significance. The symbolic distortions, the interpenetration of reality by fantasy, the confusion of sexual identity, the concerns over incestuous impulses, the attribution of omniscience and omnipotence to parental figures are all significant problems of the early oedipal or late preoedipal phases of development. Although it may be considered that disturbances in the oral phase are essential to the development of schizophrenia, they may only establish a potential for mental illness, whereas subsequent events may determine the degree and form of the individual's adjustment or maladjustment.

After lengthy consideration it became evident that circumscribed testable hypotheses could not be formulated until clearer ideas emerged concerning just what within these families might have particular significance to the etiology of schizophrenia. A careful examination of the family environments in a search for something within this sphere that might contribute to knowledge of the nature and origins of schizophrenia seemed an essential initial step. We decided not to be deterred because we could not conduct a methodologically rigorous investigation, but to carry out the necessary exploratory work. We have, therefore, conducted a study that is basically an exploration; and, by analogy, an exploration that seeks to describe and map unknown terrain, for such measures must precede efforts to compare the region with other areas.

Methods of Study

The approach adopted, despite its obvious shortcomings, was the intensive exploration of what had transpired within the family from its inception through the time of study. The core material was obtained from the long-term study of the families of patients who were hospitalized in the Yale Psychiatric Institute. This institute is a forty-four bed private university hospital in which seriously ill psychiatric patients are treated with individual analytically oriented therapy and group therapy, and in which the hospital milieu and patient-staff transactions are considered essential elements in treatment (Fleck, 1962). The Institute was in the process of being transformed into a place particularly suited to the therapy of schizophrenic reactions and other serious personality disorders of adolescents and young adults. Only families of unmarried patients between the ages of fifteen and thirty were included in the study as the parents and other members of the family had to be available. The diagnosis had to be clear-cut and beyond reasonable dispute. The series contains no cases of "borderline" or "pseudoneurotic" schizophrenia. The only other criteria for inclusion in the series were the presence and availability for study of the mother and at least one sibling. Direct study of the mother seemed essential because of the crucial position she fills in child rearing as well as because of studies and theories that indicated her potential import in the etiology of schizophrenia. A sibling was needed both to provide information about the family from the view of a member of the childhood generation, and also to provide a type of inner control through study of a person reared within the family who had not become schizophrenic. Because of the frequency with which families of schizophrenic patients are broken by the death or mental hospitalization of one parent, or by separation, the availability of both parents was not established as a requirement. However, only three of the seventeen families were broken, two by death and one by divorce, and in all but two of the cases, the fathers were available and participated in the study. Toward the end of the inclusion of cases into the series, we asked colleagues to refer patients from families which they considered to be reasonably stable and well integrated. We hoped that such families with less diffuse family pathology might provide better leads to factors that might have specific relevance to schizophrenia. However, the several families included with this criterion turned out to be just as disturbed as the remainder. Seventeen families were studied—nine of male and eight of female patients. An additional three originally included were discarded because the patients were withdrawn from the hospital within the first two months. Fourteen families were upper- or upper-middle class and capable of supporting a member in a private hospital for a prolonged period and three families were emerging from lower-middle class status. The sample had a decided bias toward intact families with status and even prestige in their communities. The bias was desired to safeguard against inadvertent inclusion of families because of their disorganization or partial dissolution, and to lessen the complexities created by economic distress and disturbed extrafamilial social environments. However, as the studies of Hollingshead and Redlich (1958) have shown, generalizations from one social class to another can be made only with great care and reservation. Indeed, we know that the families in this series are more intact than families of schizophrenic offspring in general. The incidence of homes broken before the patient's nineteenth birthday in our series is 18 per cent, about the incidence in the general population, whereas several studies have shown that about 40 per cent of families of schizophrenic patients are broken by this time (Chapter I; Oltman et al., 1952; Wahl, 1954). The study of Delay et al. (1957, 1960, 1962) which dealt with French families of lower socioeconomic levels reports even more blatant family pathology than our study.

Multiple techniques were utilized in an attempt to re-create the personalities of the family members, their interactions, the family patterns and the atmosphere. The primary source of data was gained from repeated interviews with all members of each family by the social worker and the psychiatrists. In some families, one member—usually the mother or father—was the most important source of information and was interviewed weekly for many months or even for several years. The other relatives were seen less often or only sporadically; but in some families all members were seen repeatedly. At times, a sibling, particularly one who had been in psychotherapy because of his own difficulties, was a major source of information concerning the family transactions. The social worker saw all members of all families, and thus served as one fixed point in comparing the families and their members. One of the two psychiatrists also saw almost all of the members of the families on at least one occasion to permit some check upon the social worker's impression, and usually one of the psychiatrists saw one or more members of each family on a number of occasions. In some families when it seemed unwise for the social worker to follow both parents, or when some special difficulty interfered, one of the psychiatrists saw a parent regularly. In some instances the social work and investigative relationship turned into a therapeutic relationship because of the intense need. Aside from two of the first families who were followed and studied for less than six months, all families were studied for at least one year and some for five years or longer. Whenever possible, less immediate relatives, old family friends, nursemaids, and former teachers of the patient were also interviewed. Home visits were made, in some cases on a number of occasions. Diaries kept by mothers, photograph albums and family movies, and various childhood productions of the patients were examined.

The utilization of such extensive contacts with the family for gathering material needed for the research presented problems that required study. Some of these considerations are discussed in the chapter, "Casework Interviewing as a Research Technique." Obviously, potential prejudices of an interviewer or other members of the research group concerning a family member had to be noted and discounted when they could not be overcome. The psychiatric social worker became an object of investigation, and her reactions to people, her likes and dislikes and her prejudices were a constant topic of discussion and study in order to keep these variables controlled as far as possible.

The interaction of family members with one another as well as with the members of the research team and hospital staff was observed under a variety of conditions. During the lengthy period of study special circumstances usually occurred that permitted observation of these persons under new types of stress; sometimes there were marked changes in the family circumstances, and we could observe how the various persons in the family reacted under such conditions. Toward the end of the study, greater emphasis was placed upon observing the family interacting as a group, particularly during recorded conjoint family sessions.

A battery of projective tests (Rorschach, TAT, Figure Drawing, and Sentence Completion) was administered to all family members whenever possible, aside from the first four families studied. The tests helped gain understanding of the patients and the members of their families, checking impressions gained through interviews and other contacts, and offering potential new insights. Initially, a major purpose of the testing was to seek out patterns and styles common to family members, to learn whether aspects of a child's identification with a parent could be noted in the tests, and to examine relationships of the styles of approach, perception, and thinking in parents and children. These were new uses for projective techniques which presented problems of such magnitude that they were of limited value. However, after Margaret Thaler Singer started analyzing the protocols as a consultant and in conjunction with similar work she was carrying out with Wynne (Wynne and Singer, 1963a, 1963b), new potentialities opened. Working blindly with coded material, she successfully matched the protocols of six male patients to those of their parents without error, and then did the same with four female patients. In some instances, Dr. Singer constructed descriptions of the patient's personality and problems solely from the parents' test protocols with an accuracy and breadth akin to that obtained from patient test protocols. These results together with related work at the National Institute of Mental Health led to a new series of explorations of relationships between parental styles of thinking and the offspring's thought disorder, which are still in progress both at the National Institute of Mental Health and at Yale. Dr. Singer's test analyses have been utilized primarily in the papers on the siblings and the mothers (Chapters XIV and XVII).

The material gained from family members and other sources was augmented by careful use of data emerging during the patient's therapy. However, no data offered by any person were by themselves taken as factual, but instead were evaluated in the light of total information. Efforts were made to continue gathering material until the various versions and opinions interdigitated adequately. Divergent views were, of course, in themselves a type of factual data that could be extremely pertinent.

The interviews, particularly after the initial sessions with each individual, were "open ended." They were not recorded, but the interviewer dictated lengthy notes concerning the material and her impressions of the subject immediately after the interview. The story of the family, the relationships between members, and the feelings of each member to all other members, etc., were gradually filled in by placing questions as opportunities arose. Gradually the different views and opinions of the various informants began to fit together, and the discrepancies became understandable in terms of personality differences, defenses, and divergent ways of viewing the world, etc. It is particularly important to note that little reliance could be placed in material obtained during the first interviews or even during the first months. The information often changed very appreciably as the informant gained confidence in the interviewer and the hospital, and as guilt feelings and initial anxieties diminished. The collection of data could not be pushed and hastened. At first it was discouraging when material emerged after months or even after a year or longer that completely altered the understanding of the family history and situation. Although one can gain an impression of a family from a few interviews, it was the experience of our group, probably as skilled as most investigative teams, that we arrived at some very erroneous concepts unless the work continued for many months.

Any such procedure for studying the family has shortcomings. Any attempt to reconstruct the life of a family over a period of fifteen to thirty years must contain limitations. Even though we collected far more extensive material than we had originally intended, important data concerning some of the families eluded our efforts—particularly as we sought to base our study upon reasonably ascertained data with minimal theoretical interpolations. Nevertheless, it is highly likely that the studies of these seventeen families contain the most complete, dynamically comprehensive, and personally meaningful material ever gathered about any series of families for any purpose.

The extensive material concerning each family was condensed into comprehensive summaries of the history of the family, the life and personality of each member, the interrelationships and transactions among members, the organization and atmosphere of the family as a unit; its relationships to the parental families and to the community, etc. An effort was made to include each member's views on the interrelationships among family members. As the study progressed, an increasing amount of material concerning the grandparents and even earlier generations was obtained.

The study of the seventeen families forms the core of the project, and the papers in the second part of this volume are derived from the study of these families. We avoided embellishment by illustrations drawn from other experiences, unless specifically stated, lest we slant or accentuate certain trends. However, other experiences entered into our thinking. During the project over 200 other schizophrenic patients were treated in the Yale Psychiatric Institute under the supervision of the project psychiatrists, and social work with families and group therapy with parents of patients became increasingly comprehensive. The psychiatrists were also conducting analytic psychotherapy of schizophrenic patients and with some siblings of schizophrenic patients. The material gained from these sources was confirmatory of the findings of the core study.

We have been chided for not reporting a study of a control series of families. We must hope that the reader realizes that we are as aware of the shortcoming as he is. However, a study of a real control series rather than carrying out a pretense for the sake of scientific respectability presented problems which we could not surmount. The term "control" series is in itself incorrect, but we could use a "comparative" series. Yet, the use of a series of families without emotionally disturbed offspring would serve little. It is apparent from general psychiatric experience that the families of schizophrenic patients differ in many ways from the families of mild neurotic or relatively normal persons. But which of the differences would be significant to the problem? Perhaps even more pertinently, individuals and families must be strongly motivated to work as long and intensively as did the patients' relatives, and to be willing to seek after material they have sought to conceal from themselves as well as from others. A primary motivation was the furtherance of the treatment of a family member, and other motives were such personal matters as wishing help with their own problems, justifying the self while condemning a hostile spouse, etc. A comparable study of a comparative series requires that the situations in which the families find themselves are reasonably similar.

We have conducted an intensive study of a series of ten families with a sociopathic offspring. We had decided after considerable scrutiny of the problems that these families were in situations closely analogous to the families in our original series and presumably had similar motivation to cooperate and concerns about a hospitalized offspring. A series of upper- and upper-middle-class delinquents were admitted to the Yale Psychiatric Institute for this purpose. We had intended to delay publishing this volume until we could compare the families of the two series. However, a variety of problems has made this impractical if not impossible. The families were not altogether comparable. We could not collect a series of families of delinquents and eliminate adopted children or parents with multiple marriages—neither of which occur in our schizophrenic series. The symptomatic differences between male and female delinquents are more striking than between male and female schizophrenics as the young male delinquents are in trouble for stealing, aggressive and hostile behavior, etc., whereas the females are almost all sexually delinquent. We were unable to retain many of the delinquents in the hospital for a year or longer. Parents tended not to be as cooperative, an important difference in motivation, but an uncontrollable variable. These are salient findings—or may be—but they make comparisons difficult. The main problem, however, was that the study and understanding of the families of delinquents is as arduous and complex as the study of the schizophrenic families which has taken over a decade. The matter is so complex that we decided that we must finish the work with the schizophrenic families before we could concentrate sufficient attention and energy on the delinquent families. We hope that at some future but still far from proximate date, we shall compare the two series. At present, we can state only that despite some resemblances, we have strong indications that there are profound differences between these types of families—though obviously overlap occurs—an impression also held by Morris and Wynne (1965) who believe they can differentiate these types of families by the analysis of samplings of conjoint family therapy sessions. Though differentiating families of schizophrenic patients from those of sociopathic subjects would mark a major advance in psychopathology, it is not the same as defining what is critical to the genesis of schizophrenia, but simply an assurance that our study findings are not dealing with factors common to families which give rise to offspring with a variety of emotional disturbances.

Alanen and his coworkers (personal communication, 1964) have compared the family environments in which a series of schizophrenic and neurotic patients grew up. The preliminary reports indicate very marked differences and in general substantiate our findings concerning schizophrenic patients.

The project plan provided for one type of control—the comparison of the influences impinging upon the patient with those affecting one or more siblings. Whereas such comparisons do not illuminate differences between families, they can help clarify what factors within a family are critical. The results of the comparisons will be found in the chapter, "Schizophrenic Patients and Their Siblings." Among other findings, the study emphasized the differential effects of family configurations upon male and female offspring and the need to differentiate between the family situations of male and female patients.

PROBLEMS OF ANALYSIS

The study of seventeen families did not require a dozen years. The understanding of the accumulated data has taken time, study, and re-evaluation of our psychoanalytically oriented concepts of personality development. In particular, we have had to broaden our perspectives concerning the family's influence upon the emergent personalities of its children. Psychiatric theory had been suited to the study of the individual and his intrapsychic problems, or to the interpersonal transactions between two individuals. An approach to the understanding of the dynamics of the family group did not exist in psychiatry, and sociological studies of the family were rarely suited to furthering the understanding of the individual. We have sought conceptualizations that permitted presentation and analysis of the findings: the papers in this volume indicate the searching.

Initially, we hoped that we might find some elements or factors within the family that led to schizophrenic development of an offspring. A plethora rather than a paucity of findings of potential significance created the problem. In each aspect of the family life which we examined something was seriously amiss. The parental personalities, the parents' marital interaction, the relationship of each parent to the child, the verbal and nonverbal communication within the family, the essential adherence to parental and childhood generation tasks and roles, the structure of the family as a unit, the parents' gender-linked roles, the transmission of the culture's techniques of adaptation, the relatedness of the family to the community: these and other facets were all seriously disturbed in our judgment—and various authorities who examined the protocols agreed. Further, it was not a matter of statistics, that is to say, finding that more families were disturbed in each area we examined than were not, but rather that each of the families was disturbed in virtually all of these respects—some more and some less in various areas. We examined the material in a variety of ways and sought to isolate core problems.

Now, it is evident that the various factors we studied are inter-related. We examined the individuals, the dyadic relationships, the group transactions. Rightly or wrongly, we eventually ceased looking for a specific etiological factor or factors, and instead asked what must a family provide to assure the integrated development of an offspring. As schizophrenia, no matter what else may be involved, is a gross failure to achieve or maintain a workable personality integration or ego integration, the question we asked seemed worth asking. When we reached an answer—in so far as one was achieved—we found in a somewhat circular fashion that these families did not provide the requisites.

Our findings led increasingly to a new appreciation of the extent to which the family shapes the personalities of its children and the inordinate complexity of the process by which it does. The family's influence upon the child cannot be considered in terms of maternal love or nurturance, nor through the transfer of a parent's superego to the child, nor the relationship of one or even both parents to the child, nor any other such single factor, even though it alone may be difficult enough to study. These and other elements are in themselves, of course, vitally important but insufficient. The family is a social system and its structure is also important; and it is a subsystem of the larger society holding the responsibility—albeit often unwittingly—for the enculturation or socialization of the new generation. But it has other functions both for parents and the society which influences how the family rears its offspring, and which must also be taken into account (Lidz, 1963a).

Once the question is asked, "What is the family's role in human adaptation and integration?" a new phase of investigation of person-ality development and maldevelopment opens. It is a phenomenon that is apt to occur whenever something that is so omnipresent that it is taken for granted is questioned and subjected to scientific scru-tiny. New doors open and significant questions rush in. Although the topic is considered in many of these papers, and more globally in the book *The Family and Human Adaptation* (Lidz, 1963a), little more than a start has been made. The role of the family in personality development requires, and is first beginning to receive, the intensity of scrutiny such as has been given to the unfolding of the embryo, to the directives that provide for the proper sequence of its nurturance, and to how its environment influences it.

Although the study of the role of the family in the etiology of schizophrenia requires such extensive and detailed knowledge of the functions of the family and of family functioning, the attainment of this knowledge is clearly beyond our capacities. It must await the combined and lengthy studies of many future investigators. Such ignorance has set limits upon our study, but the study has served to focus the spotlight upon this ignorance.

The papers present evidence of our changing, expanding concepts of the family, but also a final consolidation and new simplification in the last chapters written—"The Mothers of Schizophrenic Patients" and "Family Studies and a Theory of Schizophrenia." Herein we focus upon three general areas in assessing the family's influence upon a child. (1) The parental nurturance and how it alters to provide for the changing needs and capacities of the child as he matures, and how the parental nurturance influences the offspring's achievement of autonomy. (2) The family structure and how it influences the structuring of the personality of the child by channeling drives, providing relatively conflict-free areas and roles within the family into which the child can develop and motivating him to do so. We consider the family structure in terms of the parental coalition, the boundaries between the generations, and the parents' maintenance of their gender-linked roles. (3) The transmission of the basic instrumentalities of the culture, including social roles and societal institutions, but particularly a foundation in the society's system of linguistic meanings that the child requires for learning, collaborative interaction and thinking and without which no real ego functioning is possible. We wish, however, to state clearly that these constructs are tentative and not fully satisfactory. We simply consider them an advance, for they provide a means of making more comprehensive analyses of a family's influences upon its offspring, and form a basis for making comparisons between families. They permit us to formulate testable hypotheses, and with the achievement of such hypotheses, the exploratory phase of our investigations comes to a close.

ORGANIZATION OF BOOK

Lastly, we add a few paragraphs about the order of presentation of the articles. The book is divided into three sections. The second section forms the core presenting the material from the intensive study of seventeen families with schizophrenic offspring.

The first section consists of two papers by R. and T. Lidz that formed something of a prologue to the family project. The first chapter constituted the initial attempt to assess the importance of the intrafamilial environment in the etiology of schizophrenia. The second chapter, which is concerned with therapy, is not strictly germane to this book; but it is included because its orientation concerning the mothers of patients and the etiology of schizophrenia was an implicit part of our thinking at the start of the project.

The eighteen studies in the second section are arranged in the order in which they were written, with two exceptions. The dates under the chapter headings indicate the year of composition whereas the date of publication is in the footnote. "Schizophrenia and the Family" has been moved forward to serve as an introduction through presenting some essentials of our theoretical orientation which are elaborated in subsequent chapters. "The Relevance of Family Studies to Psychoanalytic Theory" has been moved backwards as it does not report data but is concerned only with theoretic considerations. Although other arrangements of the chapters might seem more appropriate upon casual inspection, such as following the material concerning the fathers with the chapter on mothers and then the chapter on siblings, the orientation of these chapters is very different. We could not have written the chapter on the mothers in its present form during the first years of the study. Placing the chapters in a temporal sequence seems necessary because our ways of viewing the material and thinking about it have altered markedly over the years.

The chapters which we consider crucial for providing an adequate impression of these families and the nature of our study of them are: Chapter III, "Schizophrenia and the Family"; Chapter V, "The Fathers"; Chapter VII, "Marital Schism and Marital Skew"; Chapter X, "The Transmission of Irrationality"; Chapter XIV, "Schizophrenic Patients and Their Siblings"; Chapter XVII, "The Mothers of Schizophrenic Patients"; Chapter XVIII, "The Limitations of Extrafamilial

Socialization"; Chapter XX, "Family Studies and a Theory of Schizophrenia." However, the other chapters also supply important data and concepts.

The third section is an outgrowth of the chapter, "The Transmission of Irrationality" and is composed of carefully controlled studies testing the hypothesis that the parents of schizophrenic patients suffer from disturbances in thinking and communicating. An attempt to replicate a study of McConaghy's because of its surprising findings was undertaken lightly, but took over three years to complete because of problems of scoring and in properly controlling the various paramaters involved. These studies also constitute the first steps in a search for a means of screening out from the general population families with a high risk of producing a schizophrenic offspring. The achievement of such screening methods, which now seems attainable, would both permit longitudinal studies of families prior to the onset of schizophrenia and also ultimately open the way for more definitive and focused preventive measures. The series of papers "Thought Disorder and Family Relations of Schizophrenics" by Wynne and Singer (1963a, 1963b; Singer and Wynne, 1965a, 1965b) are concerned with related studies pursuing similar objectives through the use of different techniques. The benefits of collaboration are apparent in the second chapter of this section, and we trust will become even more evident in future publications.

The final chapter in the book is a brief exposition on some theoretic and therapeutic implications of our findings particularly for the direction of future investigations.

PART I

Antecedent Studies

I

The Family Environment of Schizophrenic Patients

(1942)

It was noted during the treatment of a small series of schizophrenic patients that they had frequently been deprived of at least one parental figure early in life; and also that the parental home was usually markedly unstable, torn by family schisms and constant emotional turmoil, and frequently patterned according to the whims of grossly eccentric and abnormal personalities. This study, a survey of fifty case histories in the records of the Henry Phipps Psychiatric Clinic, was then undertaken to evaluate the frequency with which broken homes or seriously disturbed family environments had been noted in those histories of schizophrenic patients.

The influence of the total family life upon schizophrenic patients has been considered in at least two books. Terry and Rennie (1938) emphasized the role of the family along with other features in the developmental process. They noted that difficulties between parents or the deprivation of a parent seemed to contribute to the insecurity of the children, and that a large number of patients in their study had been in daily contact with psychotic, eccentric, or unstable parents. They stated, "It is impossible to study this material without being impressed by the importance of the family constellations and of the effect of the maladjustments within the family in contributing to the growing timidities and insecurity of the children." Pollock, Malzburg, and Fuller (1939) in their statistical search for hereditary or environmental factors in the causation of dementia praecox and manic-

Ruth Wilmanns Lidz and Theodore Lidz: The Family Environment of Schizophrenic Patients. American Journal of Psychiatry, *Vol. 106, 1949, pp. 332-345.* Copyright © 1949, American Psychiatric Association.

depressive psychoses found, among the most striking contrasts between the two groups, "that the social life of the parents [of schizophrenic patients] was singularly restricted during the childhood of the patients; [and] that there was a certain instability of the home indicated by the absence of one or both parents during the formative years."

The early family environment is commonly accepted as a critical force in personality development both normal and abnormal. Numerous other factors, some of which may be of shattering intensity, may disturb the process of personality development, but few can be as long-lasting and as pervasive as the intrafamilial relationships. Here the basic attitudes toward later interpersonal relationships are established: the formation of the projective systems by which the individual perceives the world is begun. It was considered probable, on the basis of preliminary impressions, that there might be, in general, a relationship between the severity of the personality maladjustment and the degree of the family maladjustment, and that schizophrenic patients would be found to have emerged from early family environments that were very seriously disturbed.

The material in this survey was not expected to yield detailed information with which one could trace in detail how the dynamics of the family configuration influenced the patient's personality development because these case records were compiled by different psychiatrists with differing interests. It had the advantage of being material gathered prior to the investigation, free from the bias of the investigators. As the case histories in the Henry Phipps Psychiatric Clinic usually contain reasonably detailed information concerning the parental home, most offer sufficient data to permit judgment as to the character of the family setting. This study was undertaken as a gross survey of the topic to check preliminary impressions.

METHODOLOGY

The case records of fifty schizophrenic patients, in whom the psychosis had become manifest prior to the age of twenty-one, consecutively admitted the clinic, were utilized for the study. The series was limited to patients who were youthful at the time of onset of the psychosis because their case records contained more information concerning the family environment than did records of older patients. The age limit of twenty-one was arbitrarily adopted to eliminate the necessity of further selection of records. No record was discarded other than those of a few patients who left the clinic within a few days of admission and before the admission work-up could be completed.

The fifty cases included twenty-seven males and twenty-three females. Subdivision of the data by sex did not reveal any significant or constant differences. No subclassification of schizophrenia has been made for a variety of reasons, but primarily because little value is placed upon such differentiation, particularly in youthful patients.

The case records were sifted for all information pertinent to the background afforded the patient by the family. Charts were constructed (see Chart 1) which permitted a rapid survey of the significant factors in each case, and statistical data were compiled. The topics selected for tabulation were limited to influences which seemed significant and which, when placed in apposition, would afford an impression of the background furnished by the home. Only such material as could be estimated with a fair degree of reliability was utilized. Therefore, attention was focused upon objective situations in the background of the patient rather than upon the personal reactions to situations; and single traumatic incidents as well as minor disturbances in the family life were disregarded even though they may have exercised considerable influence upon the patient's development. In particular, the obsessive, oversolicitous patterns of mothers were not taken into special consideration unless the mother's behavior reached bizarre extremes.

The division of the material into headings is obviously arbitrary, and data could often have been placed in a different column equally well. For example, instabilities of parents may be most clearly manifest in peculiar ways of raising a child, or in marital incompatibility due to peculiar choice of a mate, or in the reactive behavior of the marital partner. The loss of a parent may be due to emotional instability (suicide or divorce) but may have the serious result of changing the mode of raising of the patient. However, it is believed that the headings will serve to indicate the presence of one or several chronic conditions which adversely affected the patient. The headings utilized are as follows:

1. *Deprivation of a Parent* prior to the nineteenth birthday. The arbitrary age limit was selected as an age at which most children have gained a reasonable degree of independence from the parents. The frequency of the loss of a parent had been apparent from a preliminary survey of the material.

2. *Chronic Instability of a Parent or Foster Parent.*—Occasional and lesser neurotic disturbances and mild to moderate alcoholism have largely been disregarded, and only serious and long-standing personality disorders which clearly affected other members of the family are included.

3. *Chronic Hostility or Serious Friction Between Parents.*—The more usual degrees of friction between married couples have been overlooked in favor of estimating the general compatibility of the parents.

4. *Serious Deviations from Cultural Norms in Child Rearing.*—The topic is closely related to the stability of the parents, particularly the mother, but in some cases the eccentric methods of raising the patient were most clear-cut, and in other cases unusual circumstances led to unusual means of raising the patient. The topic deals only with clear-cut deviations from the social norm or eccentricities, such as treating a boy as a girl; extreme forms of obsessive oversolicitude or rejection; inculcation of repugnance to any contact with the opposite sex, etc. While deviations of early habit training and various more subtle influences of parents are considered of great significance, they could rarely be assayed from the case histories and are not considered in the charts.

5. *Mental Illness in the Family Tree.*—While not a real concern of this study, the data are included both to permit a general impression of the stability of the families and to allow comparison with environmental data. The information is considered reasonably accurate as one or more relatives were always questioned concerning mental illness in the family.

All patients included in the study were manifestly psychotic prior to the age of twenty-one. The ages given in the charts are the ages at the time of admission to the clinic, rather than an attempt to estimate the precise time of onset of the psychosis, which is often difficult in youthful schizophrenic patients.

The sequence in which the cases are listed in Chart 1 follows a general pattern though a precise arrangement is not possible because of the overlapping of the variables involved:

1. Patients who had been deprived of a parent by death (cases 1-14) starting with the six who also had a psychotic parent.

2. Patients whose parents had been divorced or separated (cases 15-20).

3. Patients whose parents had been seriously incompatible (cases 21-27).

4. Patients whose homes were marred by fairly serious incompatibility, an unfriendly atmosphere, or unusual modes of raising the patient (cases 28-35).

5. Patients not previously listed who had a psychotic parent (cases 36-38).

6. Cases in which insufficient information for a sound evaluation of the home situation could be gained from the histories (cases 39-45) including three in which there was fairly good evidence that the home was unfavorable to normal development (cases 39-41).

7. Cases whose family environment, despite some aberrations of parents or marital difficulties, appears from the records to have been adequate or good (cases 46-50).

ILLUSTRATIVE CASE ABSTRACTS

To enable the reader to judge how the material was evaluated and also to grasp how the various chronic disturbances in the family life impeded the maturation of the patient, the environments afforded by the families of ten patients are presented in brief form.[1] These ten abstracts are unselected, though not including any of the six cases in which insufficient data were available to form evaluations. Two of the ten are examples of relatively satisfactory homes. Although selected at random, the ten cases are typical of the fifty, though not including some in which the family environment seemed most disorganized.

---

[1] Three case abstracts presented here were not included in the original publication.

CASE 1.   W. O. is a nineteen-year-old girl, the second of four siblings whose father suicided when she was fifteen. The mother had suffered a "nervous breakdown" after bearing the oldest child and had continued to worry and be obsessively apprehensive, particularly concerning her daughters, whom she had made excessively dependent upon her. The sisters aged twenty-three and thirteen, and the brother aged eighteen, are reputedly stable.

The family was well to do and the home life relatively congenial until the patient was ten. The children were educated in fashionable private schools and became accustomed to luxury. Then the father lost his money and became depressed, sullen, and alcoholic. His repeated ventures to start anew failed. The home became gloomy, filled wih recrimination, and disturbed by the father's habitual drunkenness. The children shifted to public schools and later took stenographic positions.

When fifteen years old, the patient became severely upset when, alone in the house, she found her father's body. Little is known of the subsequent family life. The children were tied to the mother who impressed the psychiatrists as a silly, ineffectual person.

Comment.—The father ceased to be an effective parent five years before his suicide, leaving the burden of the family to the ineffectual, obsessive mother. The home was morbid during the patient's adolescence.

CASE 8.   B. R. is a nineteen-year-old youth, handicapped by a high degree of bilateral deafness, whose father died when he was four. The vigorous mother sought to dominate the lives of the children of whom she was very demanding. A sister, aged twenty-five, had married and left home as soon as possible. The brother, aged twenty-two, openly revolted and secretly married at nineteen, but the mother had the marriage annulled.

The father had been a successful attorney, but the modest income he left dwindled with the years. The older children were educated mainly in private schools, whereas the patient had to walk four miles to high school to save carfare. Money was a prime concern and a source of constant discord. The brother openly expressed hope that the mother would die and leave him his inheritance. He constantly demanded money to entertain his fiancée, and when refused, stole articles from the home and pawned them. The brother was antagonistic to the patient, stressing his faults to gain preference with the mother. The home was frequently in turmoil with open conflict and physical strife between the brothers. The mother drew the handicapped patient to her, confiding her unhappiness to him, but gave him little in the face of the brother's demands. B. R. became dependent upon his mother because of his deafness but deeply resented her domination. He tried to mimic his brother's rebelliousness by running around with girls whom his mother disliked. His attempts were half-hearted and he accepted his mother's expectation that he would support her after completing school. Deafness made it difficult to secure a position. He suffered serious guilt over his ambivalence toward his mother.

Comment.—The father's guidance ceased at an early age. The handicapped patient became extremely dependent upon his demanding mother whose domination he resented. He became guilty when unable and rather unwilling to live up to the demands placed upon him. As the youngest he felt most heavily the burden imposed by the diminishing income and the increasingly unpleasant atmosphere.

CASE 9.   F. A. is a twenty-year-old youth whose mother died when he was a year old. The patient and his six-year-old sister were taken and raised by a paternal aunt, while a three-year-old brother remained with the father. F. A. rarely ever saw his father and brother, and little of the sister after he was twelve. When his aunt died when he was thirteen, he refused to join his father who had by then married an ill-tempered woman. Instead he went to a boarding school where another maiden aunt was employed, partially supporting himself by working after school. At sixteen he was sent to a more exclusive school which his father and brother had attended. Both aunts had "spoiled" him, expecting and demanding little, catering to his desires. An attack of rheumatic fever at eight had confined him to bed for six months and thereafter prevented athletic activities. When F. A. first spent several months with the father when sixteen, he was openly hostile. He felt upon realistic grounds that his father had discriminated against him in favor of his brother, withholding similar advantages. Both the sister and brother emphasized the difference in upbringing, believing that the patient, raised by maiden aunts, was not as capable as they in combating obstacles and stating that the father had obviously rejected the patient.

Comment.—Paternal guidance was singularly lacking even though it was the mother who had died. The home life afforded by the foster parent was disrupted by her death when the patient was adolescent. The father's rejection engendered serious hostility.

CASE 10.   C. H. is an eighteen-year-old youth whose life and environment differed markedly from those of his siblings because of his severe asthma. Little is recorded concerning the home life, probably because the patient spent little time there. When C. H. was eight the family moved to the country because of the father's tuberculosis but as the climate appeared to aggravate the patient's asthma, he was sent to boarding school. Thereafter the patient was rarely at home, even during summer vacations. The father, who died when the patient was thirteen, came from a prominent family and had been a successful engineer. He was a very rigid man, incapable of compromise, who expected everyone to do precisely what was right. The mother had been a trained nurse. She tended to be oversolicitous and, even though the patient was away from home, he depended upon her for affection and help. The family, proud of its ancestors, expected the patient as the only male descendant to preserve the tradition of achievement. C. H. expected to become a famous statesman but blamed his lack of scholastic prowess upon his asthma. His limited intellectual endowment was apparent to his teachers, who finally advised that he abandon hope of a college education.

Comment.—There was little home life for this patient after the age of eight, and the father died when he was thirteen. High rigid standards were established but little guidance given. The high expectations of the family were not tempered by recognition of his intellectual limitation and physical handicap.

CASE 20.   M. A. is a sixteen-year-old youth whose conception forced the parents to marry. Both parents had immigrated from Germany during adolescence. They separated shortly after the patient's birth, reunited after a year, but there were several subsequent separations. There was little pretense of family life and no companionship between the parents, who both stated that they remained together only for the sake of the son. The father consorted regularly with prostitutes with the wife's knowledge. He is a milkman who provided for the patient financially but never showed any interest in him. The mother, a waitress in an ice cream parlor, is considered a shallow, flighty person who tried to do her best but had no understanding of her brilliant, scholarly son.

Comment.—No information was obtained from the catatonic patient during the brief hospital stay. It is evident that the patient had a father in name only, and very little home life.

CASE 21.   B. I., a fourteen-year-old Jewish boy, had a sister six years his junior. Both parents were raised and educated in Russia. They led an active social life until they married, bought a grocery store, and isolated themselves from outside companionship. The patient was born the following year and then, according to the family physician, "they concentrated all their efforts on cramming knowledge into the boy. They coaxed and encouraged him in all possible ways to skip grades, make high marks, and to keep ahead of his classmates, without any apparent opportunity for relaxation for themselves or for the boy. For fourteen years they might just as well have lived 500 miles from the city." B. I. completed high school at thirteen with the highest grades in his city, but he was eccentric, poorly socialized, and puzzled.

The parents' lives were embittered as well as narrowed. Constant strife prevailed in the rooms behind the store in which they lived. The father was an uncouth man with a terrible temper despite an unusual education for a man of his occupation. He had left home at an early age because he could not get along with his father and stepmother. At fifteen he had not talked for a year because he had heard it would improve his singing. When the patient was ten the father was depressed following financial reverses. He began to grow paranoically suspicious of his wife's fidelity. He became frenzied when the patient brought a gentile friend into the home, and once threw both his son and wife out of the home because he found the patient in the company of a gentile. The mother, though kindly, pushed the boy, centering her life about her hopes for a genius son. She confided her unhappiness to the patient and sought his help. When the patient was thirteen she left her husband but, unable to remain away from the children, begged the boy to threaten suicide unless the father brought her back home. B. I. was the hub around which the quarrels revolved. The mother, extremely orthodox, was raising him to be a rabbi, whereas the atheist father belittled all religious belief and filled the boy with poorly digested philosophical concepts. The patient resented his parents but felt bound to them by their efforts to make him great. The mother made a suicidal attempt when the son was hospitalized and the father became seriously depressed.

Comment.—The home, shut off from social relations, was filled with conflict, suspicion, and confused thinking. The unstable parents drove the boy to excel but pushed in opposite directions. The patient found no acceptable pattern in the home and came to have extremely ambivalent feelings toward both parents, who were making each other and the patient miserable.

CASE 24.   W. I. is a sixteen-year-old girl who grew up in a home with complicated interrelationships. The second of three children and the older daughter, she appeared to be the favorite of both parents. However, the family lived in the home of the divorced paternal grandmother, a fiery-tempered woman with a whip for a tongue who hated her daughter-in-law and the patient. She had opposed the son's marriage as she had made him promise to remain single and support her. The patient, as the father's favorite, became the target of her enmity. She nagged and belittled the child constantly.

The father, a heavy drinker with a violent temper, was paranoically jealous of his wife. He was afraid to sleep alone, and insisted that both the wife and the patient sleep in the room with him. When they were away the butler had to sleep in the room. He was inconsistent with all of the children, whipping them for trivialities and indulging them foolishly. The mother, supposedly of a relatively even disposition prior to the marriage, was unable to control herself when her husband and his mother lost their tempers, and violent quarrels took place almost every day.

W. I. was indoctrinated by her father from an early age with the idea that petting and pregnancy were revolting. He insisted that he would never permit her to go with boys. Her first parties created violent scenes. The father would whip her when she returned home a few minutes late, and threatened to kill the mother if the patient became pregnant. The girl had been attached to her father until this dissension started. She asked to be sent to boarding school and gained her ends with the mother's help.

However, just before she was to leave, the mother and the patient learned that the father had been keeping a mistress for years. Divorce proceedings were started but were discontinued because of the father's threats.

Comment.—The home was inordinately filled with enmity, instability, and contradictory behavior. The patient, as the favorite of the father, was more subject to the family conflicts. The father's demands upon her and the mother in regard to sexual behavior were suddenly contrasted with his own infidelity.

CASE 35.   S. I., a nineteen-year-old college girl, was born fourteen years after her sister and twenty-two years after her half-sister. The parents were both forty-two at the time, and the pregnancy continued only after abortifacients had failed and several doctors had refused to perform an abortion. The mother hid the pregnancy which led to gossip that the patient was the illegitimate child of the half-sister. The parents took no interest in the unwanted child and left her to the care of an elderly divorced aunt who lived in the home. The aunt hated the patient's mother, and taught S. I. to hate her by informing her at an early age of the attempts at abortion and the gossip about her birth. The child was never permitted to play with other children but was taken to teas at which elderly ladies gossiped. The aunt taught the child to spy upon the mother, read her mail, and report everything she heard. The aunt and the mother were openly hostile, at times having physical encounters. The aunt died when the patient was thirteen.

The family was wealthy and the parents, who led an active social life, preferred to let the patient have her way rather than be bothered. She received neither affection nor training. The family physician reported that she had not been taught to brush her teeth until the age of fifteen. Teachers, years later, recalled her as a child who had been pathetically neglected. Both the family physician and the teachers tried to intervene, but the mother only became insulted when it was suggested that the child was not being raised properly.

S. I. never had a friend during childhood, and her isolation was increased by slight lameness, the result of osteomyelitis, improperly treated because the mother had removed the patient from the hospital as she was not eating well.

Relatively little is known about the parents, but the mother was obviously a peculiar person who had been suffering from hyperthyroidism for years but refused operation. She insisted, when giving the anamnesis, that she knew nothing of sex, even though she had three children. She had placed great emphasis upon shielding S. I. from sexual contact by refusing to permit her out of the house after 10 P.M., but evidently paid no attention when the girl, at the onset of her overt psychosis, invited dozens of undesirable men into the home who broke furniture, stole, and took turns at having sexual relations with the patient.

Comment.—The rejection of the patient started prior to birth and continued to an unusual degree. The only guidance came from the unwholesome relationship with the aunt whose death when the patient was adolescent left her completely friendless. Animosity toward the parents was not only reactive but actually fostered by the aunt.

CASE 47.   Z. A. is a fifteen-year-old boy, the oldest of four children. The father was an instructor in a preparatory school who treated the boy as an equal, offering little guidance. The mother dominated the home, but seemed to be a rather good-natured woman. She had suffered from emotional difficulties during adolescence and revolted against the socialite home by becoming a trained nurse. After each of her four pregnancies she had been overactive, and at other times there had been periods of mild depression.

The home life was free of friction and the parents devoted considerable time to the children without being unduly oversolicitous. The patient's preoccupation with his relationship to his parents seemed more the result of specific interpersonal difficulties rather than a reflection of an unstable home. He resented the lack of guidance by the father, and the fact that the home was indistinguishably merged with the school that he attended.

Comment.—Although the mother suffered from moderate manic-depressive mood swings, she appeared to have been a relatively adequate parent. For the purposes of this study the family environment is considered to have been good, even though difficulties in the father-son relationship existed.

CASE 48.   N. I. is the twenty-year-old, only daughter of a college professor. According to both parents, and from information given by close friends, the parents were devoted to each other, and the home life was congenial. The parents were sociable, kindly persons who endeavored to guide their child sensibly. Difficulties for the patient arose from the father's position. She had been much attached to him during early childhood and paid little attention to the mother. As she grew up the father became prominent and had less and less time to devote to his daughter. N. I. resented the fact that she was only known as her father's daughter and that great expectations were held for her by the college community. At adolescence she became antagonistic toward her father and grew closer to the mother.

A factor difficult to assay was the burden of mental illness in the mother's family. She learned of the suicides of her grandfather and uncle with great shame. A schizophrenic aunt lived with the family until committed when the patient was seven. N. I. expressed the opinion in childhood that is was only a matter of time until she would become insane like the aunt.

The psychotic material all centered about the family relationships. The patient insisted that she was the illegitimate daughter of an uncle; and that her father abused the mother.

Comment.—Although the existence of intrafamilial difficulties might be assumed from the patient's delusional beliefs, the difficulties do not appear to have arisen from overt difficulties within the home or from gross eccentricities of the parents. The role of the schizophrenic aunt in the patient's development could not be estimated. For the purposes of this study the family environment is considered adequate.

The ten cases which have been abstracted are fairly typical of the entire group. Eight of the ten grew up amidst family relationships which were overtly disturbed and obviously deleterious to integrated personality development. Four had lost a parent during childhood: two of these (F. A. and C. H.) had little parental guidance and no consistent home life thereafter, one under circumstances that fostered deep resentment toward the remaining parent; and the other two lived in homes which became increasingly unpleasant. Two patients (M. A. and S. I.) had homes in name only, having been unwanted and rejected children in uncongenial homes. Two (B. I. and W. I.) had been favorite children, but in homes marred by constant strife which focused about them, insecure because of repeated threats of separation fostered by the fathers' paranoid tendencies. The remaining two patients came from homes which were considered reasonably amicable and constant, even though some sources of insecurity were found. The scrutiny of these synopses permits an understanding of the type of data from which the chart was constructed, the manner in which the material was evaluated, and an impression of how the more abstract data in the chart fit together.

ANALYSIS OF THE CHART

1. *Loss of a Parent.*—Data were available for all cases. Fourteen patients had lost a parent by death, and an additional six had lost a parent from the home environment by divorce or separation before the patient was nineteen. Thus, 40 per cent had been deprived of at least one parent. Pollock et al. (1939) reported a comparable figure (37.7%) in their statistical survey of 175 schizophrenic patients. As this item could be readily checked in the case records of older patients, fifty histories of schizophrenic patients whose psychosis had become manifest after the age of twenty-one were reviewed, and it

was found that 36 per cent had been deprived of at least one parent prior to their nineteenth birthday. A control survey on Phipps Clinic case records of fifty psychotically depressed patients gave a figure of 20 per cent. Pollock et al. (1939) reported 16.7 per cent in a series of 155 manic-depressive patients. Of sixty-nine medical students, twelve or 17.4 per cent had been deprived of a parent during the same age period.

These figures are highly significant, and this problem has therefore been subjected to closer scrutiny. Although it seemed reasonable to assume that the loss of a parent deprived the child of necessary guidance or might have produced unfavorable home conditions, it did not seem plausible that such deprivation could in itself bear a direct relationship to the production of schizophrenic reactions. Indeed, the possible implication of these figures was a principal reason for undertaking this study. Analysis of the data alters the emphasis. Four, and possibly five, patients had lost a parent because the parent was psychotic and committed suicide. In addition, the divorce or separation of parents was largely due to the psychotic or grossly unstable behavior of at least one parent in five of the six cases. Thus the loss of a parent in nine and perhaps ten of the twenty cases was due to the serious emotional instability of a parent.

In the control groups only one parent of a depressive patient had suicided, and none of the parents had been permanently separated. Of the medical students, three had lost a parent through permanent separation, but it is not known if any of these had been psychotic or grossly unstable.

The striking difference between the schizophrenic group and the control groups is seen to be largely a result of the psychotic or severely unstable behavior of parents which led to suicide or permanent separation.

2. *Incompatibility of Parents.*—Information adequate to form a definite impression was available in thirty-three cases. As has been noted, incompatibility led to divorce or separation (permanent or repetitive) in seven cases. An additional seven sets of parents had been seriously incompatible (cases 21-27). Four more patients had parents who were moderately but clearly incompatible, while the marriage in two other instances was considered obviously uncongenial. Thus, of the

thirty-three cases in which sufficient information was available for judgment, twenty or 61 per cent had homes that had been marked by strife. Actually only seven of the thirty-three patients had the benefit of being raised by congenial parents as four had lost a parent by death, and two had been raised in homes kept free of strife only because the father had given in and pampered the eccentric and dominating mother.

Of the remaining seventeen marriages concerning which information was deemed inadequate to judge the compatibility, six had been terminated by the death of one partner. Although none of the remainder ended in divorce, it was fairly definite that many were uncongenial, and it does not seem likely that further information would appreciably alter the calculation of the percentage of uncongenial marriages.

3. *Extreme Instability of Parents.*—Data were available for at least one parent in forty-eight cases. Twenty-three patients (48%) had twenty-nine parents who were either psychotic or chronically and seriously neurotic or psychopathic. The mother alone was unstable in nine cases, the father alone in eight cases, and both parents were markedly unstable in six. As information is not always given, this is clearly a minimal figure.

4. *Unsuitable and Unusual Raising.*—Estimation is particularly difficult for this item. Data are completely absent in six cases. The pattern of raising was bizarre or extremely faulty according to conventional standards in at least eighteen (41%) of the forty-four cases where the information permitted some evaluation. Ten patients had been rejected by at least one parent to an extreme degree such as can be noted in Cases 9, 20, and 35.

Comment on Data from Charts

The analysis of the data gives a statistical summary of some of the adverse influences to which the patients had been subjected in the early home environment, but it fails to convey the heaping up of deleterious factors which occurred in most cases. There were ten patients in whom none of the various items studied appeared to play a significant role, but these included five cases in which no information or relatively little information concerning the home life was available. The other forty patients were exposed to many injurious influences. These forty patients had been deprived of the guidance of fifteen parents by death and thirteen by separation; they had been exposed to the behavior of twenty-nine grossly unstable parents; and to the insecurity of twenty-one clearly incompatible marriages; and eighteen had been raised in unusual and eccentric fashion.

Stated conversely, only five of the fifty schizophrenic patients could be said to have clearly come from reasonably stable homes in which they had been raised by two stable and compatible parents according to fairly acceptable principles of child rearing.

DISCUSSION

A statistical or semistatistical survey cannot afford an understanding of the developmental dynamics gained through the careful study of individual cases. The ten case abstracts barely indicate the influences within the family which weigh upon the individual and help mold him, and the charts can only offer a glimpse of the manner in which the several factors studied impinge upon each of the fifty cases. Sibling relationships, often extremely significant, have been evaluated in but a few cases, and extrafamilial influences and the idiosyncrasies of individual development have been carefully screened out of the study. The study of the histories of these patients impresses forcefully that one patient after another was subjected to a piling up of adverse intrafamilial forces that were major factors in molding the misshapen personality, and which repeatedly interfered with the patients' attempts at maturation in a most discouraging fashion. The survey has been confined to the grossest features of the family environment. In their evalution the prejudices of the individual physician caring for the patient, or of the writers, play a relatively small role. The intention has been precisely this: to call attention to the unusually poor family settings in which most schizophrenic patients gain their start in life, and which play a major role in the formation of interpersonal relationships, the projective systems, and the basic attitudes with which they face life and upon which they must build.

There has been an increasing tendency of late, more so than appears in the literature, for those interested in the psychotherapy of schizophrenic patients to lay stress upon the pernicious influence of the mothers, the severely rejecting mother, the so-called schizophreno-genic mother (Fromm-Reichmann, 1948). The origins of the schizo-phrenic reaction pattern have been sought in the infantile relationship with the mother who empathetically conveys her feelings of rejec-tion to the infant (Rosen, 1948). The authors do not mean to detract from the importance of early maternal rejection. However, similar rejection or even more serious maternal rejection may be found in other psychiatric syndromes including certain psychosomatic con-figurations. If the type and degree of rejection suffered by schizo-phrenic patients can be differentiated from the rejection to which other patients are exposed, it has not yet been made apparent. This study indicates that less subtle early influences warrant careful atten-tion. The data which have been reported here would appear to in-dicate a high frequency of grossly abnormal parental influences dur-ing the childhood of schizophrenic patients. It is suggested that there may well be a direct relationship between the degree of abnormality of the early environment and the seriousness of the emotional illness.

The suggestion is offered that, whereas infantile relationships may start the patient in the direction of asocial development or form an Anlage for later regression to infantile patterns, it may be the serious difficulties that are chronically present through childhood which pre-vent the patient from fitting into the pattern offered by society. In our data it is apparent that the paternal influences are noxious as fre-quently as are the maternal. The study of some of the cases leaves the impression that, had there been a stable father to offer guidance or to serve as a source for stable identification, the patient would not have been so seriously affected by the mother's difficulties. The conflict within the patient concerned with ambivalent feelings toward one or both parents, the divided loyalties, the unstable identifications, the in-corporation of hostility directed toward one or the other parent—all these are often due to the influences of both parents. In the study of individual patients the gross abnormalities of the family background are not to be disregarded in favor of the more subtle interpersonal re-lationships, but should serve as background information which may throw light upon the reasons why the patient's emotional illness takes the drastic form.

It is recognized that the study can be taken to indicate that the instability of schizophrenic patients is hereditary. Although all the adverse familial influences are not directly to be attributed to the emotional instability of the parents, the differences between this group as a whole and some group of patients with another ailment might possibly be shown to be largely a matter of the frequency of serious instability of the parents. The problem is difficult to resolve: unstable parents tend to form unsuitable marriages and provide unstable homes. The cycle perpetuates itself. The topic will not be debated here. The emphasis of the paper, however, has been upon the survey of the environmental situation.

The question why one child in the family becomes schizophrenic when all have been subjected to similar adverse influences is frequently propounded. The problem diverges from the major emphasis of the paper, but it can be indicated that careful attention to the ten case abstracts will show that eight patients had siblings. Six of these were considered to have come from adverse environments, and all six were clearly brought up under markedly different influences from their siblings.

CHART 1

No.	Pt.	Age	Sex	Loss of parent	Incompatibility of parents	Instability of parent	Raising	Mental illness in family
1.	W.O.	19	F	Father suicided when patient was 15.	.... *	Father depressed and alcoholic for 5 years. Mother had "nervous breakdown" after first pregnancy.	Wealthy until aged 10; morbid surroundings thereafter as father was never stable after loss of wealth.	Father was depressed. Mother had "nervous breakdown."
2.	M.E.	21	F	Father suicided when patient was 15.	....	Father depressed prior to suicide.	Patient strongly attached to father.	Father depressed.
3.	S.T.	20	F	Mother absent with tuberculosis when patient 4. Father died when patient 9.	Unknown.	Father psychotic for 2 years prior to death.	Raised in orphanages from 4 to 17.	Father psychotic.
4.	M.U.	20	M	Father died of "nervous breakdown" when patient 15.	Unknown.	Father had "nervous breakdown."	Pampered excessively by mother who would not let him out of sight. Youngest sibling by 7 years. A "sissy not allowed to play with others."	Father had "nervous breakdown."
5.	R.U.	19	M	Mother suicided when patient 6.	Little known but apparently an adequate home.	Mother depressed before suicide. Aunt who raised patient "queer" and suffered an agitated depression.	....	Mother depressed. Mat. aunt depressed.
6.	W.E.	19	M	Mother died when patient 18.	Peculiar marriage of poor Protestant barber to wealthy Catholic heiress who was disowned and disinherited.	Father severely obsessive and incapacitated of depressive illness when patient 5 to 10.	Patient was mother's favorite and confidant of her disappointments; closely bound to her, he lived to make her happy by becoming wealthy.	Father obsessive with depressive episodes.
7.	K.I.	17	F	Mother died when pt. 14. Parents separated when she was 3 and divorced when pt. was 8.	Very marked, and pt. greatly upset by separation.	....	Lived with mother from 3 to 8 and then awarded to father by court.	A paternal cousin suicided in a "tantrum."

* The dotted line indicates that the record contained no pertinent data.

CHART 1 (CONTINUED)

No.	Pt.	Age	Sex	Loss of parent	Incompatibility of parents	Instability of parent	Raising	Mental illness in family
8.	B.R.	19	M	Father died when pt. was 4.	Constant strife between older brother and mother.	....	Mother domineering and older sibs revolted but pt. was deaf and dependent.	....
9.	F.A.	20	M	Mother died when pt. was 1½. Aunt who raised pt. died when pt. was 13.	....	....	Raised by aunt while brother was raised by father. After 13 raised in boarding school where aunt worked. Pampered by both aunts.	....
10.	C.H.	18	M	Father died of tuberculosis when pt. was 12.	Unknown.	....	Pt. asthmatic and raised differently from sibs, usually at schools away from home.	....
11.	B.A.	14	F	Mother died when pt. was 11.	Little known of first home, second apparently congenial.	....	Father remarried when pt. was 12, but was away from home half the time. Pt. jealous of kindly stepmother. Pt. was Catholic and father and stepmother were Protestant.	....
12.	M.O.	18	F	Mother died when pt. was 7.	Unknown.	....	Youngest of 10 sibs who was raised by older sisters. Father had no time for family but was very strict when home.	....
13.	R.A.	21	M	Father died when pt. was 2.	Unknown.	....	"Spoiled" by the maternal grandmother who helped raise pt.	Mat. grandfather was in state hosp. for 40 years.

CHART 1 (CONTINUED)

No.	Pt.	Age	Sex	Loss of parent	Incompatibility of parents	Instability of parent	Raising	Mental illness in family
14.	G.R.	20	M	Orphaned in infancy.	No data.	No data.	No data.	No data. ....
15.	H.E.	16	M	Permanent separation between mother and grandmother and between grandparents who raised pt.	Extreme open conflict between mother and grandmother and between grandparents who raised pt.	Father extreme alcoholic. Mother an irresponsible psychopath. Maternal grandmother paranoid.	Extremely wealthy boy given no benefit of wealth or position, but subject to high expectations of family. Very abnormal surroundings with vindictiveness between members of family.	Father alcoholic. Mother psychopath. Mat. grandmother paranoid. Paternal line—many severe alcoholics and eccentrics.
16.	B.R.	18	M	Permanent separation when pt. was 8.	Extreme incompatibility. Family fled to Europe to be free of father who followed and caused terrible scenes.	Father severe alcoholic who was committed several times.	Only boy with four sisters and an aggressive mother. Peculiar education in Jesuit schools in several foreign countries.	Father alcoholic. Pat. grandmother and uncle were schizophrenic.
17.	C.R.	13	F	Separated when pt. was 11.	Family was completely disorganized. Father was alcoholic and cruel.	Father paranoid and alcoholic. Mother had screaming spells and probably was feebleminded.	Family lived in a tumble-down shack. Aunt ran a bawdy house.	Father paranoid.
18.	B.A.	16	F	Divorced when patient was 6.	Extreme incompatibility. Mother would disappear for long periods. Pt. greatly concerned over incompatibility.	Mother paranoid.	Father abusive to wife and children. Pt., as youngest of seven was most exposed to difficulties in home.	Mother diagnosed as paranoid. Brother suffered a "nervous breakdown."
19.	H.F.	19	F	Divorced when pt. was 1.	Father Jewish and mother gentile. Pt. was unwanted and father unfaithful. Mother remarried when pt. was 9 but no information of this home.	....	Patient very spoiled and sheltered by the mother. Patient a feeding problem from infancy.	Paternal cousin suicided. Many divorces in family.

CHART 1 (CONTINUED)

No.	Pt.	Age	Sex	Loss of parents	Incompatibility of parents	Instability of parent	Raising	Mental illness in family
20.	M.A.	16	M	Sporadic separations.	Parents married only because of the pregnancy. No mutual life. Father took no interest in pt. and found interests out of home. Mother silly.		Little known.	Paternal grandmother in mental hospital for short time with "nervous break-down."
21.	B.I.	14	M	Temporary separation when patient was 13.	Marked discord especially on all issues concerning patient.	Father had a "nervous breakdown" when pt. was 8. Mother committed in agitated depression after patient became ill.	Brought up to be a genius, pushed by parents whose happiness depended on patient's future greatness. Strife between parents concerning patient's raising.	Father had depressive episodes. Mother an agitated depression.
22.	R.I.	20	M		Gross incompatibility. Remained married only "because of opinion of others."	Mother moody, thoughtless, rigid.	Little known.	Paternal aunt had "nervous break-down." Pat. grandfather died in state hospital at 62. Mat. cousin and great-aunt schizophrenic.
23.	R.J.	18	M		Marked parental strife and pt. very sensitive of these fights.	Mother was depressed when pt. was 8 and remained hypochondriacal.	Excessively pampered by nervous mother.	Mother depressed.
24.	W.I.	16	F		Father had mistress which caused marked dissension. Strife between parents over pat. grandmother who dominated the home.	Father highly neurotic with phobia.	Patient was favorite child, spoiled particularly by father but squelched by jealous grandmother and restricted by fearful father.	Father neurotic. Mat. aunt "unstable." Mat. great-uncle had two depressions.

CHART 1 (CONTINUED)

No.	Pt.	Age	Sex	Loss of parents	Incompatibility of parents	Instability of parent	Raising	Mental illness in family
25.	P.O.	19	F	......	Parents never got along together. Father involved in suit for alienation of affection with much scandal.	......	Mother an "unfortunate person," very solicitous for patient but devoid of affection for her.	Mat. great-uncle suicided.
26.	H.O.	17	M	......	Marked parental strife which was patient's major concern.	Mother "nervous" and quarrelsome.	Little known.	......
27.	B.B.	22	F	......	Much quarreling and suspicion between parents which caused patient much concern.	......	Oldest of four and very jealous of siblings.	Maternal great-aunt depressed.
28.	P.H.	19	F	......	Parents were not compatible; friction but not serious. Father a sort of handyman around mother's farm—a man who "never grew up."	Mother a chronic worrier, a "gloomy person." Father "immature."	Mother gloomy about children's heredity and thought them fated to insanity. Told patient that she was frigid. Mat. grandmother dominated the home.	A mat. aunt and uncle schizophrenic. A mat. aunt seclusive and suspicious. Pat. grandmother had violent and unreasonable temper. Four pat. aunts unstable and all divorced.
29.	D.A.	24	F	......	Some overt friction and patient worried about manner in which mother treated father.	......	No warmth or companionship in home. Mother a distant and aloof woman who supported and dominated family.	Maternal great-aunt was psychotic.
30.	K.E.	13	F	......	Parents never got along well. Father home but one day a week. Older sisters removed patient from home as it was "unsuitable."	Mother very peculiar, ? a socialized schizophrenic.	Mother excitable and was always at extremes using poor judgment. Very strict and overly concerned with sexual life of the children.	Mother ? Maternal second cousin schizophrenic. Pat. great-aunt in state hospital.

CHART 1 (CONTINUED)

No.	Pt.	Age	Sex	Loss of parents	Incompatibility of parents	Instability of parent	Raising	Mental illness in family
31.	L.A.	21	M	....	Not known.	Father had "nervous breakdown" and remained irritable.	Irritable father pushed patient and nagged continually.	Father had "nervous breakdown."
32.	B.L.	18	M	....	Little known but not congenial.	Father hypochondriacal and mother always "nervous" and irritable.	Not known.	Father hypochondriacal. Mat. grandmother paranoid and mat. aunt schizophrenic. Pat. second cousin schizophrenic.
33.	S.L.	17	F	....	Considerable friction but no open breaks. Both heavy drinkers with emphasis on social life rather than home.	Mother "neurotic."	Army officer family with many changes in residence and schools. Patient and identical twin became psychotic at same time with religious folie à deux.	Identical twin schizophrenic. Mother "neurotic." Mat. cousin had a religious "crack-up."
34.	T.R.	21	F	....	No overt break but a gloomy, unfriendly home with no compatibility between parents and no affection shown the children.	....	Father a physician with peculiar overconcern about patient's virginity. Would wish to perform pelvic exam. after her dates. Mother distant and uninterested in family.	Pat. uncle died of "softening of the brain."
35.	S.I.	19	F	....	Extreme hostility, suspicion and back-biting between mother and aunt who raised patient.	Aunt who raised patient was "peculiar."	Youngest sibling by 12 years who was rejected and neglected by parents who left her raising to a peculiar maiden aunt. No home life for patient despite wealthy home.	....

CHART 1 (CONTINUED)

No.	Pt.	Age	Sex	Loss of parent	Incompatibility of parents	Instability of parent	Raising	Mental illness in family
36.	J.O.	18	M	....	Fairly good as father humored mother's eccentricities.	Mother had several "nervous breakdowns," very eccentric and perhaps a socialized schizophrenic.	Mother permitted the patient no independence of action or thought, dictating all trivia. Brother left home in revolt. Patient was bound to mother but resentful.	Mother had "nervous breakdown." Two maternal aunts were peculiar and one may have been psychotic.
37.	M.O.	16	M	....	Not known.	Mother very odd. Neighborhood children would write on sidewalk, "Mrs. O. is crazy."	Patient youngest of 6 siblings by 7 years and most subject to mother's increasing eccentricity.	Mother ?
38.	D.E.	17	M	....	No information other than that older brother, a psychopath, caused much trouble in the home.	Mother mildly but chronically depressed for several years.	Father, a rather alcoholic policeman, was very strict and rigid. Mother was moody, irritable, and worrisome.	Mother depressive. Mat. aunt schizophrenic. Mat. uncle depressive. Mat. grandfather senile psychosis. Two pat. aunts and a pat. cousin suffered depressions.
39.	H.G.	22	M	....	Little known but probably fairly congenial.	Mother a "worrier."	Mother pampered the patient and shielded the 325-pound youth from his father who did not understand his "artistic" temperament. Brother's suicide affected family.	Brother suicided at 28. Sister depressed after the suicide. A mat. and a pat. uncle in state hospital.
40.	C.A.	23	F	....	No friction. Father subdued by aggressive mother.	....	Mother ambitious for patient pushed her socially and very aggressively.	....

CHART 1 (CONTINUED)

No.	Pt.	Age	Sex	Loss of parent	Incompatibility of parents	Instability of parent	Raising	Mental illness in family
41.	M.D.	21	M	....	Not known.	Mother depressed when patient was born "because of her figure."	Patient the retarded son of a university professor, raised as if normal and much out of place at home and in schools.	Pat. grandmother "nervous breakdown." Pat. uncle suicided. Pat. uncle mentally retarded. Pat. cousin and mat. aunt were schizophrenic.
42.	B.R.	16	F	....	Not known.	Mother a nervous worrier.	Spoiled by mother who always let patient have her own way. Patient married at 16 in opposition to parents.	Mother neurotic.
43.	D.O.	24	M	....	Not known.	....	Little known but patient had not talked to father in years. Rather wealthy and successful but patient looked down on parents because of lack of education.	Maternal uncle hospitalized with "nervous stomach."
44.	B.U.	19	M	....	Not known. Older brother estranged because parents would not meet his wife.	....	Rigid parents.	....
45.	C.C.	21	M	....	Not known.	Not known.	Not known.	Paternal grandmother hospitalized with "depression." "Insanity in her line." Paternal great-uncle and great-grand-uncle both insane.

CHART 1 (CONTINUED)

No.	Pt.	Age	Sex	Loss of parent	Incompatibility of parents	Instability of parent	Raising	Mental illness in family
46.	J.E.	19	M	....	Happy but odd home centering about invalid mother with father a detached research worker.	....	Patient much attached to invalid mother and jealous of any attention to siblings.	....
47.	Z.A.	15	M	....	Apparently congenial, offering good background.	Mother had severe adolescent difficulties and later brief period of depression and mild elation.	Father a prep. school teacher and home was fused with school.	Mother—brief depression.
48.	N.I.	21	F	....	Good with occasional slight friction.	....	Patient concerned about expectations for only child of a college dean and about imagined incompatibility of parents. Schizophrenic aunt in home for several years.	Maternal aunt schizophrenic. Mat. grandfather and uncle suicided in depressions.
49.	M.B.		F	....	Good home life.	....	....	Pat. grandmother had a mild depressive illness.
50.	U.L.		F	....	Good home life.	....	Both parents oversolicitous and ambitious for patient. Mother a meticulous and apprehensive person.	....

II

Therapeutic Considerations Arising from the Intense Symbiotic Needs of Schizophrenic Patients

(1951)

An attempt will be made in this paper to correlate certain observations concerning the developmental psychopathology as noted in a number of schizophrenic patients with the therapeutic approach and tactics utilized in their treatment. It is believed that the understanding of a focal problem that has blocked integrative development has helped to establish greater consistency in therapy and the avoidance of certain dangers that may disrupt the therapeutic relationship. The material is not drawn from the treatment of schizophrenic patients who have regressed into withdrawn states, and is not concerned with means of establishing a working relationship as many papers on the psychotherapy of schizophrenia have been. These patients had continued to maintain themselves in society with the aid of delusional defenses, or had even managed to remain in relatively good equilibrium except for one or more retreats into overt psychosis during periods of particular stress: some were borderline patients, including patients with certain psychosomatic ailments whose personality structure and defensive mechanisms were very similar to those of the schizophrenic. The concern revolves about the maintenance of therapy in a manner that will lead the patient into the reorientation necessary to establish adequately successful patterns of living independent of the therapist. Many of the problems are not unique to schizo-

Ruth Wilmanns Lidz and Theodore Lidz: Therapeutic Considerations Arising from the Intense Symbiotic Needs of Schizophrenic Patients. In Psychotherapy with Schizophrenics, *edited by E. B. Brody and F. C. Redlich. Copyright ©* 1952, International Universities Press. *This paper was presented at the 1951 annual meeting of the American Psychiatric Association.*

phrenic patients, but are here seen in bolder relief and as presenting more formidable hazards than when encountered in the treatment of psychoneurotics. The discussion may not be pertinent for all schizophrenic patients, but it is believed that it has application to a considerable segment.

The problems to be discussed center around the extremely passive orientation of these patients who seek a symbiotic bond with another person, to be completely protected by an omnipotent and omniscient figure to whom they are at the same time essential. The recurring theme as we have heard it does not derive from overt rejection by the mother, as occurs in some schizophrenic patients and which has received so much emphasis of late (Despert, 1942; Fromm-Reichmann, 1948; Rosen, 1947), but with the symbiotic bond to a parental figure, usually the mother. It is the pattern that Reichard and Tillman (1950) have described as most frequent in schizophrenic development. They say, "This pattern is found in mothers who batten parasitically on their children and who aim . . . to prevent them from ever becoming independent. This leads to the development of a kind of symbiotic relationship between mother and child in which the two egos remain so fused and intermingled that the boundaries never become clear. . . . The patient is not fooled . . . and never fails to indicate he was not loved as a child."[1] This statement, amplified and illustrated in their paper, is in precise accord with our observations, and the concern of this paper is with its implications for therapy and the therapeutic relationship.

What we hear from these patients when defenses have been pared away goes like this, "I could not leave mother and mother could not do without me; when I knew she was going to die the world came to an end." While at another time the patient said, "If I had died then, mother would have died; I was all she lived for." And further, "When mother died, I had to become mother—otherwise she would really be dead." And, from the same patient to the therapist, "I am just a nuisance to you—you do not need me. What other bond is there except need? I was sure of mother. She could not live without me." Another patient, whose psychotic mother had been abandoned by the

---

[1] See also Fairbairn (1940).

father after the patient's birth, said, "I knew how mother was feeling. I had to know to try to keep her out of the hospital and with me." But after mother suicided, living was directed toward awaiting the appearance of another person who would care for her and for whom she would be essential. Sometimes it seems delusional when the schizophrenic patient feels essential to another person who appears independent and strong, such as some dominating mothers of patients. Thus, the insistence of a schizophrenic woman that she could not leave her homosexual partner, an aggressive masculine type, because the partner would die, seemed a defensive rationalization. However, when the patient attempted to break the relationship, the partner became suicidally despondent and stopped eating until the patient resumed the relationship in attenuated form. Nor, in a sense, was the belief of a young man that he could destroy mother by his behavior, delusional; nor was the converse—that mother might destroy him unless he continued as an appendage of her. Despite the mother's insistence that he be a manly person, she exerted extreme pressure each time he manifested a show of independence, and fought bitterly to hold him when it became apparent that therapy would sever the bond.

It has often been apparent that to the schizophrenic as to the very young child the boundaries between the self and the mother are vague. It seems equally clear that to the mothers of some schizophrenics there seems to be little boundary between themselves and the patient. Sometimes the mother has no other reason for living and needs to have the child remain with her and in her; another type of mother feels incomplete as a woman and can accept the child conditionally only as long as he remains an appendage that completes her. Perhaps the crux of the problem lies here, that the schizophrenic patient's primary concern is not with the development and defense of his own personality and needs, but primarily with those of the mother, for without her he cannot exist. The efforts to maintain her as a benevolent figure when she is basically malevolent toward the patient as a *separate individual* may require profound distortion of reality. The basis of delusion formation is the acceptance of an axiom. The schizophrenic's axiom often is that mother is beneficent and omniscient.

The developmental difficulties do not seem to rest upon the mother alone. The patients suffered from a background of chaotic relationships from infancy through adolescence (Chapter I). Stable parents were absent, and substitutes either never appeared, or served simply to accentuate the difficulties. Neither parent was either a safe figure for identification or a suitable and secure person with whom to relate. Neither could be a model that could be followed to find security or affection. The child is burdened with the need to complete the mother's life, a task that cannot be accomplished: empathically sensing that he must, if he wishes to have a safe maternal figure for security: frightened by the covert but obvious threats of rejection if he seeks independence. He does not feel loved for himself but only as an appendage, and his personality structure is irreparably damaged. It is degrading not to be regarded as a person with desires, needs, and values of one's own. He does not develop identity with self-esteem, and he need really ask, "Who am I?" The boy cannot remain part of the mother and be a male: and the girl achieves little by identifying with mother because it is apparent *to her* that mother is basically a failure. Still the parental figure is needed, and the child learns, or rather trains himself to uncanny sensitivity toward the feelings and needs of another, so apparent in schizophrenic patients. The patient does not know the way, or the why of living, but continues to believe that omniscient parental figures know, while direction and values remain shrouded from him, leading to repeated attempts to interpret meanings from the behavior of others. Cut off from the mother or with clear-cut failure of the parental figure, he is overwhelmed by perplexity and anxiety. The way out is sought not through efforts to find his own way but in awaiting the return of a figure with whom a symbiotic relationship can be established. Repetitive disappointment is almost certain, for no one can fill the need. The therapist enters into the life, rekindles the hope, and is placed by the patient in a role that cannot be filled; and therapy will ultimately fail unless the relationship can be utilized to guide the patient into different expectations and to the assumption of responsibility for guiding his own life.

In the light of the psychopathology outlined, the general aim of therapy seems clear. It is to help the patient establish sufficient identity as an individual to make it possible to leave the need for a symbiotic relationship and the regressive, passive efforts to find an omniscient and omnipotent figure and venture actively to follow his own motivations. This means attaining self-esteem through the realization that his own desires and impulses count; that his beliefs and opinions can have value as guides to living. Through the therapeutic relationship the patient must learn of the possibility of a new type of close relationship; that another can care for, rather than just take care of; that the therapist will not "use"; set impossible conditions for acceptance; reject if the "real" self shows through; abandon after he has been trusted. These are requisites, but the patient must also learn that even though he will not be cast out while still helpless, the person he has now placed in a parental role wishes him to mature and voluntarily break the frustrating confinement of being attached to another. Thus, the parental regard and acceptance of the infantile in the patient must dissolve during treatment into regard and respect for the more mature and independent qualities (Fromm-Reichmann, 1948).

It seems to us that certain basic guides for the therapist's attitude follow. The schizophrenic patient may relate well initially to a person who presumes to know the answers, directs, and gives the needed affection. It plays into the patient's belief that someone else knows the way and will care for him magically: but it sets up expectations that cannot be fulfilled and does not lead away from the need for all-encompassing care. Indeed, the need is usually so great that the patient places the therapist in this role even when efforts are made to avoid it without rebuffing the patient. Ultimately, frustration turns the belief that the therapist is benevolent into belief in malevolence, for why does the omnipotent figure fail to protect? Delusion may become necessary to maintain the axiomatic belief that the therapist can protect. Thus, a woman who left her family despite all efforts of the therapist to block the move without disrupting the therapeutic relationship, comes, when the burden of her move becomes apparent, to believe that the therapist wished her to leave home to relieve the family of the burden of her presence. A clear illustration, though not from a schizophrenic patient, was seen in a man with a fatal illness who to protect himself from concerns over imminent death adopted the faith that his physician could cure him. When a recrudescence of his illness set in, he did not abandon his axiom, but rather believed that the physician was secretly experimenting upon him. The entire attitude of the therapist goes into avoiding being considered omnipotent on the one hand, or of needing the patient, on the other hand. The patient desires the therapist both to take care of him completely and to need him completely. Overprotection and giving the impression of intuitively or mystically understanding foster one need, while being abject or masochistically accepting the patient's condemnations may foster the other. The therapist must be willing to go a long way, to great personal inconvenience, to help the patient, but he avoids dominating as he avoids being dominated by passive measures. The strength in the therapist that must be conveyed to the patient may well derive from sufficient integrity not to need to be infallible. Nevertheless, the patient's needs to make the therapist into an all-powerful figure are so great, that as soon as feasible opportunity is grasped to work directly upon indications of such attitudes, as will be discussed later.

Many difficulties can lead to disruption of therapy, but it is considered that as long as the patient feels and recognizes that the therapist is motivated by interest in helping the patient for the sake of the patient, the disruptive forces may impede but will not sever the relationship. The patient, because of long experience, is particularly acute in his ability to recognize when he becomes secondary to the needs of another. It may be relatively obvious that therapy must not be undertaken for the sake of the parents, and even though it causes the parents to seek to interfere and terminate treatment, the hazard can usually be avoided. However, it is more difficult to elude the incorporated parent when the patient tests out the therapist by falling in line with parental wishes or acting the role of a parent. The patient can, at such times, turn upon the therapist with considerable hostility, defending against the therapist as would the mother. To ride out the upheaval without hostility toward the parent or the patient may be difficult; and it may be a long while before the therapist is rewarded by the acknowledgment that the therapist is the only person other than the patient who has seen through the parent.

Even as the patient must not be treated for the sake of another, he must not be treated for the sake of the therapist. If the therapist's prestige, self-esteem, or power needs hang upon successful outcome, the patient can sabotage even as he could with mother. He may not be able to be actively aggressive, but he can use himself as a weapon. Subtly aware of the wishes of others he can meekly be the "good" and satisfying patient while defying real change, or more frequently he can seek to injure the therapist by injuring himself through ruining whatever gains he has made outside of the therapeutic relationship.

Insistence that the interpersonal relationship between patient and psychiatrist is the only essential focus of scrutiny during treatment may be too easily misunderstood by the schizophrenic patient as an attempt to hold the patient in bondage as did the mother. The lifelong difficulty in relating to others can be accentuated during treatment by the patient's belief that the therapist will resent others and reject the patient if he forms another attachment. The psychiatrist must be careful in considering that the development of close extratherapeutic relationships is an attempt to avoid the emotional impact of the transference situation. Indeed, considerable gains can be made by helping the patient, who has always had to flee from closeness, maintain and develop friendships, and come to trust himself and the other person. In this way, a young man who had broken off all relationships with girls lest a show of sexual potency might be required, was enabled through analysis of his fears of genital harm from women and his feelings of impotence in comparison with his powerful father, to establish a love relationship and progress into marriage. He learned that the girl, no more than he, knew the answers; that her expectations were not for perfection, and that she had her own shortcomings sexually; just as at another level he learned that she neither expected nor desired great potency, nor wanted his penis.

Despite the therapist's efforts to avoid being placed in an omnipotent and omniscient role, the needs of the patient may be so great that eventually a shift in therapists may be advisable. The psychiatrist who has carried the patient out of a withdrawn state, or helped through very real problems, may have demands placed upon him that cannot be met, and the patient suffers too intensely. A change of psychiatrists can be accomplished when the patient is able to see that he will be able to utilize the gains with the first therapist better if working with another psychiatrist; usually, if the therapist can honestly state that he has become too involved to be useful; and if the patient can be made to understand that it is necessitated by the psychiatrist's shortcomings rather than the patient's.

It is particularly essential in the treatment of schizophrenic patients to be aware of attitudes which may be transferred from the childhood relationships to the therapist, for the proclivity to find rejection or persecution is likely to disrupt the relationship rather than simply impede it. However, it is the direct work with incipient delusional trends which involves the psychiatrist that can be a most useful means of clarifying the paranoid material: utilizing concrete examples to replace vague feelings, and to remove them from the area of subjective preoccupation into the light of mutual scrutiny. Usually the patient must first have become reasonably secure that the therapist is for him, but if periods of undue vagueness or recrudescence are not examined in regard to the relationship, therapy may founder. Some of the basic attitudes that are likely to be transferred to the therapist have been mentioned; and only two will be elaborated upon here. The intense jealousy of other patients, or of someone such as the secretary who seems needed by the psychiatrist, can arouse intense rage, followed by feelings of rejection. The need to be essential to the psychiatrist, rather than problems of sibling rivalry, seem important. Anything less than being the sole concern falls short of satisfying the need to be needed without which the patient cannot lose the threat of abandonment. It is difficult to handle, but permitting the problem to come into the open helps dispel the projections that may derive from the feeling. Still more important is a basic problem that seems to derive from the patient's recognition from an early age that what mother *said* meant little in comparison with her attitudes and intonations, which the patient came to learn to interpret. In treatment the patient interprets the psychiatrist's gesture and expression, often with partial correctness, but at times primarily through projection. The patient further projects, not only feelings, but his own attitudes of passive communication through symbols and indications rather than by words. Therapy is often hindered or endangered more by what the patient believes the therapist is covertly conveying than by anything actually said.

Some of these dangers of becoming involved in the delusions of the patient can be counteracted by openness with the patient provided the therapist can avoid being defensive. The psychiatrist does not insist or even imply that he is right and the patient is in error, but is willing to consider and admit his own errors, possibilities of having slighted the patient, his annoyances, and his undue expectations. The interest is in working toward gaining cognizance that more than one meaning can be placed upon an incident; and then toward having the patient become aware of his consistent biases of interpretation. Thus, when a woman interprets the psychiatrist's slight delay in rising from his chair at the end of an hour as meaning that the psychiatrist is tired of seeing the patient and wishes to be rid of her, the delay even though unnoted by the psychiatrist is not denied. He may even comment that it was thoughtless but wonder why the incident was interpreted in this manner. Later in therapy when the incident is repeated, he might wonder whether the patient had not some other grounds to think the psychiatrist was tired of treating her; or whether she had not herself been having thoughts of leaving the therapist; and even later in therapy he might wonder whether this delay in rising, as it seems to upset the patient so much, might not have had some particular significance in a previous relationship. For related reasons it seems useful verbally to express to the patient annoyances or concerns that may be apparent in the therapist's mood or behavior, rather than let the sensitive patient perceive these attitudes and interpret them in terms of his own concerns. The attitude of examining the relationship together with the patient, rather than interpreting, as has been stressed by Harry Stack Sullivan (1940), seems particularly important not only to avoid being placed in an omniscient role, but to indicate the therapist's consideration of, and esteem for, the patient's opinions and abilities. More paranoid patients, in particular, can participate in treatment but cannot be treated in the sense of having another person control or manage them.

Problems concerning the handling of content cannot be discussed aside from certain implications derived from the concepts expressed in this paper. The thoughts of schizophrenic patients are likely to be vague for they are more concerned with feelings and symbols of feelings than with activity and communication. The therapist is under no obligation to understand the verbal expressions of these thoughts, which, indeed are not at all clear to the patient. He needs to clarify what the patient is saying for himself and for the patient. It is considered best if such clarification is carried out in a manner that can be followed by the patient rather than through interpretation, so that the steps taken by the psychiatrist are apparent. The psychiatrist may comment, "You have been saying thus-and-thus. Do I understand that you are saying—this?" or, "There is something similar between what you are saying today and what you said yesterday, but I don't quite see it." However, as progress is made, firmer means of insisting upon clarification may be used: "You have said this—and—this—and—this. It seems to me that all these things mean—this."

The general policy adopted has been not to avoid topics mentioned or even hinted at by the patient because they seem too touchy at a given stage of treatment. The schizophrenic patient is so apt to assume that the therapist hears everything, that shying away from a topic may be taken to mean that it cannot be discussed with the therapist any more than it could be with a parent. The topic, or the indications of the preoccupation, can at least be acknowledged by a comment that lets the patient know that it has been heard. The decision to continue on the trend can be left to the patient. The same attitude is adopted with dreams contrary to a generally held opinion that the interpretation of dreams is avoided if possible in the treatment of schizophrenic patients. In contrast to neurotic patients, the schizophrenic is likely to be aware of the general meaning of many dreams, and avoidance of the dream would be more protection of the therapist than the patient. When the schizophrenic patient mentions a dream, the meaning of which seems quite apparent, it is considered that he is trying it out in his consciousness and with the therapist. Anxiety, which is not as useful in the treatment of schizophrenic patients as in neurotic patients, is just as likely to ensue if the patient feels that the therapist, who is now so much part of him, cannot tolerate the implications of the dream. Indeed, we have noted, in a few instances, that the acceptance and examination of a dream has led to dissolution of paranoid features. For example, the recounting and acceptance of a dream with homosexual implications directed toward the therapist has removed the need to distort and circumvent to keep the patient and the therapist from becoming aware of impulses of which the patient is already partially conscious.

PART II

Studies of the Seventeen Families

III

Schizophrenia and the Family

(1957)

The second International Congress for Psychiatry, devoted to the problems of schizophrenia, opened with an address by Manfred Bleuler which emphasized the dilemma created because virtually no two schools of contemporary psychiatry agree concerning the nature and the etiology of schizophrenia. The proceedings of the Congress confirmed his concern, and, in particular, made it clear that some American and English groups who have pursued intensive psychotherapy with schizophrenic patients regard the condition very differently from the way in which Continental psychiatrists view it. As I listened to my European colleagues at the Congress—at times with enthusiasm, and occasionally with astonishment—I became more impressed than ever that the difficulties in achieving areas of agreement do not simply follow upon different conceptualizations of schizophrenia, but stem from the more basic problem of widely divergent views concerning the nature of man and how he becomes an integrated person.

I do not believe that a satisfactory orientation for the study of schizophrenia can be achieved simply by synthesizing all approaches of possible relevance. A major task of the scientist is to seek to simplify through achieving laws or principles that unify and bring order to complex and seemingly contradictory phenomena. The present state of knowledge as indicated by the presentations at the Congress

Theodore Lidz: Schizophrenia and the Family. Psychiatry, *Vol. 21, 1958, pp. 21-27. Copyright © 1958, The William Alanson White Psychiatric Foundation, Inc. This paper, in substantially the same form, was presented at the Plenary Session on the Social Psychiatry of Schizophrenia at the Second International Congress for Psychiatry in Zurich, Switzerland, September, 1957.*

indicated a great need for a reorientation that will bring new insight, clarity, and direction.

I wish, therefore, to try to present a different way of regarding man and schizophrenia. I say "man and schizophrenia" pointedly, to suggest that schizophrenia, instead of being a *process* that has inserted itself into a person and possessed him, depriving him of reason, is rather one of the potential fates to which man is subject in his efforts to find a way of life as an independent person amid the many potential hazards that beset his path from infancy to maturity. Further, I believe that the study of schizophrenic reactions has an importance to the science of man that even transcends the relief of myriads of suffering patients. There are indications that a satisfactory understanding of schizophrenia will be synchronous and synonymous with the opening of vast new insights concerning the integration of man and his emotional homeostasis. Yet I do not consider that all is darkness and mystery even now, if we psychiatrists can but accept some facts that confront us rather than insist upon perceiving only what fits into preconceptions handed to us from our professional forebears.

In the hope of contributing to the clarification of issues involved, I have sought to set down what I consider fundamental to the study of schizophrenia as succinctly as possible and as simply as possible—for I believe that simplicity provides a test of clarity of conceptualization. I do not know if many—or any—of my countrymen will agree with me; it is my orientation, and it may also be theirs. This presentation certainly differs from the tradition generally followed in many other countries, and followed by many in the United States. But when strenuous and persistent efforts, pursued for almost a hundred years, only lead in circles, it is time to raise the question: Are the concepts and premises which guide the search sufficient?

Those who study schizophrenia as a problem of aberrant personality development, or as a type of failure to achieve a workable ego integration, are accustomed to hear that they neglect the brain and problems of physiological homeostasis. I believe, in contrast, that many of my neurologizing and chemically oriented colleagues are the ones who do not properly take into account the human brain and the nature of human physiological integration. The human brain, after all, differs from that of animals and bestows upon man a uniqueness in the way he adapts to his environment. It is just this uniqueness that must be considered in an illness that is specifically human because it involves distortions of the symbolic processes.

I consider that the critical characteristic of schizophrenia lies in the aberrant symbolic processes—in the distortion of perception, meaning, and logic. Such disturbances are usually, and even conventionally, taken to indicate dysfunctions of the brain, although careful studies and even casual observations show that the schizophrenic disorders of mentation differ critically from any produced by known toxic or deficit states, which include degradations of mental capacity along with any distortions. Schizophrenia is considered as a condition in which the patient escapes from an untenable world and his insoluble conflicts by altering his internal representation of reality. Unable to move into the future, and even unable to regain security through regression, he withdraws, and by changing the world autistically and by renouncing the logic of his culture, finds some living space and some semblance of self-esteem. The condition tends to be self-perpetuating because the patient has abandoned testing of the utility of his ideas in terms of their capacity to help him to master his environment or to further his communication with others. Since this self-contained way of life is often precipitated by fear of loss of control of incestuous, homosexual, or homicidal impulses, panic increases the disorganization of the interpersonal disorientation, but restitutive measures to re-establish some way of relating usually follow, because man cannot live in isolation.

Consideration of a few critical problems of human adaptation leads to an expectation that a schizophrenic outcome is a possibility inherent in the developmental process which must be anticipated, rather than a condition to be regarded as incomprehensible or as the manifestation of a disordered cerebral apparatus.

Man's inordinate adaptability depends upon a brain that permits abstract symbolization, including communication and its internal counterpart, mentation. Because he can communicate, man has built up over countless generations ways of doing and reacting which are termed the instrumentalities of his culture. These include his language, his ways of perceiving and thinking, and his mores and sentiments, as well as the actual tools that he has slowly accumulated. These acquisitions, of course, are not transmitted from one generation to the next within the germ plasm. Medicine has sought, by and large, to confine its considerations to the biological unfolding of the genetically endowed man, and the maintenance of his homeostasis in relation to his physical environment. Unless one understands that man is endowed with two heritages, a genetic inheritance and a cultural heritage, one can never understand him or his physiological functioning correctly. Unless the infant grows into and assimilates the instrumentalities of the culture in which he is raised, he will be no more a person than his pre-Stone Age progenitors, and no more capable of living in society. Man has, after all, developed not so much through genetic mutation as through his acquisition over generations of new and more helpful ways of living.

The infant is born with countless potentialities, but virtually no inborn direction; he learns ways of communicating, doing, and thinking through the long years of dependency necessarily provided because, unlike the lower animals, he has been freed of inborn—or instinctive—patterns of adaptation. He must find ways of solving the tasks presented at each stage of growth in order to move on to the next phase with security. By the end of adolescence or in early adult life he is expected to have assimilated patterns of adaptation in a way that is sufficiently integrated for him to leave his parental guidance, to achieve an identity of his own, and to find a role in life and a path into the future. These do not come to him as part of his biological development simply because he has matured physically, but through learning, and particularly through his interaction with the parental models with whom he must identify and whom he introjects. The process can proceed with reasonable smoothness only if these models are not impossible to follow, if they are not mutually contradictory, and if they have transmitted useful ways of living in the society into which the youth must emerge.

There are endless chances for misdirection, confusion, and conflict. The child, who must constantly gain more independence in the normal course of development, is prey to insecurity and anxiety and repeatedly seeks dependency and the security it provides despite its confinements. Repression and the relegation to the unconscious of impulses and wishes unacceptable to real or introjected parental figures are part of a development which requires delimitation and channeling to permit integrated ego growth. Regression, as well as progression, is an essential part of development. The child grows in relation to others, requiring them for his security, and man is never free of his need for others. He is moved to regain the lost union of childhood, even as he grows from it. The need gains compulsive moment because of his sexual drives. He can never be considered as an isolate, for even in isolation he is supported by his bonds to others, which are no less real because they are intangible. The loss of such bonds brings catastrophe. Nor can he be ever understood separated from the culture which he carries within him, for he has grown into it, and it has become incorporated in him.

Indeed, the problems with which psychiatry proper deals can be defined in just such terms—those problems that arise because the infant, biologically endowed with inborn drives but not with inborn direction, must assimilate the instrumentalities of his culture to become a person. Also because this assimilation must be sufficiently harmonious to permit him to function in an integrated way, it depends to a very great extent upon what is incorporated of and from the persons who raise him.

The two paths of maturation, the unfolding of his genetic endowment and the assimilation of the culture, are inextricably intertwined. His biological nature establishes certain imperatives—such as the complete dependency of the infant and the late occurrence of pubescence —and each culture must take these into account. The value systems and meanings inherent in each culture set imperatives also, to insure that each new member will be able to live in and to transmit the culture—imperatives which profoundly affect physiological functioning. Simply illustrated, a Christian's appetite and gastric juices may be stimulated by pork, but a Mohammedan will be repelled by it. In pursuit of contemporary dynamic and analytic principles one cannot afford to forget the essence of Adolf Meyer's psychobiology—that the human being is integrated at a symbolic level, and that the way in which he thinks and feels influences the functioning of the entire organism down to the cellular level.

Now, the very mechanism which permits man's inordinate adaptability contains a major vulnerability, for he depends primarily upon the instrumental utility of his thinking to master the many divergent environments in which he has learned to live in widely differing fashions. Meanings are not inborn, nor is man endowed with an innate system of logic. The brain permits thinking, but it does not guarantee its rationality. Indeed, what is considered rational varies with time and place, as history has amply demonstrated. Meanings develop through communication with others and from sorting out life's experiences, but perceptions and meanings alter in the service of emotional needs, as well as in the service of learning a utilitarian adaptation to the environment. They alter not only in the attempt to maintain a satisfactory image of oneself but also a satisfactory image of the persons who are essential to one's security. When a person's acceptability to himself and others is threatened, many self-deceptions can arise to ward off anxiety. After all, such nonperceptions or self-deceptions are what are referred to as the mechanisms of defense. When these defenses are of no avail, when essential expectations are mutually conflicting, when the path into the future is barred, and even regression is blocked because the persons upon whom one would depend cannot be trusted, there is still a way. One can simply alter his perception of his own needs and motivations and those of others. He can abandon causal logic, change the meanings of events, retreat to the period of childhood when reality gave way before the fantasy of his wish, and regain a type of omnipotence and self-sufficiency. In short, he can become schizophrenic. Perhaps not everyone can resort to such devices; they may only be open to those who have been poorly grounded in reality and who have actually been trained in irrational ways in their childhood. Indeed, this path is so clearly open to man, and so often used in culturally approved and therefore non-delusional ways, that if this analysis of man's adaptability is even approximately correct and if investigators did not know of a syndrome such as schizophrenia, they would have to search for it, as an anticipated anomaly of the developmental processes.

With this general orientation it has been natural to turn to the careful study of the family environment in which the patient grows up in a search for determinants of schizophrenic reactions. The family provides the primary schooling in social living; the person's experience in all other group and interpersonal interactions rests upon the foundations constructed within the family. Knowingly or unknowingly the family has the task of transmitting the basic instrumentalities of the culture to the offspring, including ways of reasoning and reacting emotionally, and of communicating verbally and empathically. It usually provides the models for identification which will be introjected, and the models of love objects that will pattern emotional relationships.

While the family is not all, and is not the only influence upon ego development, it provides the most consistent—or consistently inconsistent—set of influences impinging upon the maturing child. The emphasis upon the intrafamilial object relationships is not inconsistent with other analytic or dynamic approaches. It includes an interest in causes of ego weakness, of blurring of ego boundaries, of narcissistic withdrawal after object loss, of regression to infantile omnipotence and security, of withdrawal to a world free from the confines of reality testing, and so forth. However, it is considered that the ego develops in relation to objects—particularly to the parental figures—and in a world of the family created largely by the interaction of the parental figures.

Eventually a research group undertook intensive explorations of the lives of the families in which schizophrenic patients were raised. The study utilized multiple techniques in an effort to re-create the personalities, the dynamics, and the atmosphere of these family groups. I shall not attempt to review the findings here; they were unexpectedly striking. Not one family of a schizophrenic patient was found to be reasonably well integrated, although a few had difficulties which came to light only after many months of investigation.

Such studies cannot be confined to the interaction between a parent and the schizophrenic offspring. The family is a true small group with an organic life and unity of its own, and with a set of imperative functions which it must fulfill in order to raise a new generation. Such imperatives have scarcely been designated or studied as yet. The family provides a shelter for its members within and against the remainder of society. The welfare of the family, more than of any other group, requires that each member give an unspecified degree of precedence to the needs of the family above his own needs and those

of outsiders. The actions of any one member affect all, producing reaction and counteraction. Roles are assigned, according to generation
and sex, which cannot be violated without distorting the emergent
personalities. Roles also develop to fit the emotional needs of the
members, and these roles must relate reciprocally for the entire group,
or leave one or several members in a state of imbalance requiring
pathological defenses.

Stated in too summary a fashion, the family is viewed as a shaping
force upon the offspring's personality. The family provides the constitutional basis for the personality through heredity, and constantly
contributes to it by example, by teaching, and by the interaction of
its members as a social unit; within this unit the child is prepared for
existence in relation to other persons and social groups.

Thus it becomes apparent that a mother's attitude toward a child is
not simply a reflection of her capacities to mother him, but also, for
example, of her attitude toward the marriage. The father exerts direct
and indirect influences upon her ability to mother, as well as upon the
children. Yet we find in our studies that all of the marriages upon
which these family structures rest are gravely disturbed. There is
either a schismatic conflict between the parents that divides the family into two camps and that results in each spouse's destroying the
worth of the other, or the family is distorted by the passive acceptance of the serious psychopathology of the dominant spouse by the
other, with masking of the serious problems that arise, creating an
aberrant environment that confuses the child.

It is difficult to discuss the more subtle influences affecting the child
in such families, for it would require neglect of the very gross problems that are surprisingly aberrant to anyone who has not become
involved in such studies. In each of these families at least one parent
suffers from serious and crippling psychopathology. Even though in
this series, because of a bias in selection, no parent had ever been in a
mental hospital, in contrast to the many genetic studies that may be
cited, minimally 60 per cent of the patients had at least one parent
who was an ambulatory schizophrenic or was clearly paranoid. Still
others were chronic though unadmitted severe alcoholics, or severe
obsessives, and some were extremely passive-dependent—indeed "children" of their spouses and not "parents." The fathers were as patho-

logical as the mothers, and often the more serious disturbing influence in the family (Chapter V). I cannot now go into the complex dynamics of the distorted relationships and the very faulty models for identification in these families, or how these disturbances, which help to determine the nature of specific symptomatology, are reflected in the way the offspring experience the world. Suffice it to say that these families in many ways provide training in irrationality. I wish to remark somewhat parenthetically, in response to a question raised repeatedly, that the problem of why one child among several in a family becomes schizophrenic does not appear to be insurmountable when one grasps the dynamics of role relationships within the family, the vicissitudes of the family, and the different stresses linked to being a member of one sex or the other in the given family.

Many persons have made contributions from clinical observations, and our particular group is no longer the only one pursuing systematic studies in this area.[1] In contrast to the difficulties of communicating in many areas at the International Congress, it was noteworthy that at the session concerned with the family environment, people from seven or eight countries, speaking in three languages, found common ground and meaningful exchange, for they were dealing with tangible clinical findings, to which theory and speculation were secondary. Even though the family varies from one country to another, the findings seemed basically similar from Israel to the United States, and from Greece to Finland. There are no other such consistent findings of potential significance to the etiology of schizophrenia—whether interpreted genetically or environmentally—or findings which promise to give so much structure and meaning to the understanding of what the schizophrenic patient is experiencing. True, the pursuit of such leads requires that the psychiatrist become familiar with sociology, anthropology, and genetics, as well as psychiatry, rather than with biochemistry and neuropathology, but it seems incumbent to follow where facts lead rather than to cling to past training and predispositions. Now I should say that of course there are areas concerning schizophrenia that are best studied through scrutiny of the central nervous system or the metabolic processes, or through animal experi-

[1] See, for example, Alanen (1958); Bowen et al. (1957); Delay et al. (1957); Wynne et al. (1957).

mentation. One takes exception to such studies only when they seek to simplify problems concerning human behavior by confining attention to a small segment of the field, hoping thus to avoid the complexities that arise in considering human problems in terms of problems in living.

The studies of family environment to which I have referred have had many practical effects upon our therapeutic efforts—but this forms a topic in itself. The support and understanding offered these parents has led to striking changes in the marital relationship and in the attitudes toward the children. At times the parents have benefited more than the patients, but in other cases, changes in the parents have been followed by striking improvement in the patients. Communication between therapist and patient is fostered, for the meaning of what the patient seeks to communicate and what he seeks still to conceal may become apparent from knowledge of the family life and troubles. Perhaps, however, the essence of the benefit lies in the tangible meaning which the patients' behavior and symptoms take on, so that work with them becomes less evanescent and more capable of being translated into terms of concrete interpersonal difficulties with which both patient and therapist can work.

After all, the psychiatrist who wishes to learn about schizophrenia can be taught more by the patient than by laboratory samples of him. The therapist who can respect his patient as a person and can listen and dare to hear will eventually gain insights which make it an exciting privilege to work with schizophrenic patients. A Dadaist author whose identity I do not know said that to be insane is to forsake reason—to forsake reason but not truth, for the madman often speaks the truth while the sane hold their tongues.[2] And parents and siblings also have much to tell—sometimes including uncanny insights—as is shown by the profound communications concerning schizophrenia that have been offered by authors, and particularly by playwrights, who have had schizophrenic siblings.

Our family studies continue. I have sought to offer the reasons, both theoretical and empirical. We do not think that we have begun to solve the problems of schizophrenia—but we constantly find tan-

[2] Quoted by Henry Miller in *Tropic of Capricorn*. Paris: Obelisk Press, 1956, p. 307.

gible and intriguing new leads to follow, and no longer feel that we grope in the dark in hopes of somehow stumbling onto the path. We begin to think that we see the path to follow through the labyrinth; at times we dare to hope—in our dreams—that we have grasped Ariadne's thread. But the way is long and help is needed.

IV

Casework Interviewing as a Research Technique in a Study of Families of Schizophrenic Patients

(1955)

When a technique such as that of casework interviewing is used in an intensive family study, it quickly becomes apparent that it is the interviewer who is the tool and the method. It seems useful, therefore, to consider the technique as applied and experienced by a caseworker in a special project. This is a study of the families of a small number of young schizophrenic patients. We have been particularly concerned with the interaction among family members, the many kinds of equilibria which become established with varying degrees of success and stability, and the forces which act upon these equilibria, tending to preserve or disrupt them. Feelings and attitudes which may never be put into words, discrepancies between what is said and what is done or implied, must be noted along with apparently more easily interpreted historical "facts."

Quantities of material may become readily available, but major problems lie in the selection, evaluation, and interpretation of the data, and these processes are inextricably involved in the gathering of information. Casework interviewing provides a technique which is adaptable in many ways and which can be sensitive to subtleties and intricacies, changing to suit particular conditions or to take advantage of unexpected opportunities. Inherent in the technique and inseparable from these assets are certain liabilities. A very personal skill, it must be dependent upon the individual using it, his sensitivity, flexi-

Alice R. Cornelison: Casework Interviewing as a Research Technique in a Study of Families of Schizophrenic Patients. Mental Hygiene, *Vol. 44, 1960, pp. 551-559. Copyright © 1960, National Association for Mental Health, Inc.*

bility, and prejudice. Its very adaptability makes difficult the comparison of findings from one case to another and the standardization of results.

In the part of the project to be discussed here, our major concern is with the interplay of personalities in the family group. Therefore, we do not consider the mother-child relationship a closed system. We are interested in observing ways in which each member of the family affects and is affected by the patient both directly through personal interaction and indirectly through relationships with other members of the family. Social and cultural pressures which might produce stresses within the family must also be noted.

Patterns of identification are of particular interest. A successful masculine identification may be difficult for a boy to achieve when his father's bizarre manner is represented as ordinary male behavior. It may also be affected by a mother's belittling or contemptuous attitude toward her husband, the father's competitive attitude toward his son, or either parent's seductive behavior toward him, as well as combinations of these factors. Further complications are added by the presence of siblings, rivalries among them, their tendencies to form alliances with one parent or the other, etc. We may be interested in learning why one child "chose" to identify with healthy aspects of the parents and another with their more disturbed behavior.

Difficulties in perception and communication, too, are matters for concern. Has the child learned distortions in certain areas by identification with disturbed members of the family? Are these distortions perhaps related to a subtle glossing over of the unpleasant realities, actions contradictory to the apparent meaning of spoken words, or are they derived from the direct teaching of paranoid or illogical ways of thinking? Has the development of such patterns come about as a defense against an accusation, actual or implied, or some other kind of pressure?

We cannot hope to trace all the intricacies of these many networks of action and reaction, but we can keep them in mind and try to follow whatever leads we find in our hands.

An opportunity for observation of these phenomena is provided in the long-term casework treatment of problems brought to us by these families. There is sufficient motivation for both family and interviewer to engage in extensive exploration of troublesome areas. A gradual unfolding takes place in which, it is to be hoped, both the relative and interviewer can see the situation with increasing clarity. We recognize that in entering the situation at all, we are changing it. Doing this by means of a planned therapeutic approach gives an opportunity to test hypotheses, explore otherwise inaccessible areas, and observe new phases of interaction.

SOME PRACTICAL ASPECTS OF THE METHOD

Since, for many years, casework with the patients' families has been an integral part of the treatment program in this hospital, it has not been necessary for the research worker to depart very far from routine procedures. For purposes of the study, a more determined effort may be made to have all family members keep regular weekly appointments even when it seems unlikely that they will make constructive use of the service. Some information not immediately applicable to the therapeutic approach may be sought, but, in general, these cases are handled more intensively rather than differently from others.

The social worker's contact with the relatives begins as soon as the patient is admitted to the hospital, sometimes even before his admission. Several reasons may be given for the appointments with the caseworker, and the order and emphasis with which these are presented may be varied, according to the individuals. Relatives are encouraged to use the caseworker as their liaison with the hospital, discussing with her their questions regarding hospital procedure and regulations; what they may or may not bring to the patient and why; what changes might take place in his behavior toward them, etc. They are told that we believe we can understand the patient better and work with him more effectively when we know his family and can learn about him from them. We tell them, also, that, because we realize that the hospitalization of a family member is upsetting, we believe the relatives should have available to them for regular appointments a social worker, a specialist in family problems. Group interviews such as those employed by Ackerman (1958b) and Bowen et al. (1957) have recently been initiated with some families. In all cases, parents have met a few times with one of the psychiatrists, generally for discussion of particular questions related to planning for the patient. With some individuals, the interviewing has been done by one of the psychiatrists on the research team. This arrangement was made in some cases because a parent seemed unusually disturbed, and in others, because it seemed desirable to have husband and wife see different interviewers. Possibly because these have happened also to be the senior staff psychiatrists of the hospital, one result of such an arrangement has sometimes been that other family members lose interest in seeing the social worker.

Most of the relatives assume that in a university hospital, our data will also be used for study purposes, but this is not discussed specifically with them unless they bring it up. Usually, it does not occur to them during their initial anxiety over the patient's hospitalization. After the relationship is established, the idea of research is accepted, if it arises at all, with little evidence of concern.

The initial reactions to appointments with the social worker vary. A few may want her to run errands or listen to complaints about the hospital and see that things are changed. Some want to see only the administrative head of the hospital and are indignant at having to settle for less. Nearly all are very anxious and defensive, and those who are aware of it are grateful for the special attention and the opportunity to unburden themselves. Whatever the initial reaction, most accept the contact readily enough to permit establishment of a workable relationship.

A number of different and sometimes changing motives serve to keep the relatives in contact with the social worker. Most hope to learn about their patient, his life in the hospital, and his progress. Plans for the patient's employment, tutoring, school, and, eventually, discharge arrangements may need to be discussed. Parents, and often siblings, feel intensely guilty, and this can lead them to wish to prove their willingness to help. A few relatives would like to escape from the situation. Many are frightened about themselves and seek reassurance that they are not sick, too. Some feel the need for help in learning to cope with family problems bearing on the patient's illness.

As many sources of data and opportunities for observation as possible are explored and developed. Regular attendance at staff conferences and frequent discussion with the patient's therapist are essential, of course. In addition, the caseworker spends time on the ward, making the acquaintance of the patient and gathering impressions of patient and family visitors from nurses and ward aides. Home visits yield particularly valuable data, and the social worker is sometimes able to participate in family parties, birthday celebrations, etc. Whenever possible, schoolteachers, old family friends, nursemaids, etc., are interviewed.

Notes are dictated, usually on the day of the interview, from memory alone. This is a personal preference. Recorded interviews would give accuracy of a sort but would produce masses of unwieldy material. A few recorded interviews with each individual could be valuable, but we have not yet used them.

All family members are asked to take psychological tests, and these are studied to determine what can be learned from them of family relationships, patterns of identification, etc.

Case material has been discussed regularly at weekly meetings of the research team.

Usefulness of Combined Casework Service and Research

The patient's stay in the hospital, as well as the project's study of the family, may depend upon successful work with the relatives from the start. Many parents are not sure they have made the correct decision in hospitalizing their son or daughter, and the patient, ambivalent toward both family and hospital, will often make destructive use of the family guilt and fear. Immediate evaluation of the parents' anxieties and efforts to meet some of their needs may reduce considerably the danger of discharge against advice.

A history obtained over a period of time from several informants in free and spontaneous discussion is particularly rich in color and depth. Accounts of the same incident by various family members may be pieced together to give a rounded picture. It is often possible to evaluate contradictions and to make a fair guess at the degree of distortion in the material provided by each informant.

Mrs. Lerner described a visit to her daughter, in which, she said, the girl had flown into an entirely unprovoked rage at her father. Mr.

Lerner, in his interview, reported that, in spite of the patient's obviously irritable and upset mood, he had involved her in a complicated legalistic argument in which he exposed and ridiculed irrationalities in her thinking, and it was then that she had attacked him. When this is brought together with other similar incidents, we can see the mother's protective and subtly belittling attitude toward her husband, Mr. Lerner's provocative behavior toward his daughter, and Mrs. Lerner's denial of it.

Long contact makes possible observations of the family through major and minor crises and also induces spontaneous revelations of a more intimate nature than are obtained in a few interviews.

Mrs. Lerner did not confide for almost a year that her husband had suffered a mental breakdown many years before, and, since he had never fully recovered from it, the major responsibility for supporting the family fell upon her while he kept up appearances but remained relatively inactive. This gave us both important historical material and a sample of behavior to compare with that in the relatively trivial incident described above.

Changes in the family which appear to result from our therapeutic intervention may shed light on some of our hypotheses. We noted that the mother of a sixteen-year-old schizophrenic son clung very tightly to her children, particularly the boys. It appeared that this might be at least partially explained by her difficult marital situation and consequent need to obtain affection and gratification elsewhere. We found evidence to support this when, after the stress in the marriage was eased, partly through our efforts and partly through external events, she became less indulgent with the patient's younger brother and set more reasonable limits when responding to his demands.

Much can be deduced about the family from the relatives' behavior toward the interviewer. An apparently routine event or casual conversation may be far more revealing than the replies to direct questions.

When Mr. Nussbaum, the father of a schizophrenic adolescent girl, wanted to entertain the social worker accompanying his daughter on her first visit home by telling sexual jokes, the worker's dilemma in handling the situation revealed much about the pressures the patient has experienced in her life in this family. Laughing at the jokes would offend the mother and the patient, who were maintaining a stony silence; not laughing would inflict a painful wound in the father's very tender narcissism. Considering this, together with the patient's propensity for playing off hospital versus family and staff member against staff member, we can see the total situation with greater clarity. This was further illuminated in a quarrel between the parents, which took place in the interviewing room. They had been informed that their next week's appointment would be canceled because the social worker would be out of town. They assumed that it was to be a vacation, and Mr. Nussbaum insisted Florida was the place. His wife said Florida was a dreadful spot. Suggestively, he remarked that he was going there soon for professional meetings. She glowered. Suddenly, he proposed the city where they lived, and both were in immediate, if brief, agreement. The worker could stay in their apartment and sleep in their daughter's bed. He said she could go to the theater every night. Mrs. Nussbaum said grimly that he never takes *her* to the theater, and so it went, giving a clear picture of a scene which must have been re-enacted many times over in their home with their daughter.

In the same way, childlike dependency, hostile condescension, supplicating, friendly, aggressive, or ingratiating behavior toward the social worker all demonstrate much of the family patterns of interaction. While complaints are an interesting area for studying some situations, the absence of justifiable complaints is equally revealing. In these situations, the "feel" of the interaction is at least as important as what is discussed directly.

SOME PROBLEMS IN APPLICATION

A few special problems arise in this application of the casework technique.

There are times in the combined approach of service and research when one must be adapted to give way to the other. In occasional instances, the two may be in direct conflict, but these have been relatively rare. Often the two are closer together than is immediately apparent.

An invitation from the Newberg family to go with them to the ward for a celebration of the patient's birthday was accepted eagerly for research purposes, but reluctantly, because their son, who was depressed at the thought of a second birthday in the hospital, might be even more disturbed by the presence of a guest invited by his family. He was upset, but the party itself provided valuable material for discussion with the parents regarding their difficulty in recognizing his rude and ill-mannered behavior. A week or so later, the patient spontaneously asked to talk over the incident with the social worker. He apologized, acknowledged his need for control, and indicated anxiety at being offered his family's explanation that he "was not feeling well." It was, therefore, unexpectedly useful from a therapeutic point of view.

Pressing an anxious informant too far might arouse resistances which would defeat research as well as therapeutic goals. In one or two cases, we became concerned for fear we might be upsetting the families too much. Their anxiety subsided, however, and it seemed that it represented a necessary phase.

In order to have a degree of uniformity of data, it was decided that one interviewer should, whenever possible, see all family members. Problems of transference and countertransference have, therefore, been very complex. The social worker does not relate in the same way to all people interviewed. She has likes and dislikes and personality traits of her own which make for more productive relationships with some individuals and less productive contacts with others.

Some families are very free and probably fairly reliable when giving historical data. In a few cases, there is only a very scattered and "unreliable" family history. Always, we have our own observations of current behavior in a stress situation, which is fairly constant from one case to the next, although, even in this, there are variations if there have been previous hospitalizations.

When there have been sharply divided allegiances within a family, it has sometimes been hard to avoid taking sides. Furthermore, even a mild demonstration of interest in the marital partner's history can aggravate the conflict and reinforce resistances with results which might interfere with the achievement of either therapeutic or research goals. A mother who was inclined to project all her problems onto her disturbed and very difficult husband brought up dramatic historical information concerning him, of a sort which he would be likely to conceal just at the time when it seemed wise to try to help her check these projections and encourage her to think more about herself and her own part in the family difficulties. Interest shown in this material at this time would probably tend to reinforce her projections and to close off useful data concerning herself, but the information was valuable; it would probably not come up again or be available through other family members. Bringing it up later would only give it more emphasis. It was discussed but in less detail than might have been desirable from the point of view of our research interest in the husband's psychopathology.

Relationships of the social worker with other members of the staff, both research team and other hospital personnel, have a marked effect on the data. Suggestions may be made concerning new lines of thought or other ways of working with the case. This can be both stimulating and reassuring. It introduces some checks on the subjectivity of her impressions but adds, of course, other subjective impressions. At times, the combined hostility of the group toward a particularly trying parent has complicated the worker's efforts to handle her own hostility. In other instances, she has felt pressed to protect a relative from attack by the group or by the patient-therapist combination. No doubt these circumstances affect both the data and the relationships concerned. Mutual confidence and understanding between therapist and caseworker can facilitate the free exchange of ideas. The occasional lack of it limits understanding of the case and affects the worker's relationships with family members.

The fact that the relatives are not told of the research probably complicates the social worker's feeling about her work with them. The decision to omit discussion of the use of data for research purposes was based on a pilot study made of four families by Dr. Beulah Parker. Two who were told of the research became uncooperative and suspicious, fearing that they and their patient were being exploited, even though they were, in fact, receiving extra care and attention in addition to the reduced rate then available. The other two families, who were not informed of the research, were much more inclined to participate in a helpful way. At that stage in the research planning, efforts were made to avoid therapeutic intervention with the families, but these were not very successful. It seems possible that this, together with the fact that the families were singled out in seeing a psychiatrist rather than a social worker, might have affected the findings, but we have not tested it.

A related problem, still unresolved, is that of confidentiality. In a comprehensive study such as this, it is difficult to work out satisfactory disguises. Even if we could make the families unrecognizable to their friends, it would be next to impossible to disguise them from themselves. A father who has confided in us his extramarital affairs would not like to have his wife read their case history. It might be a shocking discovery for a mother to learn that we believe she needs her child's illness in order to give her life a focus and direction, or for a father to read that his son considers him strongly homosexual. Since our families are relatively sophisticated, we cannot be sure that they will never pick up a book or article signed by people they know, coming from the hospital where they have had a patient. This thought poses a serious problem for the caseworker who is seeing the families. At times it is possible to repress it, but there is no doubt that it is always present, and that it does interfere.

Occasionally, the caseworker experiences a kind of pressure from the fact that she needs something from these relatives even when they do not feel the need of anything from her. Parents in one family were exceptionally anxious at the thought of the interviews and found innumerable reasons for not making or keeping appointments. They insisted upon evening appointments which they canceled minutes before the hour "because they were tired" or kept the appointment and then let it be known that they could as easily have come during the day. Had they chosen to come because of their own need, this might have been interpreted as provocative behavior, hostility, resistance, etc. Here, however, we needed them more than they thought they needed us, and the worker's resentment could not be so easily dissipated.

Data obtained by casework interviewing are open to challenge on the basis of the subjectivity of the approach. It is true that even in the broadest aspects of the consideration of such material as this study provides, the part played by personal biases is great. It is possible in extensive and detailed case histories to find or to project evidence in support of almost any hypothesis. Collection of data cannot be separated from interpretation, and the impressions of the interviewer are, of course, subjective ones.

Personal biases of other members of the research team and the various personalities play upon and interact with the various aspects of the interviewer's personality, checking the subjectivity of her observations in some ways, complicating it still further in others. In another similar project, an analyst, having no investment in the outcome of the study, was found to be very helpful in conferences with those collecting the data, but this, of course, adds another subjective impression, and this could go on *ad infinitum* (Bott, 1957).

We are dealing here with changing quantities, shifting equilibria, subtleties which are observable at some times and not at others, and intensities which can be compared roughly, but only roughly. Only a sensitive and adaptable method could provide the material necessary to such a study. The same factors which we hope may contribute these qualities will also produce unevenness and distortion in the data. Paradoxically, when such "errors" are discoverable, they can further our understanding of the families. The value in the procedure lies in the color and depth and intimacy, the richness of detail, in the picture of life in these families as we see it unfold before us.

V

The Fathers

(1955)

As part of our intensive study, we here present an initial compilation of material concerning fathers. We are not studying such fathers apart from their interaction with the remaining members of the families, or from their role as partners in marriages in which the wives are often, if not usually, very difficult women who also have serious neurotic or psychotic needs that tend to disrupt the marriage and the family life. We are here focusing upon the father because so much attention has been focused on the mother, with little recognition of the difficulties frequently imposed upon her and the children by the father, and because, in order to understand these marriages, which are predominantly unsuccessful and often torn by intrafamilial schism, we must understand the husband as well as the wife.

In the orientation that permeates our work, there is no incrimination of the parent, such as often develops from receiving the story from the patient's point of view. One rapidly realizes that these parents are struggling with their own problems and defenses and, with very rare exceptions, have striven to do their best for their children within their abilities and the limits placed by their own emotional difficulties. Too often the psychiatrist forgets his psychiatric understandings when dealing with parents and expects them to have been

Theodore Lidz, Alice R. Cornelison, Stephen Fleck, and Dorothy Terry: The Intrafamilial Environment of the Schizophrenic Patient: I. The Father. Psychiatry, *Vol. 20, 1957, pp. 329-342.* Copyright © 1957, The William Alanson White Psychiatric Foundation, Inc. *This paper was presented in November, 1955, to the Joint Meeting of the Washington Psychiatric Society, the Washington Psychoanalytic Society, and the Medical Society of St. Elizabeth's Hospital, Washington, D.C.*

able to be different from what they were, or to change through reading a book or just because he tells them to behave differently. They,
too, are as much bound to their unconscious conflicts as the patients
and could not have been other than they were.

THE SCHIZOPHRENIC AND HIS FAMILY

Our focus has been on the entire period of maturation, seeking to
grasp the complex interplay of forces that may prevent the patient
from achieving an individual identity or an integrated self at the end
of adolescence or early in adult life, very much as Erikson (1956) has
been focusing on ego diffusion at the end of adolescence. The emphasis is upon the inability to find a "role" in life, a way into the future, a
way of relating meaningfully to persons in and out of the family. The
cause is not sought in a particular developmental period, nor in a
single family relationship or traumatic experience, but rather in the
confluence of factors that hem in the patient and prevent movement,
perhaps even successful regressive movement. Of course, it is considered that in some instances the earliest mother-child relationships may
have been so unsatisfactory that the ego was bound to founder, or
that after a close mother-infant relationship the mother would not
permit any independent movement of the child because of her anxieties, and so forth; but we conceive of the possibility that, even later in
the process of maturation, reality factors, including parental attitudes
and intrafamilial schisms, can warp or block further development so
that the child or adolescent loses his way. It might be said—to return
to the earlier frame of reference—that we are, in part, seeking causes
for the withdrawal from reality in the nature of the reality in which
the patient lived, not out of neglect of problems of ego strength and
weakness, but rather because we believe that the ego is formed in relation to and in interaction with the "reality" in which the patient
grows up, through reciprocal interaction with the people who sur-
round and nurture him.

According to early analytic theories, the massive narcissistic regression of the schizophrenic indicates serious fixation at the early
oral phase. The ties to reality are weak because of the libidinal impoverishment of the ego due to the early fixation of the libido, and,

when objects are relinquished, regression to the earliest developmental stages follows. A major reason for such hypothetical frames of reference follows the reasoning of Abraham (1908, 1916), that schizophrenia, as the most profound disorganization of the ego, indicates the most profound regression. The symptoms indicative of later developmental stages are considered clear evidence of restitutive attempts to restore object relationships.[1]

This outline is, of course, only a condensed approximation of one of several related hypotheses; but if it is correct, the need to concentrate on the earliest period is obvious. Efforts to study the later family relationships may seem unwarranted, and the space left for consideration of the role of fathers is very narrow, although not entirely absent. However, a hypothesis serves only to direct investigations, and if it fosters neglect of facts it must be altered or discarded. At the moment, it seems pertinent to examine the understanding of some facets of the hypothesis. If one accepts the concept of early oral fixation in schizophrenia, one has not of necessity arrived at a concept of etiology. One can say that early infantile deprivation is necessary to the occurrence of the illness, but one must remember that an Anlage is not a cause. Patients with other entities, such as certain antisocial personalities and psychosomatic illnesses, have yielded clearer evidence of seriously disturbed mother-infant relationships than have schizophrenics. The specificity of illness may depend upon additional, later causative factors. Indeed, the paucity of evidence from case material of a qualitative or quantitative difference in the early deprivation of schizophrenic patients as presented in the literature is most

[1] A review of psychoanalytic concepts of schizophrenia can be found in Brody and Redlich *Psychotherapy with Schizophrenics* (1952), and a brief review of psychoanalytic theories of the psychopathology in Freeman et al. *Chronic Schizophrenia* (1958).
Psychoanalytic ego psychology has broadened the understanding of schizophrenia, but many of its contributions concern suppositions about the psychic apparatus. Hartmann (1953) conjectures that deficiencies in primary autonomous factors in the ego contribute to the vulnerability of defense, of neutralization, and perhaps still other ego functions. Though recognizing the importance of early object relations, he leaves open the relative importance of various innate and environmental factors. Federn's (1952) contributions concerning ego boundaries helped clarify the phenomenology and the nature of the patient's problems. Fairbairn's (1944) studies of the endopsychic structure consider the nature of the internalized objects to a greater extent than Melanie Klein's theories, but they are also concerned primarily with the mother.

striking. Hajdu-Gimes (1940) is among the few writers who present fairly clear evidence, and she invokes two other major factors—the cold, sadistic character of the mother and the passivity of the father— as etiological essentials. Further, there are other ways of regarding the extent of the regression in schizophrenia. L. B. Hill (1955) who has had extensive experience with schizophrenics and their mothers, believes, somewhat paradoxically, that the mother-infant relationship was usually satisfactory, despite his devastating description of the mothers. He adheres to the view that the intense fixation results from undue or untimely indulgence, impeding advance to the next developmental phase in which the child suffers deprivation, and that regression occurs to a pretraumatic period in the effort to regain gratification. There is good evidence in at least some cases that the mother badly wanted the schizophrenic child and was reasonably capable at mothering the infant. Severe and unqualified rejection, such as propounded by Rosen (1953), is probably not productive of schizophrenia.

What requires emphasis, however, is that the stage to which regression occurs need not indicate the period of deprivation, or even the level of the fixation. Leaving aside Freud's analogy to the dammed river breaking through the banks at a weak point upstream (Freud, 1911), and using instead his analogy to a migrant people's constructing fortified points to which they can retreat (Freud, 1916-1917), one can recognize that, in panic, an army can run past all shelters and fortifications until it reaches the ships from which it disembarked— or at least so went one campaign—even as the patient seeks the shelter of the womb.

Of course, the army may be overcome in battle because it has left too many behind to garrison the outposts or fortifications; that is, fixations may deprive the patient of libido to invest in the advance; but the defeat can also derive from split objectives, overwhelming opposition, difficult and uncharted terrain, dissension in the forces, defects in training, lack of grasp of reality by the generals—a very pertinent factor, we believe, in both military maneuvers and child rearing—or failures in the supporting troops. It is possible to continue the analogy, but what we wish to emphasize is that one cannot focus prematurely on a single explanation for all of the catastrophic defeats in living that are termed schizophrenia. The need to withdraw from reality can, and probably does, involve factors other than the early weakening of the infant who must find his way to achieve an independent and integrated identity.

The concept of regression as an entire explanation seems to contain a major defect. The primary schizophrenic maneuver, or at least *a* primary maneuver, is withdrawal and, although regression is a withdrawal maneuver, it is an attempt to find security in the dependency of infancy or childhood. The schizophrenic usually withdraws from reality and from object relations. The withdrawal of the schizophrenic is a "distance" maneuver and is often singularly ineffective in gaining for the patient the closeness attained by regressive efforts. The classic onset is a withdrawal from the love objects he desperately needs, with consequent feelings of catastrophe and annihilation. The regression, in itself, is of a delusional nature in the schizophrenic and is, by itself, an insufficient explanation.

There are further reasons to be cautious about accepting the concept of fixation at an early oral level as an adequate hypothesis. The belief that the schizophrenic regresses to this level is not clearly confirmed by observation. The critical symptomatology focuses on later developmental stages: the eluding of the painful confines of reality by reversion to a time when a private fantasy world did not conflict with reality; the escape from the demands of masculinity by a feminine identification with the mother; the striking revival of the oedipal conflict; the manipulation of symbols to personal needs, and the concreteness of meanings. All focus on the early oedipal and immediately preoedipal periods when the child must reluctantly come to terms with the inevitable force of the reality principle, the primacy of parental authority, the formation of sexual identity, and problems pertaining to the adaptation to extrafamilial influences. It is the narcissism of the schizophrenic rather than the level of regression that is the most forceful reason for considering the earlier level of fixation, for the cardinal defects mentioned are scarcely restitutive. There is ample narcissism in the early oedipal child. One should add that the earlier consideration of catatonia as a regression to an early infantile, helpless state also does not hold up, for the catatonic is immobile and mute because in his omnipotent, narcissistic state any movement or word can change the fate of his needed love objects or of the world. He is protecting himself against the catastrophe which follows upon his hate and withdrawal of cathexis from his love objects.

THE FATHERS

The fathers in the families under consideration were found to be very important, albeit often extremely disturbing, members of their families, whose presence and influence cannot be neglected. We would like to make room—theoretical room—for the consideration of the potentiality that the father requires scrutiny in the effort to understand schizophrenia and the schizophrenic patient.

The reasons for the predominant interest in the mother and the early mother-child relationship in schizophrenia derive principally from two considerations. Psychiatrists have not been able to avoid mothers of schizophrenic patients, and the obvious eccentric and paralogical characteristics of some of these mothers make a lasting impression upon the psychiatrists whom they harass, who tend to generalize from them to all mothers of schizophrenic patients. This does not appear clearly justified on the basis of our intensive studies, however. The dominant analytic theories concerning the etiology of schizophrenia have also warranted the close scrutiny of the mother-child relationship during the first year or two of life.

The father, however, also plays an essential role in the development of the child, and the child who grows up with a grossly maladjusted father or father image will undoubtedly have serious difficulties in maturing properly. The father's place in the developmental process of the child is, of course, extremely involved, and his deficiencies can impede or prevent the child's progress in many ways at all stages of development. Perhaps in the most general terms one can follow Zelditch (1955) and Parsons and Bales (1955) in pointing out that the father is the leader of the family in adaptive-instrumental roles, as against the integrative-expressive primacy of the mother, and, therefore, a "weak, ineffectual" father is more significant than a "weak, ineffectual" mother, whereas a "cold, unyielding" mother is more of a problem than a "cold, unyielding" father. It is usually the father in middle- or upper-class families who represents the family to the extrafamilial world, establishes the family position in society, and forms the major source of the family's prestige, pride, and self-esteem. Perhaps more than the mother, his friendly or suspicious attitudes toward outsiders cultivate the group attitudes of the family to the environment. To the child, he is the first intruder into the child's feelings of unity with the mother, and the child should develop a sense of identification with the father—one of mutuality as against the rest of the world. The mother's ability to mother and to be secure in mothering cannot be divorced from the support she gains from the father and his ability to share her with the child. Fathers who resented or could not endure the intrusion of the child and became rivals of the child or of the mother are common in our study. The child's appraisal of the worth of the mother as a love object and as a secure, sheltering figure also involves the father, through the father's esteem for her or enmity toward her. To a daughter, the father should be a suitable early love object, so that she can seek to gain the love of a man by growing into a woman like the mother—a course that can be impeded if the mother is despised or unwanted by the father, as well as if the mother forms an impossible model for identification.

A crucial event of the oedipal phase for children of both sexes is the achievement of sexual identity as a male or female. The boy has the difficult task of overcoming the primary identification with the mother, and the ambivalent fear and hostility directed toward the father, to enable identification with his father and thereby feel lovable to women in his male role. If the father is realistically jealous and hostile to the boy, if he is a weak figure, completely subservient to the mother, or if he is unacceptable to the mother, who constantly derogates him, then the assumption of a workable male role can be extremely difficult for the boy. It will be noted that few of the fathers in our study presented masculine images for their sons to incorporate that were even vaguely satisfactory. Whereas the girl need not shift her sexual identification, she must come to terms with her castration feelings and the worth of her sex. She has, however, a potential model in the home and can remain relatively passive after her emergence from the family, provided the mother as a mothering figure is appreciated. The boy, however, cannot grow in the image of the mother. A father figure, albeit simply the ideal of a father figure, which he can follow in his emotional development is essential—a father who is a representative of the outside world and who can get along in it without being overwhelmed; and a father who can show the way in relating in a masculine way to the mother, to guide the boy in the difficult turn-about from being a child dependent on a mother to becoming a man who can permit a woman to be dependent upon him. For a son to find his way in life—into a career role as well as a marital role —the covert as well as the actual support of an acceptable father is important. It may well be easier for a son to grow up without a father than to grow up with a father whom the mother cannot tolerate, or who is too aloof or grandiose to serve as a figure for identification. Too often schizophrenic patients must exclude such fathers and continue a mutuality with the mothers.

We have not sought to cover all of the needs for a satisfactory father figure in the family, but have only sought to emphasize the vital role which the father fills in the development of children. We should like to add one further consideration which has many ramifications, but may best be summed up by saying that the family structure and the proper development of children require that there not be confusion of the generations between parents and children. For the child's normal development, he must know that he cannot take one parent's place with the other, and that while he may identify with a parent, he does not become a parent figure in the familial home. The father who competes as a son of his wife, or remains a passive child who is displaced in the wife's affections by his child, or, on the opposite side, seeks to substitute a daughter or even a son for his wife, threatens this necessary division between generations that offers the child security against incestuous and castration anxieties, for his attitudes rather realistically foster one or the other fear. Parsons and Bales (1955) emphasize such considerations in slightly different terms.

Fathers have not been altogether neglected in the study of schizophrenic patients. Lidz and Lidz (Chapter I) indicated in their survey of fifty families that "... the paternal influences are noxious as frequently as are the maternal ... study of some cases leaves the impression that had there been a stable father ... the patient would not have been so seriously affected by the mother's difficulties." The ineffectiveness of the father in the paternal role, his passivity or weakness, his aloofness from the patient, have been noted by Gerard and Siegel (1950), Hajdu-Gimes (1940), Ellison and Hamilton (1949) and Frazee (1953). The last three investigators noted that a fair proportion of the fathers were cruel and rejecting, or domineering and sadistic, and both commented on the unfortunate combination of cruel fathers and overprotective mothers. Reichard and Tillman (1950) describe a schizophrenogenic type of father who is domineering, sadistic, and overtly rejecting. They pertinently note that these fathers are basically weak and ineffectual and that their jealousy of the children and rivalry for the mothers' attention prevent the mothers from giving the children adequate care and attention. This formulation appears to us to be highly pertinent, although more of a composite of outstanding traits than a description suited to any one father.

There are fourteen fathers whom we have now studied and understand reasonably thoroughly. None filled his paternal role effectively, although several were ineffectual primarily because of their passivity rather than because of positive deleterious traits. In the following pages, we shall discuss these fathers in terms of five groups, which we believe are useful for demonstrating the types of tangible problems created for the mothers and children concerned and also for purposes of broad theoretical conceptualization. The groups are not to be regarded as clear-cut and mutually exclusive; they are, rather, five somewhat overlapping patterns which seem to be of significance, practically and theoretically.

The first group, comprising fathers of some female patients, is made up of men who are in constant, severe conflict with their wives, undercutting their authority with the children and derogating their worth as persons, while seeking to win the daughters to their own side of the controversy. They rigidly and unrealistically expect that their wives will docilely conform to their own peculiar ways of regarding the world and of raising children, probably wishing for wives who would agree constantly with them and build up their self-esteem. Disappointed in their wives, they would like to mold their daughters to fill their needs. They are paranoid in their distrust of people, and when their unreasonable demands force the wives to subterfuge, their mistrust is heightened.

The conflict antedates the birth of the children, who simply become the focal point in the struggle between the parents. Although these fathers have tyrannical tempers and are habitually cruel in their attitudes, if not physically, to their wives, they are not necessarily strict with their daughters. Rather, they are constantly in opposition to their wives' expectations for the children. The wooing of the daughters is designed primarily to gain their allegiance, although it may also be sexually seductive.

The father is highly inconsistent, and the children, who seek to satisfy him, are confused by his demands, for the behavior he requires of them depends upon his neurotic or psychotic needs. Furthermore, the children are disillusioned by his basic though unconscious dishonesty, which seems to derive from his projection of his own wishes onto his wife or daughter.

In our experience, it is the daughter who sides with the father and seeks his love who becomes psychotic. She seeks to differentiate herself from the mother, rather than to follow the mother in her development; but the father's demands are too inconsistent and unrealistic to allow her to establish a satisfactory relationship with him. Moreover, the father's hostility to the mother is crippling to the daughter, for the daughter needs the mother in order to develop a secure feeling of feminine identity.

The Grau's marriage has always been seriously disturbed; almost from the beginning Mr. Grau would frequently become violently infuriated with his poorly organized wife, and spells of gloomy depression would punctuate his chronic irritability. He has always believed his way of doing things to be right, and his wife's failure to comply with his set notions has been unbearable to him. They married several years after his graduation from college, where he had been ill at ease, unrealistically feeling handicapped and unwanted because of his rural background. He had never dated a girl before his brief courtship, and he married without concern over the fact that his wife was a devout Catholic, agreeing to raise the children as Catholics.

Soon after marriage, he informed Mrs. Grau that the children's religion would not create a problem because they would not have any children. Although he made the religious difference the reason for not wanting children, his wife believes that he could not tolerate having her pay attention to a child. Continuous conflict began with the first pregnancy. He accused his wife of conceiving to prevent the marriage from breaking up, although he had assumed responsibility for the contraceptive practice. His refusal to let the children be baptized Catholic began a conflict which continues to the present time.

As long as the children can remember, there have been incessant strife and threats of separation; Mr. Grau's instability and outbursts have kept the home in a state of chronic tension. This became more pronounced when he became ill during the patient's ninth year. He was invalided for the next eight years, stubbornly refusing a necessary operation. His disposition worsened as he became physically dependent upon his wife, and his leadership and authority were impaired, further diminishing his effectiveness as a father. His illness also caused considerable economic insecurity for the family.

He always not only has been constantly critical of his wife and oblivious to her feelings, but has pointedly sought to hurt her. Thus, perhaps jealous of her devotion to the Church, he blames Catholicism for all her faults and for the wrongdoings of any Catholic miscreant of whom he reads in the paper. The younger daughter, who is not the patient, has espoused Catholicism, but she keeps it secret from her father, for she is certain that he would turn against her as violently as he has turned against his wife. However, religion, while a focal issue, has not been the only cause of strife; for instance, Mr. Grau constantly belittles anyone without a college education, derogating his wife because she attended only a two-year junior college. He has always made it clear to his daughters that he hates and scorns his wife, at the same time letting the patient feel that she is more important to him than his wife. However, he has been inconsistent with the daughters, being overly permissive but also harsh, critical, and cynical. In general, he is lax concerning their supervision and their dating, but he forbade their dating before the age of sixteen and he objects violently if they go with a boy who is a Catholic or who does not have a college education. His unfeeling and thoughtlessly cruel remarks to his schizophrenic daughter, even though she has always been his favorite, reflect his disappointment in her and in his own life.

Although Mr. Grau is fairly successful in his career, he is suspicious of his superior and his coworkers. He has also inculcated in his daughters a suspiciousness of outsiders and a feeling that one lives in a basically inimical world. His own suspiciousness is reinforced by his bigotry against his wife's religion, but more specifically by his distrust of her. Mrs. Grau, who has always been very insecure and rigid in raising the children, has met constant opposition from her husband in her efforts to raise the children according to the only pattern she knows—that of devout Catholicism—and her worth and authority have been constantly undermined. While she has also undercut Mr. Grau's authority with the children, this has been primarily because of her own struggle to retain her children's loyalty. The fact that Mr. Grau has turned to his older daughter to fill the emptiness left by the mother has involved confusion of the father-daughter roles.

The second grouping concerns the fathers of some of the male patients, whose hostility turns toward the offspring rather than the wife. These men are rivals with their sons for the mothers' attention and affection, behaving like jealous older siblings who must outshine the patient. They are extremely self-centered and eager for prestige, sometimes resenting their children as impediments to their success and hence to the admiration due them. They advertise their successes to their sons, at the same time belittling the boys' efforts and sabotaging their self-confidence. These fathers do not participate in raising the children, but interfere with their wives' efforts to be mothering. Their effectiveness as fathers is further diminished by absence from the home or withdrawal—in some instances, apparently because they cannot endure the attention the wife must give to the son.

The wives are torn between the jealous demands placed upon them, and either the husbands or the sons, or both, feel the deprivation of their attention. The father's behavior is sometimes such that the children feel ashamed of him. The son, recognizing the father's inadequacies as a husband, seeks to fill the gap in his mother's life, which, however, increases his fear of the jealous father.

The inconsistent behavior, the temper outbursts, and the personality disturbances of these fathers create great tension in the home, just as in the case of the fathers of the girls who have been described. Some of the mothers in this predicament have given the impression that they could have been reasonably satisfactory mothers had the fathers not resented and opposed their efforts.

Mr. Lamb is a forceful and successful businessman. At the time he met his wife he was feeling dejected and disgraced because he had been dropped from college for cheating on exams. Nevertheless, he was considered to be a glamorous figure. For a year prior to the marriage, they lived together in a Bohemian atmosphere, and their relationship seems to have been happiest during this period. Difficulties began with their marriage, for Mr. Lamb tended to separate sex from marriage and found it hard to feel sexually aroused by a woman who was his wife. Thus early in the marriage he began to drink and consort with other women. Nevertheless, he expected to be his wife's sole concern. When a son, the patient, was born seven years after the marriage, Mr. Lamb showed a great deal of jealousy of the infant, objecting to any interference with their social life because of the child, and engaging in violent outbursts whenever his wife could not pay immediate attention to his own wishes.

During the following years he became increasingly irritable and demanding of his wife's attention, and also more alcoholic and promiscuous. Mrs. Lamb, striving to satisfy his need for companionship and at the same time to care for the son, found the situation intolerable; thus when an opportunity arose for him to take a promising traveling position which would keep him away from home except for occasional week ends, she agreed, feeling that this was the only way in which the marriage could continue.

Mr. Lamb, who had been an outstanding athlete in his youth, found no common interests with his son, who shared his mother's intellectual and artistic interests. However, it became clear that although the father was disappointed in not having a manly son, he could not have tolerated one; for instance, instead of coaching or encouraging his son in athletic endeavors, he criticized his son's efforts and lost his temper over them. It developed that he had, as a boy, squelched the efforts of his own younger brothers in the same way. At the same time, he belittled the interests or achievements of the son in other fields, and mocked at his effeminate traits and artistic inclinations.

Even though Mr. Lamb was now away from home most of the time, his brief sojourns with his family were always unpleasant. He was usually partly or completely intoxicated, and he sought to take his wife away from the children.

During the patient's adolescence, Mr. Lamb's affair with a woman in the neighborhood created considerable scandal. His wife considered getting a divorce and told the patient that he might have to assume more responsibility for the family if she did so. At the same time, the patient's efforts at masculine achievement, made in a desperate effort to gain recognition from his father, were continuously belittled by Mr. Lamb.

Despite the disturbances throughout their marriage, a definite attachment and fondness has persisted between the spouses, and Mr. Lamb has been eminently successful in his job.

This case illustrates how a father can intervene in and seriously affect the mother-child relationship from the early months of the child's life. There was no possibility that Mrs. Lamb could care for the child with equanimity. Most striking among the noxious influences were the father's constant derogation of the son and his failure to offer any support to him.

Although neither parent overtly discredited the other to the children, the father's extramarital affairs, which were obvious to the adolescent son, indirectly devalued the mother. The mother, along with trying to meet the father's needs for attention, tried also to bolster his prestige with the children. Such efforts, however, presented an inconsistent and contradictory image of the father to the children, for the father's defects as a husband and his weaknesses as a man were apparent to them. Similarly, a perplexing discrepancy was presented by the father as they knew him and his reputation as a strong man among his business associates. Thus he was not a reasonable figure for identification for the son; the boy could not follow the pattern of a father who caused intense unhappiness whenever he was at home. The mother's efforts to make up for the father's deficiencies led to overindulgence and inconsistency, which weakened the son and increased the father's jealousy.

Other fathers in this group tend to be paranoid, suspicious of the motives of others and grandiose in their notions of their abilities, and to have distorted concepts of causal relationships.

There may well be a relationship between the two types of fathers who have been presented. Both types are unable to tolerate lack of admiration or the failure of their wives to center their lives about them. Of the cases presented, one father was paranoid and the other alcoholic, and both required bolstering of their masculinity. The fathers of daughters turn against the mothers and seek to gain the daughters' support and admiration. The fathers of sons become rivals of the sons, but some of them lose their wives' esteem in the process.

A third group of fathers presents a somewhat different problem, or perhaps one which is not fundamentally different, but simply brings into sharper focus a characteristic of many of the fathers in our study by presenting it in exaggerated form. These are fathers whose exalted concepts of themselves contain features of paranoid grandiosity, even though they have realistic abilities and achievements. The mothers and the children, and sometimes people outside the family, may share the fathers' estimation of themselves, being impressed with the importance of their positions and of the people with whom they associate. These fathers are aloof from the children and physically distant, conveying the impression that their offspring cannot reach their stature, and giving little or no support to their sons, in particular. The mothers are needed as adulatory admirers, and their attention to their fatherlike husbands may result in lack of attention to the children; or, conversely, they too may feel their husbands' distance and seek to complete their lives by attaching a child to them. In either case, a son becomes too weak to emulate his father and is apt to become a sham shell, assuming his more bizarre characteristics.

Mr. Dolfuss was a European-born manufacturer and inventor, whose grandfather had been a prominent statesman, but whose father had been an alcoholic. He married an emigré member of the nobility, and they settled in a Boston suburb, living in the rigid and formal tradition of European landed gentry. This unrealistic life in terms of their environment isolated them from the community, where they felt rejected as enemy aliens. The household was organized so as not to disturb the father, the children being raised by a seductive governess and permitted to see their parents at specific times in a formal relationship. The father studied Eastern mysticism with a close friend and felt that this set him apart as a select, superior being. The mother, and, to an even greater extent, the governess idolized him and considered him a sort of demigod, catering to his whims and hypochondriacal needs and accepting his beliefs implicitly. When the father died, the family believed that he still lived in a sense, but had been removed for more important tasks elsewhere in the universe.

This family, upon casual observation, seemed to be very superior, but actually the children were being raised in a paralogical atmosphere divergent from the culture in which they were living. While this is an extreme example, it is not the only instance of a father who is so positive and dominant that the mother and even the children go along with his beliefs in a sort of *folie en famille*.

As we have suggested earlier, the grandiose type of father, which we have illustrated by the case of Mr. Dolfuss, cannot be clearly separated from our other groupings. While these characteristics emerge most predominantly in our upper-class families—using class in a strict, sociological sense—they are clearly present in ten of the fourteen fathers, although somewhat obscured by the lower social status of the families in some cases, or by the fact that the fathers' evaluations of themselves, in other instances, receive less emphasis because they are unsupported or openly opposed by their wives and associates.

To discuss this particular tendency further, as it appears in varying forms in the greater number of our cases, the fathers exhibit an almost insatiable need, which has the quality of an addiction, for narcissistic satisfactions in the form of adulation from others. They expect to be the foci of their wives' attention and admiration, but, even if this is forthcoming, they require other sources of supply. Thus, Mr. Lamb required admiration as an athlete, and his extramarital relations were with women who flattered him and made him feel that he was outstanding. Another father had become a livestock auctioneer as a compromise between his interests in acting and farming. A physician turned from his home and built up a following of admiring women patients, listening to their personal problems and being unduly available to them at all hours of the night. Even though these men are assertive and often domineering, their fundamental lack of self-esteem and their insecurity in their masculinity are apparent. One such father, a man who has achieved unusual prestige, explained his intolerable marriage by saying that at the time he married he "had felt only half a man and would not expect to find a wife who was more than half a woman." Few wives can consistently supply the admiration that is needed. Furthermore, many of these wives require a man who can help them overcome their own narcissistic cravings, and clashes soon ensue. Whether the persistent need for admiration in these husbands was very marked before marriage or whether, in some instances, it was heightened into a serious problem by the wives' undermining or attacking of their masculine self-esteem, is a question which may be answered eventually by further scrutiny of the husband-wife interaction.

At any rate, the offspring, particularly the son, is in a difficult position, for if he is really successful, he may threaten the father's need to be the shining light in the home. The child may recognize that much of the father's greatness exists only in his own self-evaluation and self-deceit; this contributes to the child's faulty and corrupt superego formation and distrust of others. Wedge and Fry (1955) have called attention to the predicament of college students whose parents are unusually successful, but the difficulty is considerably more pronounced when the father's greatness is unreal and his weaknesses as a father and husband are apparent.

We shall now focus upon a group of fathers who have failed in life and become virtual nonentities in the home, scarcely participating in the responsibility for the children. The children are left virtually fatherless. Some of these fathers had earlier seemed infallible, but collapsed when their efforts to maintain their prestige collapsed, while others slowly faded, striving at the same time to retain their self-esteem by projecting the blame. Some had been unable to cope with their wives' coldness and exclusion. Thus these fathers have become rather pathetic figures, without prestige in the family and, at times, treated with disdain by their wives. The children are apt to be caught up in the fathers' failures and the social decline of the family.

Mr. Lerner had, before the business depression, been an outstanding and scholarly attorney who provided extremely well, if not lavishly, for his family. He considered himself to be superior, and much of his conversation was about his very prominent associates. His wife regarded him as a fatherly figure who admired her but who also had an intense need for her. While he was kindly toward his children, he was never an effective father, for he was always an aloof man who related to his wife to the exclusion of the children. He was only passively appreciative of his unusually gifted daughter, the patient, although she was the center of the larger family's attention.

When his partner committed suicide during the depression, Mr. Lerner was unable to gain new clients, since he was primarily a scholarly brief writer, and he withdrew into obsessive studies that shut him off from the plight which now faced his family, as well as from outside contacts. The entire burden of support of the family fell upon his wife, who went to work, and the economic status of the family declined severely in ways which were very apparent to the children —for instance, while they had always been encouraged to be proud, they now found themselves wearing hand-me-downs from relatives. Yet both the husband and wife pretended within the family and to his associates that he was still a busy and important man, and the wife helped support this pretense by maintaining his office. She dared not press him to any practical steps for earning money to support the family for fear that he might become overtly psychotic or commit suicide. Yet to the children, the failure of the father whom they had been taught to regard as a great man was apparent, and the very fact that it was hidden and made mysterious by the mother made it all the more frightening.

One of the problems of the patient was her difficulty in choosing between marriage and the chance of success in a career, and this conflict appeared to be heightened by the disgrace of the father's failure and the burdens of the mother's role.

While some of the types described so far are overlapping and have been differentiated largely to illustrate the varieties of difficulties that arise, the next and final grouping appears to be quite distinct.

These men are very passive and demand little for themselves, acting the part of lesser siblings in the family, and accepting their wives as grown-up authorities. They are not masculine figures to their wives, who seem to have married them because they did not wish to be dominated by a man. While they offer their wives passive support, implementing their decisions and wishes, they are unable to assert needs of their own or to express any ideas concerning the raising of the children.

To the children, these fathers are pleasant, even mothering figures, but they offer weak models to their sons. Moreover, they fail to counter the eccentric and bizarre patterns of child rearing which tend to be established by their wives—perhaps the most pathogenic feature of these families, and a situation which the sons come to resent, feeling that the father has abandoned them to the mother's whims. These fathers accept without apparent resentment the fact that the sons are their wives' primary concerns, and do not impede their sons' growth into the passive role which seems to fill the mothers' needs. The wives, who have little real respect for their husbands, anticipate that the sons will live out the lives which are closed to them as women. It is interesting to note that the two most striking examples of such passive fathers were themselves adopted children.

There is very little of a definite nature to say about Mr. Newcomb other than that he is a good breadwinner and a competent accountant, and that he is very meek. In his visits to the hospital where his son was under treatment, for a long time he scarcely said anything to the personnel except what his wife wished him to convey; he served primarily as an apologetic mouthpiece for her. It was not that she was inarticulate, but that she could not repeat the same unanswerable questions or the same set ideas concerning the etiology of her son's illness often enough to overcome her belief that no one listened to her. However, after a time Mr. Newcomb began to speak securely and sensibly, mildly blaming himself for never having taken a stand against his wife. He had never intervened in the relative social isolation which Mrs. Newcomb imposed upon the children nor contradicted her bizarre ideas. After the son became ill, he accepted his wife's dictum that their lives must be devoted to the son's recovery, for "we have no life while he is ill," and for many years Mr. Newcomb scrimped and saved to maintain the son in private hospitals despite very pessimistic prognoses.

Mrs. Newcomb had married him after the death of her fiancé of five years' standing. She had not been aware that Mr. Newcomb was courting her, simply considering him a young man who went along with her group. When he proposed, she was taken aback and blurted out, "But how old are you?" However, he apparently had an unusual asset as a suitor, for in one of her most insightful statements Mrs. Newcomb said, "He didn't get as annoyed with my talk as most men." The hospital personnel who have listened at length to Mrs. Newcomb agree that it takes an unusual man to live with her.

Mr. Newcomb is a conscientious and pleasant man and is a "good" father in the sense that he does his best for his son. It is essential to realize that his wife forms the paradigm of a "schizophrenogenic mother" in her impervious solicitude for her son and her bizarre reasoning and ways of rearing children. However, in a sense Mr. Newcomb is not a father, for he has permitted his wife to try to be both mother and father, and to completely dominate him and the home, while he has found refuge and solace in his work. He has not been a satisfactory masculine figure to his wife, even though a satisfactory husband to her. The son has never received protection or support from him in his efforts to grow into a man, and both the son and the daughter—who once verged on a schizophrenic break—have gained from him an unrealistic image of a man.

A more striking illustration is afforded by the father of schizophrenic twin sons. While the father was a competent man at work, he went along with his wife's bizarre use of the twins as obvious phalluses, building up fantastic expectations of their greatness and refusing to accept the reality of their semidelinquent behavior. The pattern of this family was so extraordinary that it cannot be presented in abbreviated form, but suffice it to say that the father was excluded from his wife's room, was banned from using the family toilet because he was "dirty," and was generally treated with contempt and disrespect by his wife and sons (see Chapter XII).

These fathers cannot be considered apart from their wives, because the wives, who follow closely the descriptions of domineering mothers of schizophrenic patients frequently found in the literature, are virtually schizophrenic themselves. In the case of the mother of the twins, her narcissistic injury—rather clearly related to castration—dominated the scene, and the father was a pawn in maintaining her restitutive maneuvers.

There are other implications in the material presented that the narcissistic needs of one and often both parents are deleterious to the formation of a family that can foster the child's growth into a mature and independent person. However, it is premature to focus upon specific dynamics. The primary purpose of this paper has been to call attention to the deficiencies of the fathers of these patients, which often impeded the mothers' efforts to be mothering. The fathers presented poor models and offered little support to the children and, quite aside from the mothers' deficiencies, went a long way toward creating a family environment which was distorted and rent by schisms between the parents over the fathers' bizarre ideas about the raising of the children. However, it must be repeated that although few, if any, of these fathers functioned effectively as parents, we do not believe that such fathers are specific to the families of schizophrenic children. Indeed, we know that they are not. We are, as we emphasized earlier, concerned at present with the integrative and disintegrative forces in these homes and the constructive and destructive models and patterns afforded the children. The father contributes but part of the family environment; he is only one of the parents. The difficulties of the mothers of schizophrenic patients have been presented by others, and we ourselves will in future studies attempt an analysis of them for the families we are investigating.

Still, lest it seem that this series of fathers does not differ very much from the usual assortment in the population, let us consider them not as individuals but as a group. We will simply focus on their propensity for paralogical reasoning, which was also amply fostered by many of the mothers. Five of the fourteen were clearly paranoid, particularly in their distrust of outsiders. Another, although not definitely paranoid, had a grandiose concept of himself and rigid and bigoted ideas, and finally withdrew in unrealistic fashion. One father's obsessive needs were rationalized in a fashion that seemed both dishonest and perplexing to his family, who were expected to act in accordance with his incomprehensible ideas. Another father, who was eccentric and chronically depressed, was treated as a handyman around the home. Three fathers went along with their wives' distorted thinking, and, for practical purposes, shared it. Of the remaining, two were alcoholics and one was overtly seductive of his daughter.

COMMENT

We have been concerned largely with the role of the father in the family environment in which the patient grows up and have not gone very far in offering specific characterizations of such fathers. Indeed, we feel that efforts to specify a type of father, or necessary characteristics of fathers of schizophrenic patients, might be misleading, for we are not seeking the cause of schizophrenia in the fathers' characteristics. We have, however, noted certain characteristics which seem to occur frequently. It has been noted that the fathers are frequently insecure in their masculinity and need admiration and undue attention to bolster their masculine self-esteem. A goodly proportion are paranoid or given to paralogical or irrational behavior that dominates or seriously affects the attitudes of the entire family. One characteristic which we have not emphasized in this paper, that quality which seems to us to epitomize best the mother of the schizophrenic—imperviousness to the feelings and needs of others—also applies to a number of the fathers. We have attempted to indicate how the father can interfere with the mother's ability to be mothering, even in the first months of a child's life; how he can foster a confusion between the roles of the two generations in the home, and how, by his own insecurity as a husband and father, he can fail to provide the necessary object of masculine identification to a son and can interfere with a daughter's identity as a woman. The fathers, as are so many of the mothers, are so caught up in their own problems that they can rarely satisfactorily fill the essentials of a paternal role.

VI

Interaction between Hospital Staff and Families

(1955)

In the course of our study we have become increasingly aware of the need for constant examination of the interrelationship between the hospital staff and the families of patients. Without attention to this relationship, family attitudes toward the hospital or staff attitudes toward the family may affect the patient deleteriously or even catastrophically. We wish to report on a few of the many significant problems that can arise between staff and family.

The hospital as a social system has been scrutinized repeatedly during recent years, with particular emphasis on the effects of staff attitudes and staff disharmony upon patients. While Simmons and Wolff (1954) have studied the social hierarchy in the general hospital, Caudill and Stainbrook (1954), Jones (1953), Stanton and Schwartz (1954), and others have reported in detail on the interaction between the mental hospital team and their patients. Some attention has also been given to the relationship between the patient and his family during the period of hospitalization (Devereux, 1949; Rose, 1952; Szurek, 1952), but few systematic studies have been carried out. On the practical side, therapy has been provided for the mothers of hospitalized children by Szurek (1952), for mothers of schizophrenic patients by Abrahams and Varon (1953), and for the marital partners of patients (Brody, 1956; Inwood, 1952).

In many hospitals, social service casework with the families of psy-

Stephen Fleck, Alice R. Cornelison, Nea Norton, and Theodore Lidz: The Intrafamilial Environment of the Schizophrenic Patient: II. Interaction Between Hospital Staff and Families. Psychiatry, Vol. 20, 1957, pp. 343-350. Copyright © 1957, The William Alanson White Psychiatric Foundation, Inc. This paper was presented in part at the annual meeting of the American Psychiatric Association, May, 1955.

chiatric and other patients is carried out routinely, with varying degrees of intensity (M. Faris, 1955; Tennant, 1954). However, the interaction between hospital personnel and the families of psychiatric patients has been almost completely neglected, even though it has commonly been recognized that families can disrupt the therapeutic relationship between the patient and the hospital, and that what transpires at home can influence the hospitalized patient profoundly. Richardson's (1945) pioneering book, *Patients Have Families*, which focused attention on some of the problems involved, has not been followed by studies of the families of patients in mental hospitals. However, Inwood (1952, 1953) has described his experiences with complaining families of psychotic soldiers; Fetterman (1948) has considered assigning participant roles to family members in the treatment of psychotic patients whether hospitalized or not; and Tennant (1954), Brody (1956), and Faris (1955) have studied the effects of careful casework service for families of patients in private psychiatric hospitals.

The Yale Psychiatric Institute long ago established the policy of providing social casework for family members of every patient, in order to obtain essential data from families, to provide adequate liaison between the family and staff, and to clarify and seek to modify family problems that affect the patient.[1] In the research reported here the same worker interviews all families to provide a more uniform screen against which family reactions can be observed and evaluated. Her interaction with each family member is discussed regularly with the entire research team, and the information is shared with the staff. Only upper- and middle-class families have been studied, who are usually well educated and sophisticated, and less likely to be awed by the authority of the hospital personnel than those of lower socioeconomic levels.

GENERAL OBSERVATIONS

Admission to a psychiatric hospital differs from admission to a

[1] As a result of this and other studies, the Yale Psychiatric Institute carries on group therapy sessions for groups of parents of patients, and at times, conjoint family therapy. Our psychiatric service in the Yale New Haven Hospital under the direction of Dr. T. Detre includes family members in the therapeutic process from the moment of admission.

general hospital. The former often occurs under duress; the patient may be committed despite his expressed opposition to hospitalization, and responsible family members may also act under pressure from neighbors, friends, or even the authorities. Family members may disagree as to the necessity or wisdom of commitment, or may experience the same conflict within themselves. Other more tangible differences concern the usual curtailment of visiting, the indefiniteness of diagnosis and prognosis, the greater difficulty in understanding psychiatric treatment methods as compared to medical or surgical procedures, and the comparatively personal information requested, often by social workers rather than a physician.

Furthermore, the families of schizophrenic patients may themselves present many problems, which may or may not have something to do with why the patient is schizophrenic, but nevertheless must be taken into account. Among these are the following:

1. Frequently one parent—usually the mother—is overambitious and obsessively anxious, believing that no one can understand or properly care for her child except herself. Such a mother suffers severe anxiety when separated from the child. She may have to withdraw the patient from the hospital to allay this anxiety, just as earlier she had to fasten her child to her to be secure. While she may withdraw the patient early in the hospitalization, she is more likely to do so later, when the patient shows signs of independence which the therapist considers improvement. This rather classic occurrence of a parent's sabotaging treatment just as it begins to work can be avoided by appropriate attention to the parent's needs. Recognition and amelioration of the parent's plight are in order, rather than rebuffing an "intolerable schizophrenogenic mother" or an "intractable domineering father."

2. Divisions or schisms between family members which have existed openly or covertly long before the hospitalization of the patient are apt to become disagreements about what needs to be done for the patient. The more dominant spouse may insist upon hospitalization, while the other may consider loving care at home essential. The one who does not have his way can still sabotage treatment. Or one parent likes one hospital, while the other prefers treatment elsewhere. The hospital staff can be caught up in such struggles just as the patient has

been, and must guard against antagonizing one parent by seeming to side with the other.

3. Intense guilt reactions may occur in parents who feel that they are to blame for the patient's illness. Such parents feel impelled to do everything for the patient, even to the detriment of their other children. The guilt is often so extreme that it must be projected onto the doctors or the hospital, expressed in incessant fault finding with the therapy. Other projections may lead to shifting blame to the other parent, to outsiders such as teachers, or to some happenstance. There may ensue an extensive search for etiological factors, in which the parent scrutinizes every detail of the patient's history and solicits opinions from every conceivable source.

4. A serious product of the parental disharmony and the parental guilt is the recrimination by one parent against the other. The manifest or latent hostilities gathered through the years break forth when a parent, guilty concerning his or her own deficiencies as a parent, condemns the other for shortcomings that he thinks made the child ill. The battle is noted by the patient, who is often an artist in splitting the parents, and affects his hospital course even though the family discord remains unnoted by his psychiatrist. Often, however, the hospital is involved in the struggle, as each parent seeks to gain the solace of having hospital personnel side with him against the other.

The task of the hospital is to treat the patient and prevent the family's problems from interfering with the therapeutic program. Even though understanding of the parental problems is not a primary interest, the parents' disharmony may be a prime source of the patient's dilemma, and modification of the family environment can be useful or even essential to promoting improvement in the patient. From among the numerous problems that can arise to disturb the family-staff relationship, we shall select two of significance to serve as illustrations, which we shall call the problem of *family decompensation* and problems which arise through *staff exclusiveness*.

FAMILY DECOMPENSATION

The schizophrenic illness of a family member can change the tenuous equilibrium of the family and precipitate disorganization that deprives its members of emotional support from each other just when they need it most. The patient, who already feels overwhelmed, may be caught in the midst of the family disorganization. The disruption of the object relationship can precipitate illness in other members of the family, further increasing the stresses on all of the members.

The critical situation of the Newberg family following the admission of Arthur, their fifteen-year-old son, in a state of catatonic excitement will illustrate some of the problems involved.

The Newberg family equilibrium had been precarious for many years. Mrs. Newberg had married her strange but ardent suitor after becoming pregnant with the patient. Both parents were strongly attached to their parental families; this had fostered jealousy and strife, and had resulted in the Newbergs' failing to establish a nuclear family of their own. For instance, the mother refused to move from the apartment house in which her married sisters lived, although this meant that Mr. Newberg had to travel over two hours each day to work. Mr. Newberg felt that he was excluded from the family and that his wife was more attached to her family than to him; on the other hand, he spent much of his free time with his mother, whom his wife would not visit. During the year before Arthur's admission Mr. Newberg had planned to move the family to the West Coast when his mother and brother moved there, but Mrs. Newberg had threatened to separate from him rather than go along.

Mr. Newberg had unusual aptitudes, but the plans he evolved for utilizing them were often impractical, if not paranoically grandiose. He worked hard at his hobbies and schemes, completely neglecting his family. Mrs. Newberg became increasingly resentful that the entire burden of raising the three children rested upon her. She resented her husband's absences from home, but could not tolerate his incessant talk when he was at home, and disapproved of the bizarre ideas he expressed to the children.

When Arthur was admitted to the hospital, Mr. Newberg was in a highly excited state, showing signs of paranoid distortion. He sought to blame Arthur's illness upon any one of a number of events in Arthur's recent or distant past: his guilt over an injury to his sister, masturbation, overwork in high school, disappointment in his first crush, and so on. Mr. Newberg circumstantially repeated one such story after another to the staff, elaborating the details in his effort to convince them.

It was soon apparent that the long-standing conflict between the parents had now flared into mutual recrimination. The father felt guilty because he had often been reprimanded for his neglect of his family; the mother felt guilty because she had raised a schizophrenic son and because she had not left the father, whom she privately believed was an ambulatory psychotic. The father was openly blamed for the son's psychosis by the wife and her family, particularly by one sister who attacked him viciously, with complete disregard for his despair over his son's illness. Mrs. Newberg, whom the social worker found to be feeling depressed and lost, confided that she would leave her husband now that she saw that maintaining a home with this bizarre man had damaged the family.

The first crisis arose because of Mr. Newberg's energetic and excited efforts to treat his son, which were disturbing and could not be controlled, and made it necessary to stop his visits. Separation from his son heightened his anxiety, and led him to feel that the hospital also blamed him for his son's illness. He wished to remove his son from the hospital and devote all his time to caring for him. Mrs. Newberg was terrified lest he be permitted to carry out this plan. The social worker recognized Mr. Newberg's incessant talk as paranoid and possibly psychotic and arranged that a senior psychiatrist see him regularly. It proved possible to allay his guilt, by permitting expression of the hostility toward his wife's family. This helped to diminish the projection of blame onto his wife and onto the hospital. Through regular discussions of his problems and of the difficult family situation, he gained the support he needed during this critical period and quieted down so that he could resume visiting the patient.

At the same time, with the help of the social worker, Mrs. Newberg began to recognize that her husband was not solely responsible for the family problems, and that the difficulties had been heightened by her attachment to her family and the meddling sabotage of her sister. She realized that she was fond of her husband, who was childishly dependent upon her, who deeply admired her, and who had sought to be a good husband and faithful provider. Through further discussion, she recognized that her son probably had been frightened by the threats of separation, and needed his father despite the difficulties in the father's relationship with all members of the family.

It was possible to re-establish and maintain some degree of family unity, so that each parent could give the other some support and so that both could strive to attain a new equilibrium. Mr. Newberg began to spend more time with his other children, and sought to help his wife. Mrs. Newberg came to recognize, at least in part, that she did not have to rely on her sister but was herself able to guide her children.

A later crisis arose when Mr. Newberg impetuously decided to remove his son, in response to the boy's pathetic pleading. This was headed off by the social worker, who understood his need to prove that he would sacrifice anything for his son, by suggesting that leaving the boy in the hospital and waiting patiently for his recovery required a great deal of self-sacrifice and self-restraint.

The differences between the parents again threatened to become acute during preparations for the patient's discharge, and once again it seemed that the patient would become the focal point of their controversies. The staff had suggested that they send the boy to a boarding school for a year. Mr. Newberg agreed, despite the severe financial burden, expecting his wife to object. She did object, taking our recommendation as an implied condemnation of her and the home. Moreover, the prospect of further prolonged separation from Arthur virtually precluded re-establishment of the close relationship between herself and her son, just as it deprived the father of the much-desired opportunity to demonstrate that he was a good father for Arthur. However, when she saw the patient's enthusiasm for the school plan, she agreed. Then her husband, who had very easily agreed at first, changed his mind and had to be persuaded again.

We felt that unless the parents had been permitted to voice their objections and work through their resistances, they might have agreed to the plan without expressing their opposition, but they probably would have eventually undermined the patient's adjustment at school. Actually the parents have been pleased, because the patient has been doing very well since discharge. Had he returned home, the family would have had to readjust again after having barely achieved a tenuous equilibrium.

STAFF EXCLUSIVENESS

Staff exclusiveness is manifested by prohibition of family visits and by ineffectual communication by the therapist and staff with the family. Sometimes all communication between family and hospital ceases. Families may find this isolation intolerable, and it is rarely helpful to their efforts to adjust to the hospitalization. Moreover, the therapist may deprive himself of useful information or may even be misled by the patient's statements or behavior, and both can impede or even stop therapeutic progress. For instance, Arthur's fear that the family might break up was quite realistic, but this could be established only from the family's communications and not from his psychotic productions, which avoided the topic.

Since the tendency is to concentrate all efforts upon the patient who is admitted to the hospital for treatment, the psychiatrist is apt to resist and resent forces that interfere with his relationship with the patient. Yet the very complex relationship between the patient, the family, and the hospital can, unless given careful consideration, impede or even founder the therapeutic effort. This is particularly true of young schizophrenic patients who are still deeply involved with their parents, and are often in a close relationship with a parent who is seriously disturbed. The family disequilibrium or schism may have much to do with the patient's illness and can continue to affect him in the hospital. Isolation from the family is sometimes necessary, but in itself it is not an effective means of coping with the problems, for they cannot be dodged indefinitely. The hospital must endeavor to modify the parents' attitudes toward the patient and toward each other, particularly when the patient remains dependent upon the parents.

The Lamb family may be used as an illustration of some of the ways in which excluding relatives may affect therapy. This family appeared less bizarre and pathological as individuals than did the Newberg family, in part because we had little contact with them for many months after their son Daryl's admission.

The Lambs had had serious difficulties for many years, chiefly because of Mr. Lamb's infidelity and drinking and his jealousy of Daryl, the oldest child. Daryl had not been wanted by the father, and was never permitted to interfere with their social life or with Mr. Lamb's interests. Mrs. Lamb, however, was happy with her mother role, although beset by many difficulties caused by her husband's jealousy of the child. As Daryl grew up, Mr. Lamb always belittled him and mocked at his effeminate traits and artistic inclinations. The father had much less difficulty, however, in accepting Daryl's only sibling, a sister seven years younger. Mrs. Lamb's submissiveness and indecisiveness were pronounced in her dealings with the entire family. In particular, she could not impose realistic restrictions upon Daryl; she attempted to compensate for her husband's contemptuous treatment of him, and she feared to undermine or block his artistic inclinations.

Daryl was a very sensitive child whose social awkwardness had been noted as early as kindergarten. Although above-average intelligence, he did poorly in the early grades. Later he received superior marks but encountered many difficulties in school because of his bizarre and effeminate behavior and his mendacity. This behavior led to psychiatric treatment during his senior year at a boarding school and, when it continued despite therapy, to hospitalization. He was eighteen when admitted, a shy, sensitive boy whose appearance and awkwardness suggested very early adolescence. In the hospital, he at first isolated himself almost completely, hardly communicating with anyone and then only in a haughty, contemptuous manner. After several frustrating months of extremely patient and persistent effort on the part of the therapist, Daryl began to communicate meaningfully with him, although not with other staff members and patients; and when the therapist left the hospital, about six months after Daryl's admission, he refused for some time to communicate with his new doctor.

From the time of his admission Daryl insisted that his parents did not love him and demanded that they not be permitted to visit him. Moreover, we knew that Daryl's father was openly jealous of his son, which placed both Daryl and his mother in a particularly difficult position when the patient visited at home. Both therapists feared that opposing Daryl's demands to exclude his family would destroy their relationship with him.

Lacking adequate contact with the family, we had no evidence that the isolation from the patient bothered them. The mother, passive and fearful, abided by our decision, made soon after admission.

When she was seen again, she appeared quite depressed, and Daryl's sister, his only sibling, had also become disturbed and was worried about the absence of contact with her brother. Mrs. Lamb began to discuss her own indecisiveness and indulgence of Daryl's demands with the social worker, and we came to realize that the hospital was behaving as the mother had in the past, by permitting Daryl to decide if and when she could visit. The staff finally persuaded the therapist to insist that Daryl see his family.

Later it came to light that, as Daryl had perceived it, we had not only behaved like the undemanding mother by giving in to him, but also had unwittingly imitated the father, who explicitly expected nothing from Daryl, and who also sought to separate his wife and son. At the same time, the fact that the parents abided by our decision meant to Daryl that they were less interested in him than ever. The mother, on the other hand, needed the social worker's help to be more assertive with both her children. Her guilt feelings had been aggravated by our stand, because she took it as confirmation of her fear that she was an unfit mother, making her more uncertain than ever in her relationships with her children.

Although the social worker helped Mrs. Lamb considerably, enabling her to deal more effectively with both her children, we were unable to influence the basic family difficulty. Amelioration of Mr. Lamb's severe alcoholism and rejection of his son, which were rooted in similar experiences in his own background, would have required intensive individual psychotherapy, which he was unwilling to undertake. He rarely came to the hospital even after we permitted it, and continued to maintain the pretense of being a highly competent and self-sufficient person.

Therapeutic benefits for the patient ensued from the mother's visits, not from the separation. Some months later home visits became possible, and Daryl's interest in life outside an institution was thereby stimulated considerably. He finished his high school work successfully while still a patient in the Institute, and this achievement, together with his regular trips home, facilitated therapeutic consideration of his ambivalences in all his personal relationships. The ultimate prognosis for him and the family, however, remained guarded.

In this case, as in others, staff exclusiveness had undermined an already precarious family equilibrium, had deprived the staff of important information, and had interfered with therapy instead of facilitating it.

We have presented only a few of the very complex interactions among young schizophrenic patients, their families, and the hospital staff, from the wealth of material made available through the study. While it is true that the hospital team's tasks can often be eased temporarily in many respects by exclusion of the family from the hospital experience, such simplification of a complex problem ignores reality, necessity, and opportunity.

We believe that maximal inclusion of certain family members, if not the entire family, in the hospital experience opens important new therapeutic potentialities. The aim should be to reconcile therapeutic indications for both patient and family. Young schizophrenics are still closely attached to their parents, and it is unrealistic to try to sever such bonds abruptly upon hospital admission, no matter how unwholesome the attachment may seem at the moment. The patient's effort to withdraw from his family is often motivated by fear of his hostile or libidinal aggression, or by disillusionment, but it is usually highly ambivalent, for there are also deep needs for attachments to one or both parents. Many patients, however, are excited by contact with a parent who is also upset, and in occasional extreme cases this disturbing interaction must be prohibited (Tudor, 1952).

It is quite common for inexperienced therapists to encourage the expression of hostility and even rebellious behavior against parents, because it is sometimes wrongly believed that such behavior indicates developing independence and maturity (Semrad et al., 1952). We have found the reverse usually to be true. In such situations, the patient uses the staff as a shield from behind which he can safely attack his relatives without assuming responsibility for his behavior, instead of examining his impulses and feelings in treatment.

No matter how desirable prohibition of family visits appears to be on therapeutic grounds, it becomes a wise decision only if there is evidence that the family can tolerate it. Otherwise, family disorganization may be transformed into interference with treatment. Even if the patient is not removed from the institution altogether, disagreement between staff and family may affect the patient adversely, just as does disagreement among staff members, so aptly described by Stanton and Schwartz (1954). Moreover, we have evidence that chronic controversy and disunity have characterized many of these families throughout the patient's life, and that, not infrequently, the patient has been caught up in this schism. It is incumbent upon hospital staffs to make certain that the patient does not simply move from a position of being the focus of family disunity to one of being the center of a struggle between staff and family.

It has been stated that if a recovered young schizophrenic patient returns to live with his family, the likelihood of recurrence is increased (Federn, 1952). We can neither confirm nor deny this principle at present. We have found that preparation for disposition of the patient must begin at admission, because the success of any plan, whether the patient returns home or not, depends upon the family's readiness and ability not only to accept it but also to feel comfortable with it. Active cooperation cannot be expected unless the family is helped to recover, first of all, from the disorganizing and possibly overwhelming experience of the hospitalization of the patient. The expectation that relatives of patients will differ from other human beings in the possession of some miraculous ability to change unconsciously determined behavior, simply because they are told they must, disregards all psychodynamic knowledge. A tacit hope prevails, however, that families will quickly give all the necessary information and then disappear to leave the staff alone with the patient. Such assumptions may prepare the way for therapeutic failure for which staff and family will blame each other. If the relatives are to participate in the management of the patient, as we believe they should, continued contact with them is necessary, because the family situation is not static.

Here we would like to make a few observations and speculations concerning the patient committed to a state hospital—a more common situation than those discussed in this paper. Whereas in the upper-middle-class families we have studied it is often difficult to persuade the family to accept a plan which entails having the patient live apart from them following recovery, a reverse situation often exists in families of lower social class. They frequently break off contact with the hospital altogether if hospitalization goes on for any length of time and are quite unprepared to receive the patient back following his discharge. This happens even in families considered "cohesive" on cultural grounds. It has also been observed that, to some extent, the state hospital patient's fate and recovery actually depend on the family's activity and the interest which they maintain in him, as well as on their prodding hospital staffs into renewed therapeutic efforts with chronic patients (Meyers and Roberts, 1959).

The details and dynamics of family equilibrium cannot be discussed here, but our findings suggest that two things may happen following the commitment of a family member: First, the family may remain in a precarious state of equilibrium but make recurrent efforts to reunite the family, including the patient, and this results in such active behavior with hospital staffs as just mentioned. Second, the family may re-establish equilibrium by excluding the patient and then be hard put to it to shift toward an older equilibrium which may have been less stable, or to a totally new state of balance required by the readmission of the patient into their midst. This second group may well contain the families who discontinue contact with patient and hospital, or who make no effective demands for treatment or discharge. Probably there are many gradations between these alternatives, and further research will be required to establish the validity of these hypotheses.

Hospitalization of psychiatric patients occurs at various stages of illness, and also at different stages of family disorganization. It is not known at this time whether class differences are a significant factor in determining how early or late hospitalization occurs, in terms of either illness or family disorganization. However, it is obvious that the upper-middle-class families we have studied have recourse to many more facilities short of hospitalization than do families from lower socioeconomic groups—for instance, special schools, long vacations, and private psychiatric care. Occasionally, the moment of hospitalization may be determined by agencies outside the family, such as school authorities, employers, or neighbors, but in most instances the family's capacity to tolerate the disturbed member in their midst and their attitude toward mental hospitals appear to be the decisive factors.

We have also found that the reactions of relatives to hospitalization offer an important opportunity for research into the interaction in families under stress and provide data which transcend our immediate goal of studying the families of schizophrenic patients. Opportunities for research aside, we conclude with Fetterman (1948) that "he who neglects the family neglects the patient."

VII

Marital Schism and Marital Skew

(1956)

We wish to report briefly on another fragment of the work in progress, namely, on the defects in the marital relations of parents of schizophrenic patients. The topic is selected because, like the psychopathology of the fathers and mothers, the marital difficulties stand out in bold relief; and also because these marital problems are basic to the study of the intrafamilial milieu. The potential relationship of these parental difficulties to the maldevelopment of the children will have to remain largely implicit in this paper.

We must emphasize as strongly as possible that we do not seek to establish a direct etiological relationship between marital discord between parents and the appearance of schizophrenia in an offspring. It is obvious that bad marriages do not, in themselves, produce schizophrenic children, but it is unlikely that they do not have some relevance to the problem of schizophrenia.

The deficiencies in the relationships between parents of schizophrenic patients have been noted and studied by relatively few investigators. Lidz and Lidz (Chapter I) called attention to the frequency of broken homes, markedly unstable parents, and unusual patterns of child rearing, and found that at least 61 per cent of thirty-three patients had come from homes marked by strife. Tietze (1949) reported that thirteen of twenty-five mothers of schizophrenic patients said that their marriages were very unhappy, but that the state-

Theodore Lidz, Alice R. Cornelison, Stephen Fleck, and Dorothy Terry: The Intrafamilial Environment of Schizophrenic Patients: II. Marital Schism and Marital Skew. American Journal of Psychiatry, *Vol. 114, 1957, pp. 241-248. Copyright © 1957, The American Psychiatric Association. This paper was presented at the 1956 meeting of the American Orthopsychiatric Association.*

ments by nine that their marriages were "perfect" did not stand up under investigation, for the marriages were strained and far from happy. Frazee (1953) found that fourteen of twenty-three parental couples were in severe conflict and none was "normal" or had "only moderate conflict," whereas thirteen of the control parental couples were near normal or showed only moderate conflict. None of the parents of schizophrenic patients revealed any degree of marital stability, whereas well over one-half of the control group manifested only moderate conflict or had made a good marital adjustment. Gerard and Siegel (1950) found open discord between 87 per cent of the parents of seventy-one male schizophrenics as against 13 per cent in the controls. Reichard and Tillman (1950) cite the unhappy marriages of the parents of schizophrenics and analyze the sources of discord in terms of parental personalities. Of interest, too, is Murphy's report (1952) of the family environment of two adopted children who became schizophrenic, in which the marital relationship was filled with hostility and mutual recrimination between two seriously disturbed parents. Many individual case reports emphasize or mention the bad marital relationship between the parents.

In our efforts to study and describe marital relationships, it has become apparent—as it has to others—that one cannot adequately describe a family or even a marriage in terms of the personalities of each member alone. A family is a group and requires description in terms of group dynamics and the interaction among its members. We are indebted to Parsons and Bales and their coworkers (1955), to J. Spiegel and F. Kluckhohn (1954), Nathan Ackerman (1954a), Reuben Hill and his coworkers (1953), Bradley Buell and the Community Research Associates (1953), and others for their efforts to analyze marital and family interrelationships. We are still searching for suitable frames of reference, but the deficiencies of descriptive method should not blur the basic consideration—that the parental relations are highly disturbed in all of our fourteen cases.

The requisites for successful marriages are unfortunately far from clear, but some essentials are emerging. A couple must find reciprocal interrelating roles with each other and in their respective roles with their children. Absence of such role reciprocity means making constant decisions, self-consciousness, and tension. As Spiegel (1957) has pointed out, role reciprocity requires common understanding and acceptance of each other's roles, goals, and motivations, and a reasonable sharing of cultural value orientation. Mutual trust and effective communication between partners are important requisites given effect by support of the spouse's role and self-esteem during periods of loss of confidence. We have been particularly impressed by the need to maintain lines between generations: that is, not to confuse or blur distinctions between parents and children. Spouses cannot remain primarily in a dependent position to their parents to the exclusion of an interdependent marital relationship; nor can one behave primarily as the other's child; nor as a rival with one's own children for the spouse's attention, nor reject a parental role completely. The need for both parents to form sources of primary love relationships for children and objects for stable identification will not be entered upon here, as we are concerned primarily with marital interaction.

It seems helpful to follow the lead of Parsons and Bales (1955) and consider the father's role in the family as primarily "adaptive-instrumental" and the mother's as "integrative-expressive." In broad terms, which may differ somewhat from Parsons', the father supports the family, establishes its position with respect to other families, determines prestige, and the social patterns of interaction with other groups. The mother's basic functions pertain to intrafamilial interactions; tensions and their regulation; supplying the oral needs, both tangible and affectional. Each parent, in addition to filling his own role, must support the role of the other through his or her prestige, power, and emotional value to other family members.

The marriages of these parents of schizophrenics are beset by a wide variety of problems and ways of adjusting to them. However, the fourteen marriages can be placed in two general groupings, which, of course, tend to overlap in places. Eight of the fourteen couples have lived in a state of severe chronic disequilibrium and discord, which we are calling marital schism. This paper will focus primarily upon these eight couples. The other six couples have achieved some state of relative equilibrium, in which the continuation of the marriage was not constantly threatened; and the marital relationship could yield some gratification of needs to one or both partners. However, the achievement of parental satisfaction or the sacrifices of one parent to maintain marital harmony resulted in a distorted family environment for the children.

MARITAL SCHISM

In the eight families in which the state of disequilibrium designated as marital schism existed, both spouses were caught up in their own personality difficulties, which were aggravated to the point of desperation by the marital relationship. There was chronic failure to achieve complementarity of purpose or role reciprocity. Neither gained support of emotional needs from the other; one sought to coerce the other to conform to his or her expectations or standards, but was met by open or covert defiance. These marriages are replete with recurrent threats of separation, which are not overcome by efforts at re-equilibration, but through postponement of coming to grips with the conflict or through emotional withdrawal from each other—but without hope or prospect of improvement or ever finding any gratification in the marriage. Communication consists primarily of coercive efforts and defiance, or of efforts to mask the defiance to avoid fighting. There is little or no sharing of problems or satisfactions. Each spouse pursues his needs or objectives, largely ignoring the needs of the other, infuriating the partner and increasing ill-will and suspiciousness. A particularly malignant feature in these marriages is the chronic "undercutting" of the worth of one partner to the children by the other. The tendency to compete for the children's loyalty and affection is prominent; at times to gain a substitute to replace the affection missing from the spouse, but at times perhaps simply to hurt and spite the marital partner. Absence of any positive satisfaction from the marital relationship (excluding the children) is striking, though strong dependency needs may be gratified in a masochistic fashion in a few instances. Mutual distrust of motivations is the rule and varies only in the degree to which realistic causes for mistrust extend into the paranoid.

In seven of these eight families, the husband retains little prestige in the home and with the children, either because of his own behavior or his wife's attitudes toward him. He becomes an outsider or a secondary figure who cannot assert his instrumental leadership, and when he strives to dominate in tyrannical fashion, he eventually forces the family to conspire to circumvent him. His instrumental role is basically limited to financial support, which he may have originally considered as a husband's basic function, or he is relegated to this position. The ineffectual role of the father applies equally to five of the six marriages in the other group in which marked schism is not present.

The wives will be considered only in respect to their wifely functions, excluding the complex maternal relationships which also cause marital discord because eccentric, cold, rigid, or overindulgent attitudes toward the children antagonized the husband. All distrusted their husbands and had no confidence in them. They were openly defiant in major areas of interaction and rather habitually disregarded or circumvented their husbands' demands. They were emotionally cold and distant and, with one or two exceptions, sexually aloof. They competed for the attention and affection of the children and tried to instill their value systems, which differed from those of their husbands.

Communication in these marriages is greatly impeded by mutual withdrawal and by masking of motives from one another, but is further hindered because four wives show seriously scattered thinking and four husbands show paranoid thinking and rigidity. The imperviousness to the feelings of others, characteristic of many parents of schizophrenics, also creates communicative difficulties.

It seems of interest that in five of the eight marriages, the focus of the partners' loyalties remained in their parental homes, preventing the formation of a nuclear family in which the center of gravity rests in the home. The grandparents or the parental siblings often carried out much of the expressive and instrumental roles rather than the marital partners. The cardinal emotional attachment and dependency of one or both partners remained fixed to a parental figure and could not be transferred to the spouse.

The eight families can be grouped into three categories, according to the groupings of the Community Research Associates in their "Classification of Disorganized Families," which describes ten combinations of masculine and feminine personalities which are potentially hazardous to successful marital and family relationships (Buell, 1953).[1]

Four marriages seem best described as "Man-dominated Competitive Axes." The husband strives to assert his male dominance to a pathological degree, rather clearly in reaction to his feminine dependent strivings. He needs an admiring wife who supports insatiable narcissistic needs and complies with his rigid expectations, and is angered when she reacts with defiance and disregard. Indeed, her inadequacies as a wife or mother may well produce exasperated frustration. He distrusts her increasingly and undercuts her prestige with the children. The wives are disappointed and disillusioned in the father figure they married who cannot grasp their needs, and, if they are overwhelmed by force, they manage to gain their ends through circumvention. The husbands are rigid paranoiacs or obsessives, and the wives are poorly organized obsessives or schizophrenics. The marriages are marked by chronic severe mistrust without (except in the least serious instance) any semblance of affection. The family is split into two factions by the conflict and mutual undercutting. Although both members are fighting, it is the husband's moral brutality, his disregard and contempt for the wife whom he tries to force into compliance that dominates the picture.

Mr. Reading, a forceful and successful but paranoically suspicious man, sought to control his wife's behavior from the start of the marriage. He was infuriated and disillusioned when she joined a church group against his orders to remain aloof from any organizations. He was dependent upon his mother, who lived in the home for many years; he followed her advice in household matters in opposition to his wife's, whom he considered incompetent to furnish the house. Marked strife began with the birth of the elder of two daughters, for he was clearly jealous of the attention the wife paid the child. He disapproved of everything she did in raising the child, often with good reason, but he competed rather than supported. Mrs. Reading was obviously overprotective of the children, whereas her husband wished to inure them to the hard knocks of life. Violent scenes, filled

[1] The classification used to find common ground with other members of a panel has not been used by us again, as it added little to the understanding of the families.

with Mr. Reading's dire threats and marred by occasional violence, were commonplace. The marriage further disintegrated into a hostile battleground after Mrs. Reading discovered that her husband was having an affair, which she reported to her mother-in-law to gain an ally her husband feared. Mr. Reading never forgave his wife for this betrayal and, apparently to spite her, sold their home in the best section of the city to move into a two-family house in an undesirable neighborhood. Thus, he struck a foul blow at Mrs. Reading's major preoccupations—her social aspirations and her insistence that her daughters associate with only "proper" companions. The family, previously split into two groups, now united against Mr. Reading and refused to eat meals with him. The difficulties engendered by the wife's indecisive obsessiveness and the husband's paranoid trends cannot be depicted here. Both partners used interviews primarily to incriminate the other and persuade the interviewer to judge in their favor against the spouse.

The second group of two families may be categorized as "Woman-dominated Competitive Axes," according to the "Classification of Disorganized Families." The outstanding common feature is the wife's exclusion of the passive and masochistic husband from leadership and decision making. She derogates him in word and deed and is emotionally cold and distant to him. Her attention is focused on her narcissistic needs for completion and admiration. These wives are extremely castrating and their husbands are vulnerable. The husband withdraws from the relationship in an effort to preserve some integrity when defeated in the struggle, and may find solace in alcohol. The husband's function in the family is restricted to providing a living or, if willing, to supporting the wife in her domination of the family. The wife does not fill an expressive, supportive role to her husband and her expressive functions with the children are seriously distorted.

Both Mr. and Mrs. Forel were closely tied to their parental families. Mrs. Forel, the youngest of three sisters, was very dependent upon her eldest sister, a masculine aggressive woman with open contempt for men, who tended to dominate the Forel household. Mrs. Forel refused to live at any distance from her family and spent two months each year with them away from her husband. She was an extremely cold, narcissistic woman and a "tease," who flirted constantly but denied her husband sexual relations. Mr. Forel was a passive man who sought to assert a pseudo domination of his family when his men friends were about. He formed fawning attachments to men, which increased his wife's contempt for him. He was excluded increasingly from the family circle, his opinions disregarded; and felt like an outsider who was barely tolerated. He was closely attached to his mother, whom he helped to support. Mr. Forel finally took steps to separate unless his wife would detach herself from her sisters. She capitulated but became pregnant in the process of reconciliation. She was ashamed and concealed the pregnancy, and then took it out on her husband. Separated from her sisters, she began to drink heavily and carried on open flirtations, or perhaps affairs, neglecting her baby. The discord heightened. After Mrs. Forel was seriously disfigured in an accident for which her husband was responsible, she became depressed and withdrew into seclusion until plastic surgery restored her appearance. Mr. Forel then tried to make amends through becoming a weak and spineless husband who mothered the youngest neglected child. However, he soon developed cancer and his wife displayed a physical abhorrence for him, fearing that she might catch the disease. She refused to nurse him during his terminal illness.

The remaining two marriages may be classified as "Dual Immature Dependency Axes." Mutual withdrawal of the spouses and dependency on members of the parental families were outstanding. It is difficult to say which spouse dominated the marriage, though both tried and at the same time resented not having a strong figure who would provide leadership. Resentment of the mates' attachments to their families was prominent. The inability to gain mutual gratification of needs and support led to mounting disregard of the other and increasing emptiness of both lives. These marriages were replete with threats of separation by both members, but each tended to go his or her own way, undermining the other to the children by deeds and attitudes more than by words. Despite the long duration of both marriages, they remained tentative, as if both partners were awaiting and contemplating release.

The Nussbaums' dissension had started shortly after their marriage twenty-five years ago. Mr. Nussbaum had been largely supported by his elder brother, whom he regarded as a father. Mrs. Nussbaum's father had suicided following business reverses, which her family blamed upon his affiliation with Mr. Nussbaum's brother. Mrs. Nussbaum appeared to side with her family in their accusation of her husband's brother. Mr. Nussbaum considered her attitude to show utter disloyalty as it furnished the finishing blow to his feelings of being excluded by her close-knit family. There was little or no discussion of the matter, but they drew apart. Mrs. Nussbaum was very sensitive lest her husband dominate her, and stood her ground with the help of a violent temper. She refused to accompany him on social engagements essential to his career and antagonized his friends. Mr. Nussbaum felt unloved and unwanted and constantly deprecated. He stayed away from home much of the time, and fostered the impression that he was having affairs, either to spite his wife or to mask his impotence, or both. Weeks would pass when the couple would not speak to each other. The wife found solace in her relationship to her son, and the husband in his seductive attachment to his daughter, our patient.

Although the Newbergs had been in violent disagreement and there had been repeated threats of separation, some elements of goodwill toward each other could be uncovered. Mr. Newberg is a very disturbed man, pushing numerous impractical schemes that are often grandiose; talking incessantly in a loud voice; seeking to dominate but with faulty judgment and, although a steady and hardworking provider, he had frightened his wife for years lest he leave his job and launch upon one of his impracticable schemes. He spent little time with his family, partly because of his attachment to his mother and partly because of his wife's attachment to her sisters, which forced the family to live in a home two hours from his job. Mr. Newberg resented his wife's attachment to her three sisters and mother, and her domination by one sister who constantly disparaged him to his wife and children. Mrs. Newberg claimed that she remained dependent upon her sisters because her husband provided her neither emotional support nor help in raising the children. She considered him impossible to live with because of his demands, his thoughtlessness, and the constant confusion he produced in the home. She remained with him only because she felt the children needed a father but found she had to treat him as a child, humoring him to avoid strife. They blame each other's families for interfering and discourage and disparage each other's interests. The situation reached a crisis when Mr. Newberg wished to move to the West Coast because his mother and brother were moving there. He threatened to leave his wife if she would not move and she threatened to leave him if he tried to force the move. Both had intense needs which the other could not begin to satisfy. Although Mr. Newberg had strong paranoid trends and Mrs. Newberg had difficulties in being close, and the hostility was marked, this family offered the best chance of any for some reconciliatory movement, because both showed potential ability to recognize the other's needs as well as their own difficulties.

The portrayals of these marriages are little more than symbolic fragments of the wealth of material collected. Still, they indicate the virtual absence of complementarity in each marriage. Husband and wife do not support each other's needs, and the marital interaction increases the emotional problems of both, deprives the spouses of any sense of fulfillment in life, and deteriorates into a hostile encounter in which both are losers. Instead of any reciprocal give and take, there is demand and defiance leading to schism between partners that divides the entire family, leaving the children torn between conflicting attachments and loyalties.

Marital Skew

In six of the fourteen marriages, this type of schism did not exist, although the family life was distorted by a skew in the marital relationship. In all, the rather serious psychopathology of one marital partner dominated the home. In some, the dissatisfaction and unhappiness of one spouse is apparent to the other and to the children, but husband and wife manage to complement or support each other sufficiently to permit a degree of harmony. In the others, the distorted ideation of one partner was accepted or shared by the other, creating an atmosphere of *folie à deux*, or even of *folie en famille* when the entire family shared the aberrant conceptualizations.

In all of these families, one partner who was extremely dependent or masochistic had married a spouse who had appeared to be a strong and protecting parental figure. The dependent partner would go along with or even support the weaknesses or psychopathological distortions of the parental partner because dependency or masochistic needs were met. In contrast to the marriages with overt schism, one partner could gratify rather than combat a spouse's narcissistic needs. It may be significant that no member of these six marriages had intense emotional bonds to the parental family, and it is possible that absence of such alternative sources of gratification tended to hold these spouses together. A striking feature in all cases was the psychopathology of the partner who appeared to be dominant, creating an abnormal environment which, being accepted by the "healthier" spouse, may have seemed to be a normal environment to the children. Considerable "masking" of potential sources of conflict occurred, creating an unreal atmosphere in which what was said and admitted differed from what was actually felt and done. Two and perhaps three of the marriages may be classified as "Woman-oriented Self-depreciatory Axes," according to the "Classification of Disorganized Families," in which the wife's masochistic self-sacrifice to support a narcissistic and disappointing husband was striking. One, and perhaps two of the marriages could be designated as "Man-oriented Self-depreciatory Axes" in which a husband with a meek and self-effacing disposition supported a wife who was an ambulatory schizophrenic.

We shall cite examples in cursory fashion, primarily to illustrate that even though these marriages provided some gratification to the marital partners, the family milieu was as distorted and disturbed as in the case of the schismatic marriages.

The Schwartz family was completely dominated by a paranoid mother who supported the family. Her husband had left her on one occasion, unable to tolerate her demands, but had returned long before the patient, the youngest son, had been born. Soon thereafter the father suffered a nervous breakdown, after which he lived as a sort of handyman around the house and worked as a menial helper in the wife's business. The wife was extremely ambitious for her four sons, pushing them and dominating their lives, as well as making it clear that they must not become like their father. She was paranoically fearful of outsiders, believing that their telephone was tapped and that the family was physically endangered because they were Jewish. A severe schism actually existed despite the peace between the marital couple. The mother was intensely protective of her oldest son, a gambler and embezzler, who consumed all of her attention as well as much of the family income. A chronic ambivalent conflict existed between them that tended to exclude the husband and the other sons. The husband did not intervene, but merely told his sons that the trouble in the family existed because they did not obey their mother as he did.

Here the father had abdicated and the mother was a paranoid instrumental leader, while the father supplied no masculine image with whom the younger sons could identify.

Illustrative of the *folie à deux* and the *folie en famille* group, the Dolfuss family lived like European landed gentry in a New England suburb, isolated from their neighbors. The family life was centered in the needs and opinions of Mr. Dolfuss, a successful but paranoically grandiose inventor. The children were raised by a seductive nursemaid of whom the cold and distant mother was intensely jealous. However, Mrs. Dolfuss devoted her life to her husband, catering to his whims, and keeping the children out of his way. Mr. Dolfuss' major interest was an oriental religious sect. He believed that he and a friend were among the few select souls who would achieve a particular type of salvation. Both Mrs. Dolfuss and the nursemaid virtually deified him. They and the children shared his beliefs as well as his grandiose notion of himself, living in what we termed a *folie en famille*. Here, the children were largely excluded from the lives of the parents, the model of the father was an unrealistic one for the son, and the intellectual and emotional environment was estranged from that of the larger culture into which they had to emerge.

In all of these six families, the fathers were particularly ineffectual, assuming little responsibility for family leadership other than earning a livelihood. They were either weak, ineffectual men who went along with wives who were schizophrenic or at least questionably so, or they were disturbed men who could maintain an outward form of capability and strength because of the support of a masochistic wife. In all instances, the psychopathology that pervaded the home was masked or treated as normal.

The analysis of the pathological environment in these last six cases, and of the effects upon the children, cannot be gone into here, but we trust we have shown that we have not simply discarded less disturbed family environments in choosing to focus this paper upon the eight marriages in which overt schism between the partners existed.[2] In considering the eight schismatic marriages we do not seek, as emphasized previously, to relate directly the appearance of schizophrenia in an offspring to the marital disorganization. There are many other factors in the family environment which we are studying that affect the children, but they all bear some relationship to the personalities of the parents and the atmosphere created by their interaction. We are only seeking to describe bit by bit what this family environment is, until we can assemble the fragments into a meaningful description of the whole. We are still occupied with the grossest factors, for unless we start with what appears fairly obvious, these factors may be overlooked during our preoccupation with subtleties. In this presentation, we have paid minimal attention to the individual personalities of the parents in order to concentrate upon problems created by their interaction.

DISCUSSION

We find a number of features in these marriages that are theoretically adverse to the "normal" developmental process of a child. In these families each parent constantly denigrates and undercuts the other, making it clear to the children that each does not respect or value, but rather dislikes or hates, the other. Each parent more or less openly expresses fears that a child will resemble the other, and a child's resemblance to one parent is a source of concern or rejection by the other parent. One or both parents seek to win the child away from the other. The boundary between the generations is violated. A child may feel the burden of being expected or required to complete the life of one or both parents; and this creates a block to growth into an independent individual. A child may be used and needed as a replacement for the spouse. There is excellent oppor-

[2] The Newcomb, Lerner, and Lamb families, described in other papers in this volume, are other examples of skewed families. The Nebb family also had schismatic elements.

tunity for intensification of the oedipal rivalry rather than for its resolution. The child can insert himself as a wedge between the parents, becoming inordinately adept at widening the breach and becoming caught in the incestuous concern that the parent can be seduced or might seduce, as well as in the guilt over hostile-destructive impulses toward the other parent. A parent of the same sex with whom the child should identify during latency and adolescence, who is not an acceptable love object to the other parent but is hated and despised, cannot provide a model through which a child can achieve mature identity. Potential homosexual trends, which play a large role in schizophrenia, are opened. Many other serious impediments are placed in the way of the child's achievement of a stable identification with a parental figure, a requisite to the formation of a stable ego identity by the end of adolescence. In addition, children of a rejected marriage are likely to feel rejected themselves. Caught in the anxiety that a needed parental love object can be lost through separation of the parents, the children may devote much energy toward balancing the precarious marriage. The stronger the incestuous tendencies, the greater the need for protection by the presence of both parents. When one or both parents have paralogic and scattered ways of thinking and behaving, the difficulties are further heightened.

VIII

Parental Personalities and Family Interaction

(1957)

The family's subtle task of transmitting acquisitions of its culture essential to the new generation and of shaping personality has been largely implicit, guided by custom and pedagogic and religious precepts. Only in recent years have scientific attempts been made to analyze this process in which so many factors have been taken for granted that they have not been scrutinized. As with many other human functions that transpire almost automatically, study of the pathological helps focus attention upon essential functions and processes.[1]

The study of the family has been approached in very many ways. The approaches may be said to vary from the sociological, concerned primarily with the effects of the structure of society upon the structure of the family and vice versa, and then upon the functioning of the persons involved, to psychological approaches focusing primarily upon the effects of personalities upon one another and upon the family organization. Our studies have certainly rested heavily upon a variety of certain sociological orientations. We have found it useful, following Parsons and Bales (1955), to consider the family in terms of small group dynamics. The nuclear family is a true group; all mem-

Theodore Lidz, Stephen Fleck, Alice R. Cornelison, and Dorothy Terry: The Intrafamilial Environment of the Schizophrenic Patient: IV. Parental Personalities and Family Interaction. American Journal of Orthopsychiatry, *Vol. 28, 1958, pp. 764-776. Copyright © 1958, American Orthopsychiatric Association, Inc. This paper was presented at the 1957 annual meeting of the American Orthopsychiatric Association.*

[1] See, for example, Ackerman (1954a); Bott (1955); Dicks (1953); Foote and Cottrell (1955); Group for the Advancement of Psychiatry (1954); Handel and Hess (1956); Hill (1954); Jackson (1957a); Jensen (1952); Kluckhohn (1952); Locke et al. (1955); Spiegel (1954, 1957).

bers are interdependent, the actions of any member affecting all, and because the family provides a protecting shelter for its members both within and against the society in which it exists. Still the family differs from all other small groups in that its organization follows a number of imperatives that must be taken into account. One approach to family interaction is to study how each family or any given type of family seeks to fulfill these imperatives in comparison with other families, and the effects upon the personalities involved. The most categorical of these imperatives derive from the biological structure of man born either male or female helplessly dependent and requiring prolonged nurturance and protection, with a set of basic drives and needs, but developing into a self-sufficient person by assimilation from the persons who rear him the instrumentalities of the culture in which he happens to be born. Other imperatives are implicitly set by the culture to ensure that each generation will be able to live in and transmit the culture.

We can but touch upon the nature of our thinking in this area to designate how it can lend coherence to the diffuse material gathered in a family study. The family contains two categories of members according to generation, and two categories according to sex. The parents raised in two differing families seek to find a permanent union by finding reciprocally interrelating roles and a shared set of values for living with each other and for raising children. The children, however, in contrast to members of any other small group, receive their primary training in group interaction within the family. The child learns largely through interaction in this group how to emerge and live in other groups, including how to start one of his own as a parental figure. He is trained to belong and yet to leave. The functions of the two generations differ; for example, parents can be dependent on each other, and children must be dependent upon parents, yet limitations must be set on parental dependency upon immature children. Or, as another example, sex taboos exist between all family members except the parents, for whom sex relations are more or less obligatory.

Similar analysis can be made of the division according to sex. The female role, linked to child rearing and mothering, is more confined to the home, permits a more sheltered and dependent life for the woman, and promotes her greater dependence upon the emotional relatedness of family members. The total care required by the newborn dictates that the father provide subsistence and protection for the family, and that he assume a more instrumental role, forcing him to emerge more from the family into society. The mother must possess skills, patterns, and emotional ability to care for children, with graded patterns for abrogation of total care commensurate with the children's increasing abilities and with instilling confidence in them. The long dependency of the child causes a blending of parent-child and sexual love, which must, however, become differentiated. As the family is a mutually protective group, some undefined degree of primacy must be given by all members to the needs of the family group and by the family as a whole over the needs of outsiders.

The requisites within the family to provide for the gradual socialization of the child cannot be reviewed here. We shall simply mention that parents must provide models of identification for children of both sexes which can be incorporated smoothly only if the models are not conflicting and mutually exclusive. Each parent's worth as a primary love object depends not only upon that parent, but also upon the spouse's esteem for that parent. Also, a parent's own self-esteem helps build the child's ego strength. If parental personalities or the interpersonal processes within the family are too aberrant, children may be able to live within the family, but will become perplexed when they emerge from it and may be unable to socialize harmoniously.

In some families, such as those we have studied, gross failures in carrying out essential functions like the few enumerated are apparent. Even within this framework a great many variant approaches to a study can be undertaken. Here, we shall pursue the effects of parental personalities on the family interaction. It seems apparent that whatever the approach, parental personalities and their interaction will provide a uniqueness to each nuclear family, influencing its structure and functioning, and the children's personalities. However, families cannot be understood through the study of individual personalities alone, but only through the interrelatedness of these persons. Their behavior evokes reaction and counterreaction, and creates an environmental atmosphere which exists over and above the influence of individuals. We wish to emphasize particularly that the personality of each parent contains resultants of his own parental family interaction and the social culture in which he was raised, so that a study of parental personalities implicitly or explicitly includes consideration of many basic sociological factors. In a strongly antitraditional society with rapid changes in mores, as in contemporary middle-class United States, where the nuclear family tends to be isolated from collateral kinship systems, the influence of parents upon family interaction is unusually strong. Neither the structural pattern of the family nor parental and children's roles are as clearly defined as in more static societies, and there is a dearth of paternal and maternal figures to provide security and models along with the actual parents. Here the two parents come together from two differing families, having had a relatively narrow experience with family life and parenthood, largely confined to their own parental families. The actual pattern of the family, the harmony of the home, the security afforded the children, the skills and knowledge to be imparted, etc., all depend upon what the parents bring with them, including their value systems, and the interaction between these personalities.

The families that we have studied are all disturbed. However, this does not interfere with the intent of this paper, but rather may simplify the task because of the exaggerations involved, which permit us to note specific types of failure in essential areas of family interaction. In Chapter VII we divided the disturbed marriages we were studying into two general types: marriages marked by severe marital schism that split the family into two opposing camps, and "skewed" marriages in which serious strife was avoided because the dominant parent's seriously distorted ideas were accepted by a more normal but very dependent spouse, giving rise to a deviant and paralogic family environment. Here we wish simply to present a single family and some of our efforts at analyzing its structure and interaction by starting with the personalities of the couple who married.

We have selected the Grau family for presentation because the pathology was not too extreme and because the parents came from sufficiently divergent backgrounds to illustrate some areas of interest with reasonable clarity. It is an upper-middle-class suburban family, relatively aloof from kin. The family, when the study was started four years ago, consisted of the father, fifty-two; the mother, fifty; Nancy, a twenty-one-year-old schizophrenic daughter; and Ellen, a college girl of eighteen. The marriage was troubled from the start because both parents were strange, showing many psychotic features both in our contact with them and on projective tests.

Let us first look at the persons who married twenty-five years ago. At twenty-six, Mr. Grau had never dated a girl before meeting his wife. He was a shy chemist who even then viewed the world with a jaundiced eye, and was given to depressive moods. He came from a Dakota farm family of German Evangelical origin. His father, a relatively wealthy man, must have been rigid and somewhat paranoid. We know, for example, that his wife was not permitted to leave the farm to shop in town more than once or twice a year. Born in Germany, she was better educated than most farm wives of her generation. Our patient's father had little use for his numerous siblings, except for one sister Ellen, and retained little contact with his married sisters and one bachelor brother, all of whom settled on farms near the family home. Mr. Grau had always been aloof and without close friends. He felt an outsider in high school because most of the others came from Scandinavian families, and in college because he was a "hick" even though it was a state college. He had difficulty finding himself after high school, and was permitted to go to college by his father only when he promised not to study agriculture, as his father had set prejudices against scientific farmers. After completing a year of graduate school, Mr. Grau accepted a position with a large chemical firm in upper New York state, and remained with it. Just how and why he married his wife remains obscure, because he talked as if he had been an unwary country boy who had been trapped. We know he could have escaped since she agreed to marry only after he had willingly given his written promise to raise their children as Catholics.

Mrs. Grau's father was a German Catholic and her mother a devout Irish Catholic. The father was a strict man, cruel to his wife and sons, but he favored his only daughter. According to Mr. Grau he was a tavern keeper, while Mrs. Grau said he was a restaurant owner—at any rate he ran a speakeasy at the time of the marriage. Mrs. Grau's mother managed to get along with her difficult husband. The bond between mother and daughter was very close. Mrs. Grau had an adequate social life before her marriage, and had just completed two years at a junior college. She had set ideas of right and wrong and adhered strictly to her Catholicism. For many years before our study started, at least, she had been vague and scattered in her talk, conveying the impression of being childish and feebleminded, but it soon became clear that her intelligence was not defective. Though perhaps attracted by a scientist from a well-to-do family, she certainly married a man who resembled her father in being stubborn, German, and set in his beliefs.

Trouble started almost immediately. Mr. Grau, insecure as a man, followed his father's pattern and expected his wife to obey and to mother him. He deeply resented her attachment to her church as an infidelity to him. He claimed that he had known few Catholics, and had not understood that Catholicism was a way of life as well as a religion. He was suspicious of his wife's fidelity without provocation, and he trailed her on occasion. He developed great contempt for her "stupidity." The arguments soon focused on religion, because Mr. Grau decided not to have children as a way out of his pledge to raise them as Catholics. Evidence indicates, however, that he could not tolerate having rivals for his wife's attention.

When Mrs. Grau became pregnant three years after they were married, Mr. Grau felt that his wife had trapped him, following her mother's advice to have a child to preserve the tottering marriage, although he had assumed responsibility for the contraception. Fighting raged constantly, and Mr. Grau struck his pregnant wife in the abdomen, a fact which she never forgot. Thereafter, the marriage became a hostile encounter, focusing on the daughter's religion. Mr. Grau refused to allow her to be baptized Catholic. Mrs. Grau felt betrayed and attacked by his assault on her religion. She considered leaving him but was advised by her priest to stay for the sake of the child. Mrs. Grau could not accept a situation that left her child living in sin. Her insecurities in raising the child were heightened because she could not rear her in the tradition in which she felt secure. In any event, she was very rigid with Nancy, following to the letter the strict schedules taught in her book, and she was apprehensive of any initiative the girl showed. Nancy became a docile, conforming child who never stood up for herself with her mother or playmates when small. Her birth had clearly separated the parents, rather than bringing them closer together. Three and a half years later Ellen was born—also unwanted by her father but welcomed by the mother. The birth did not arouse such violence, but the discord continued. The father, having gained his way with Nancy, expected his wife to follow his orders with Ellen. However, hopeless about ever gaining his consent, Mrs. Grau secretly had both children baptized, justifying herself because of her husband's broken promise. When, at some later date, Mr. Grau learned of her action, he became infuriated and grew increasingly distrustful of her.

Mrs. Grau, however, was much less restrictive in raising Ellen, having learned that raising a child required more than providing for physical needs according to schedule. Ellen soon showed herself to be more aggressive and less compliant than her sister.

Several attitudinal patterns were permanently established in this family. The father constantly displayed a peculiar paranoid attitude about Catholicism, blaming his troubles and many of the troubles of the world on the way Catholics raised their children. He could not tolerate the acceptance of a belief which conflicted with his own cynical suspiciousness of people's motives. He constantly deprecated his wife as a Catholic, contemptuously calling her a fisheater and still less complimentary terms, and never missed an opportunity to call attention to Catholic miscreants he read about in the newspaper. He had fixed ideas about education, derogating anyone without a college degree, and considered his wife in particular stupid, and her views worthless because she had attended only junior college. Mrs. Grau received no emotional support from her husband in raising the children. He constantly deprecated her to the children and she responded in kind. The family had almost no social life: the mother saw a few women friends, and the father stayed home in what seems to have been a disinterested and almost apathetic state. Communication had descended into irritable fights over trivia, always turning into conflicts over religion. Under stress, the mother became even more scattered than usual. As Nancy grew older, the father wooed her to win her to his side of the conflict.

This couple, who had hoped their needs would be met in the marriage, floundered in a hapless situation. Mr. Grau, whose insecure narcissism needed constant support through admiration, became jealous of the attention his wife gave the children and attacked her and her way of life. Mrs. Grau, who had been her father's favorite, married a man like her father, but found no fatherly support but only criticism from a husband who favored the children and rejected her. Mr. Grau, who tried, like his father, to insist upon his pseudomasculine dominance, only provoked defiance. They were enemies but could not get along without each other. They could not avoid fights because Mr. Grau could not forego cynical comments, and Mrs. Grau, with remarkable tactlessness, did not know when to keep quiet. Afraid of her husband, she often pretended to agree but then did as she wished, further infuriating him. Talk of separation became common, but they stayed together "because of the children."

When Nancy was nine, the situation deteriorated further when Mr. Grau developed a chronic disease which incapacitated him for long periods, and forced dependence upon his wife. He was an irritable patient with a violent temper at home, and apparently preferred the hospital. When Nancy was fourteen and Ellen ten, Mr. Grau became completely invalided for three years because he refused an operation which would improve his condition. Mrs. Grau worked, and with liberal help from both grandfathers, the family managed without notable change in economic status. Mr. Grau could not take the pressing needs of the family into account and undergo the operation for their sake. Eventually he had to accept the operation, after which he was able to return to work though he continued to suffer considerable pain at times.

When, during her father's invalidism, Nancy entered adolescence, she changed markedly. Mrs. Grau had continued to be distrustful and extremely intrusive, wanting to know exactly what Nancy did whenever she was away from home. Nancy began to fight back, and unable to retain some privacy by maintaining silence, because her mother would nag and insist that she tell, she learned to talk but reveal nothing. She purposely became vague and confusing—in a sense all that she had to do was copy her mother's confused talk and her father's evasiveness. Her father would not permit her to date until she was sixteen—but then Nancy focused her attention on boys, dressing in a dramatic and inappropriate fashion that infuriated her mother and made her suspicious. If Nancy went out with a Catholic boy, her father was infuriated; if with a non-Catholic, her mother hounded her. Aside from his concern about the boy's religion and education, Mr. Grau showed a peculiar neglect concerning whom she dated, as if in collusion with Nancy to aggravate and worry her mother. Nancy went with some rather questionable characters, and Mrs. Grau would chase her about the house, insisting on hearing every detail of the evening, and slapped her when she would not tell. Fights between Nancy and Ellen would soon turn into fights between Nancy and her mother, with Mr. Grau on the sidelines making no effort to head off the battle.

Entering upon the genesis of Nancy's illness would require too much detail for this presentation. We wish only to note that by the time Nancy entered college she clearly sided with her father, insisting that her mother had deceived him in having her baptized and that she was a Protestant. She considered her father to be the perfect man, a judgment which made the hospital staff shudder, for he was a bitter, cynical, and verbally sadistic person who consciously sought to make his daughter cynical and suspicious. Nancy felt that completing college was essential, as her father could not respect her unless she gained her degree. She wished to become an interpreter, a meaningful and necessary occupation in this family. Hating her mother and seeking love from her father, she sought to become totally different from her mother.

Whereas Nancy always got caught between her parents and became the focus of their hostility to each other, Ellen managed differently. There had been notable differences in the way the two girls had been raised. Ellen had not been a source of conflict or a substitute conflict for the parents, nor had her mother restricted or nagged her as much as she had Nancy. Her father had become seriously incapacitated when Ellen was only five or six.

Ellen considered that she had profited greatly from seeing how her sister got into trouble, and sought to avoid repeating her errors. She patterned herself to be different from Nancy. She managed to pick the strengths of each parent, and warily and diplomatically placated both of them. She sought to gain their trust by being the type of daughter each wanted. Even when she was permitted to go out with boys at sixteen, she disclaimed any interest in boys, and concentrated on studies and athletics. Above all she gained her mother's approval and confidence by letting her know that she espoused Catholicism, a fact which through silent collusion they hid from Mr. Grau. As a Catholic she was not so restricted by her mother, and since she did not go out on dates, she avoided the Catholic boy vs. non-Catholic boy controversies. To all except the father it was clear that the family was divided into two camps: mother and Ellen as against father and Nancy. How well Ellen concealed her loyalty to her mother became apparent when Mr. Grau and Ellen were interviewed together, Mr. Grau acting as if Ellen were on his side and shared his contempt for her mother. Ellen considered such concealment essential, for if her father knew, for instance, that she had joined a Catholic society at college, he would hate her as much as he hated her mother. Ellen saw her mother's shortcomings, and considered that she had handled Nancy very badly; but she had few misconceptions about her father.

When Ellen went away to college she joined the Catholic society and started dating Catholic boys. Ellen chose strength, for Catholicism was her mother's strength and the only consistent guiding principle in the family. She also chose to study science, for her father's strength lay in his profession, and she also thus bought his interest and approval. Her father had sent her to a western college to lessen the chances of her meeting Catholics, but he could not observe what she did away from home. There are many such details, but the essence of her ways was shown in her choice of a husband. He was Catholic, and a chemical engineer. Her father's violent objections to his religion were dissipated in his interest in finding that his prospective son-in-law shared his professional interests. In a sense, Ellen was correcting the error her mother had made twenty-seven years before in marrying a non-Catholic, as if this had been the source of her unhappiness. Although Ellen was reasonably well adjusted, in fact, a master at tightrope walking, she paid a price, for both interviews and projective tests clearly indicated that this highly intelligent girl was seriously constricted, deprived of imagination and inner stimuli.

In leaving the description of the family at this point, we wish to comment that attention to these family problems proved rewarding therapeutically. Mrs. Grau came to believe that the constant conflict over religion was largely responsible for Nancy's illness. Knowing that her husband would never give in, she did. She encouraged Nancy to become a Protestant, and her father to take her to church. Perhaps this shift was made possible because she now knew that she had been victorious with Ellen. Mr. Grau, pleased by his Pyrrhic victory with Nancy, managed to restrain himself in his quarrels with his wife to some extent.

We have examined these twenty-seven years of family interaction, abstracted briefly here, according to a number of systems of reference which have contributed to the understanding of the problems involved. Sociological approaches which pay minimal attention to the individuals concerned and their personal assets, idiosyncrasies, and problems do not meet our needs. Still, consideration of family dynamics must include the value systems and cultural usages that fuse along with the parents to form the new family unit. We cannot understand the functioning of a family, its assets and liabilities, without grasp of its structure in relation to the society in which it exists.

We are struggling to achieve a dynamic approach useful for the study of the influence of the family upon its component members. We are not concerned with the problems of each parent taken singly, or with why these two people could not get along together; we are concerned with how the behavior of each produces reaction and counterreaction in the entire family, creating difficulties over and above those arising from the shortcomings of individuals. Such understanding moves beyond the level of blame and recriminations. We see both parents coming into the marriage carrying with them entire systems of social and personal values, but also with unfilled unconscious needs that they hoped would be fulfilled in the marriage.

Like most people, the Graus came to marriage incomplete, and with unresolved oedipal problems that helped dictate the choice of a partner. They not only failed to achieve such fulfillment, but in the marriage they could not even maintain the ego defenses that they had managed to erect before marriage. Needing and wanting more than they could give, they became insecure and vulnerable, and fell back upon new and more regressive defenses which further separated them. The advent of children created still more adult demands of the parents, which heightened the conflict and intensified their regressive needs. These children, then, were needed not just to fill normal parental desires for relationships with children, but even more to satisfy unconscious and regressive needs unsatisfied by the spouse. Such unconscious demands form serious impediments to the children's ego development, for they are in contact with and reacting to—and thereby are prone to introject—the immature narcissism of parents rather than adult models. Such children are also caught in a conflict, for responsivity to the needs of one parent means disloyalty to the other and provokes the latter's antagonism and rejection.

In this family, the husband, who was very insecure as a man, expected to set the pattern for the family and gain admiration and conformity from his wife. He considered her dependence upon the church and the priority she gave its rules and mores as disloyalty to him. His furious opposition to the church threatened to deprive Mrs. Grau of a major source of strength to her ego which she could not afford to relinquish. She could not replace her premarital dependence upon the church or supplement it with confidence in and dependence upon her husband, particularly when his anger and broken promises forced her to be distrustful and defensive. Of course, Mrs. Grau's seemingly naïve faith in her religion as well as her unintelligent overgeneralizations and clichés conflicted with her husband's paranoid cynicism and need for an intelligent and admiring wife in the image of his mother. We can assume that his need for attention and mothering, which led to his refusal to have children, and his temper outbursts and accusations when his wife was pregnant were related to inability to tolerate sibling rivalry in his childhood. The struggle between the parents could now be displaced onto a struggle over the children, and depersonalized in part by becoming a conflict over religion. The children were from the start caught up in this contest to gain their loyalty and affection away from the other parent.

In raising children, the mother followed her lifelong pattern, and fell back upon authority, rigidly adhering to the rules found in books. Her own needs for conformity were transferred to the child's behavior. Her insecurity as a mother had been further undermined by her being forbidden to follow a Catholic pattern as well as by her husband's biting devaluation of her efforts. Her capacities as a mother were diminished by her characteristic insensitivity to the needs and feelings of others, which permitted adherence to the set prescriptions of a book. The father remained aloof from Nancy when she was small, but later he seductively wooed her, seeking someone to give him the admiration and affection he could not gain from his wife. He could also use the child to hurt his wife, and his efforts to win the child increased Mrs. Grau's intrusiveness into Nancy's life lest she should fail to mold the child into her way of life. The father thus was breaking the necessary boundaries between the generations. Then his worth as a father figure and instrumental leader was further diminished by the chronic illness that made him pathetically dependent on his hated wife. The mother was forced to fill the instrumental role, but she was constantly being undercut and devalued. Her worth as a mother was not only weakened by her own imperviousness, but also by her castigating husband's derision and contempt. The father's value as a father was, of course, similarly being diminished by his own behavior as well as by the mother's disregard for his wishes.

In this family, the oedipal situation could not be worked through normally because of the parents' problems. Nancy's desire to be loved by her father meant that she must avoid identification with her mother and become unlike her. She could not follow her mother's model into womanhood. The mother's restrictiveness and rigid disciplining while the father was seductive led to accentuation of Nancy's choice of the father as a love object—a primary model of a love object that was distorted—an image of a castrated, hostile man, generally antagonistic to women. He trained Nancy to hate her mother and be suspicious of everyone. Nancy's turning to the father then increased her mother's feelings of inadequacy as a mother and made her even more intrusive and suspicious of Nancy. The efforts of each parent to win the girl away from the other opened the way for Nancy to separate her parents, which she continually did by fomenting dissension. Alliance with her father while he rejected her mother heightened Nancy's incestuous wishes and fears. When she became ill, her solution of her difficulties and those of the family lay in the fantasy that her mother and sister would go away to live, and leave her father to her. At the time she became psychotic, she feared leaving home lest she lose her father to her sister, just as she had lost her mother.

However, Ellen could manage the situation. As noted, her early training was different and her father was an invalid during her oedipal period. Ellen recognized her mother's shortcomings but did not accept her father's exaggerations of them. To Ellen, her mother was the potential source of security, and her father's affection was secondary. She could identify with her mother, follow her pattern, and imagine a more satisfactory outcome of a similar life if she married a Catholic husband. She became adept at mother's ability to dissemble to avoid father's wrath and still gain her own ends. From watching Nancy, she learned that it would be easier to handle her father than to oppose her mother. She gained stability by choosing her mother's religion and way of life, and in the process gained her mother's favor and room to live. She grew up to become an improved version of her mother. She bided her time, hiding her choice of religion, and avoided going with boys until she was free at college. She would not return home after college, and soon found a husband to provide a new home for her. We should note that Ellen's marriage finally established some degree of balance between the parents, for with Ellen in the fold of Catholicism, Mrs. Grau could relinquish the ancient struggle over Nancy's religious upbringing and cede her to her father.

Such consideration of the interpersonal dynamics of the family, even if greatly amplified, still omits an essential ingredient. The parental personalities also create a domestic atmosphere that affects everyone living in it. This family never formed a real entity which served as a protective shelter for its members. Indeed family members were more exposed to attack and required stronger ego defenses within the family than outside the family. A spirit of mistrust pervaded the home, and each person had to protect himself from derision and hurt. Feelings and motives were concealed, for open expression brought attack and rejection. Things were not done to please another, or through sensitivity to unspoken needs, but often to hurt or spite. The family failed to provide a place where one felt wanted despite failings. The parents' preoccupation with their own defenses left little room for sensitivity to the needs of others, causing them to be impervious to the emotional needs of their children. As the parents could not share the children, loving one person came to mean hating the others. There was intolerance of difference, blame for error, projection of one's own deficiencies onto other family members. The home seemed temporary, apt to dissolve from one day to the next, even though the parents were firmly tied by their dependency. Here, there was no hope of gaining happiness or satisfaction, but only effort to avoid the intolerable. There was little leadership, for the father's pseudo dominance was not so much leadership as intrusion into and sabotage of the mother's efforts. The conflicts, whatever their origins, could not be resolved, because of the failures in communication. Not only did each person hide his real feelings and intentions, but each parent had his own strange paralogic reasoning. The mother was vague or stereotyped and seriously scattered under stress, and the father rigid and paranoid. Then Nancy's vagueness, at first purposeful and later schizophrenic, added to the confusion.

It seems natural that the two girls shared nothing but were wary rivals, jealously protecting their own interests. They, too, found ways of playing the family game, playing one person off against another, seeking allies, concealing real interest, and in the process heightening the discord between the parents.

This study of a family includes psychodynamic aspects as well as some basic sociological and biological considerations. The family is studied in terms of the dynamics of a small group which has certain structural requisites dictated by both biological and cultural imperatives. Individual families or categories of families can be compared in terms of how these requisites are met. The personalities of the parents serve as a focus for such study, for the parents carry into the marriage and the family that they form resultants of their own family origins, including ethnic, religious, and class mores, as well as conscious and unconscious attitudes toward marital and parental roles, and unresolved needs they hope will be met in the marriage. The fusion of two individuals provides a uniqueness to each family, which cannot be grasped by the study of individuals alone. It requires scrutiny of their interrelatedness; the reactions and counterreactions engender an atmosphere that in itself exerts an influence on all family members. Similarly, the model afforded by one parent as an object for identification and as a primary love object for a child cannot be considered simply in terms of a dyadic relationship. The differentiation of the intrafamilial forces impinging upon schizophrenic and non-schizophrenic siblings which was only incidental in this paper will be elaborated upon in Chapter XIV.

IX

The Understanding of Symptomatology through the Study of Family Interaction

(1957)

We have found that some schizophrenic symptoms can be related in detail to individual behavior in the family through the process of imitation, parental tuition, and identification (Cameron and Magaret, 1951; Fleck, 1953; Miller and Dollard, 1941; Chapters V and VI). In addition to the parental models, however, family interaction and deviant family organization also are reflected in the schizophrenic's personality and behavior. To illustrate this thesis in some detail, we have selected one patient and his family. This is a skewed family whose life was so bizarre and deviant from its social environment that we coined the phrase *folie en famille* to characterize such maladaptation. We shall first describe the patient's illness and his symptoms which, as will be seen, leave no room for doubt concerning diagnosis. The patient's behavior and personality organization reflect, often in caricature, not only one parent's characteristics, but also show a combination of the parents' attitudes and their perception of each other.

THE PATIENT

Emil Dolfuss was twenty-six years old when he was transferred from another hospital to which he had been admitted for the second time following a serious suicidal attempt. At the time of admission to

Stephen Fleck, Daniel X. Freedman, Alice R. Cornelison, Theodore Lidz, and Dorothy Terry: The Family Environment of Schizophrenic Patients: V. The Understanding of Symptomatology Through the Study of Family Interaction. Unpublished paper presented at the May, 1957 meeting of the American Psychiatric Association.

the Yale Psychiatric Institute, he conducted himself in a haughty and pompous manner, choosing his words and accent carefully. He spoke calmly of his suicidal attempt which, he explained, followed a quarrel with his mother. He answered most questions in vague generalities and stated that he was in the hospital because, "It's usually the case that one hopes to become more stable and achieve a more harmonious relationship to one's self and to one's family and others."

Overt psychotic behavior first appeared when Emil was twenty-one, although we later learned that shortly after his father's death when Emil was fourteen symptoms in the form of ideas of persecution had occurred. Although Emil was highly intelligent, his school record had been so poor that he could not gain admission to college and after a few years of aimless studying, he traveled alone to the Orient although his family recognized then that he was severely disturbed. While abroad, he developed ideas of saving the world, lived out religious delusions, and was returned to the United States by consular authorities after he persistently attempted to contact the President. Emil was then hospitalized for the first time for approximately eighteen months; he received insulin and electric shock treatments and psychotherapy. During this hospitalization he was catatonic and exhibited many rituals, most of which were derived from various Eastern religions or philosophies; and he would periodically refuse to eat meat. He declared his only sibling, Adele, a goddess, and knelt and prayed in front of her before speaking to her. For a period he became mute and refused to see his family.

Between hospitalizations, Emil maintained a marginal adjustment, changing occupations often, but gradually he again became preoccupied with Eastern religion and, at times, believed himself a God. He insisted on having such brilliant lights turned on constantly within and around his garage apartment that it disturbed the neighborhood. After the argument with his mother which concerned a religious trinket that belonged to a friend of his father, Emil offered an engagement ring to his sister's friend whom he knew but slightly, and ostensibly his suicidal attempt followed the rejection of his proposal.

In our hospital the patient's behavior gradually deteriorated. Because of his many pompous and unreasonable demands, he found himself increasingly isolated from other patients who resented in particular his attempts to enforce his belief that all rooms must be fully illuminated around the clock. These and other demands made it extremely difficult for the staff to maintain a harmonious and consistent attitude toward him, a factor which contributed to his behavioral incontinence. At first he was immaculately overdressed, as if he were at an exclusive English country club, but then his dress became increasingly slovenly, and he refused to shave or have his hair cut. Following a major crisis about the lights five months after admission, Emil became combative, remained mute for weeks, and refused to eat. He then demanded and ate enormous quantities of beef for a period, after which he put himself on a strictly vegetarian diet. From this time on, he also steadfastly refused to wear trousers. He would remain attired in shorts, a checkered waistcoat, and a heavy jacket even on very hot days; later he wore only shorts even in winter while insisting that his windows be open. He refused to sleep in bed throughout the remainder of his hospital stay and slept either standing up or in a chair. Emil was never without light in his room. Although he acted as if he had the right to command the staff to carry out his wishes, it was clear that the absence of light caused him to panic and become combative. He communicated with the staff by signs, charades, or in a foreign language. He refused to wash or to be bathed, and while quite oblivious to certain health hazards, he also propounded many faddish health theories and was deeply worried about insufficient food supply. He hoarded food, especially candy, fruits, and nuts in large quantities, and when his mother objected to these foods for health reasons, he accused her of stinginess.

Emil also became quite interested in Jewish customs and history (he had a Jewish therapist) and even wished to be circumcised, but in his behavior continued to adhere to the dicta of a mysterious Eastern religion. In observance of the latter, he counteracted gravity by never lying down, worshiped light, and avoided "animal excitation" by not eating meat.

A vignette of Emil's life in our hospital follows: a tall, bearded young man with hair to his shoulders, dressed only in shorts stands in a room stacked with magazines and fruit, or sits on the toilet in the adjacent bathroom reading the *Wall Street Journal*. The doors and windows are open; he motions to a passer-by in the hall to come into his room. There he forces a sticky fig into the visitor's hand and makes a request in sign language. When he is refused, he listens carefully, then shoves the visitor out and shoots him with mock gestures.

The Family

Mr. Dolfuss, of a wealthy middle-class background, was sent from Austria in early adulthood to conduct the American branch of the family business. Mrs. Dolfuss who came from an Austrian family of considerable renown also immigrated to this country as a young adult. After they married, they moved to the home near Boston which Mr. Dolfuss had established as a bachelor. He ran his well-appointed home in the manner of European nobility which set the family apart from the rest of the community. The formality of the household was un-usual—the chauffeur wore white gloves even to shop for groceries, and all members of the household had to dress formally every after-noon to receive the master at the door. The children were permitted to be with their parents only during specific hours. When at home, Mr. Dolfuss spent much of his time in his bedroom, where he was not to be disturbed, and only his wife or the "Fräulein" was permitted to look after his needs. He was mortally afraid of drafts, and frequently suffered from colds. Usually he spent his time reading about Eastern religion and philosophy while dressed only in his underwear. From his reading he evolved a peculiar cult which the family shared, but which allegedly was understood by only a few select people. This Eastern philosophy somehow included certain Christian traditions so that Christmas and winter-solstice celebrations were combined. A ceremony of the lighting of candles was preceded by a long speech by Mr. Dolfuss on the holiness of light during which the entire house-hold were required to stand listening.

Mr. Dolfuss' intelligence and ingenuity were put to a test when the family business failed. He invented a device which he manufactured and sold with great success, so that no change in the family's income or living standard occurred. Mr. Dolfuss claimed other inventions, however, and the family believes that he was cheated out of several patents.

Mrs. Dolfuss considered her primary duty to be at the service of her husband: she felt he was a great man and came to share his beliefs to which she still adheres. After his death she continued to believe that her husband was still alive, dead but in another reincarnation. The family members refused to elaborate their religious beliefs to us because the religion was not to be discussed with people not devoted to it. Even the daughter maintained this reticence out of reverence for her father, although she supposedly disavowed the creed.

The patient and his sister as children were cared for by the Fräulein since the parents were frequently absent on long trips. The Fräulein favored Emil over his sister, she treated him like a little prince, and habitually slept with him. This nursemaid also worshiped the father and claims even now that she understood him better than did Mrs. Dolfuss. Thus, to the patient, his mother who devoted most of her time and energy to her husband represented remoteness, whereas the Fräulein mixed motherliness and seductiveness with rigid reinforcement of the father's cold formality and religious preoccupations. She had used harsh methods of toilet training.

When the patient was seven or eight, the nursemaid was dismissed by Mrs. Dolfuss, partly because of their competitive feelings, but also because Emil's teachers complained that he had not been taught the rudiments of self-care and that he was being severely "spoiled" by his nurse. Supposedly, Emil did not react to this separation. He showed little emotional disturbance until shortly after his father's sudden death. For a few days following this crucial event, Emil behaved appropriately, acting as the head of the household during his mother's transient incapacitation in the period of her acute bereavement. The patient has been quoted as saying, "I have to be the man in the family now." Soon thereafter he became delusional, believing that a light beam from a tall building was following him. He told one of his psychiatrists, "The loss of my father set me back, and I don't know how to describe the incomparable harm it did to my development of all descriptions."

Other characteristics of the family interaction and attitudes must be mentioned. In line with his beliefs, the father disapproved of and never expressed any hostility. Everybody was "happy" in this family. The mother, however, despite her subservience, belittled and criticized the father's disinclination for fresh air, sports, and physical activity. She was a food faddist and considered physical culture extremely important for herself and her children. She was always very parsimonious, leading the patient to say, "I always gave my family large presents, but they never gave me anything."

COMMENT

It is easy to note the many parallels between the parents' behavior and the patient's symptoms. Their haughty demeanor, their withdrawal into a religious world accessible only to a selected few, their preoccupation with health and food, their demands for ritualized service, and much of their detailed thinking seem of one piece. However, because of overdetermination the patient's symptoms also contain minor but important modifications and indicate some of his distorted primitive object relations (Szasz, 1957). For instance, during one of the accidental periods of darkness in his room, Emil became frightened, grabbed a flashlight, and held it erect over his penis, thus revealing castration fear. Between hospitalizations he made sexual overtures to his sister. His oral dependent needs also asserted themselves. As his father might have done for business trips, Emil studied airline time tables to find interconnecting flights that could provide him with a continuous food supply from all over the world. Moreover, the symptomatology was based not only on identification with his father, but also contained important elements of the mother's overt and covert attitudes and of the entire family interaction. Emil's hostile insistence upon fresh air parodied the father and ceded a point to the mother. Hoarding was a mockery of her stinginess, and he collected and ate foods which she avoided.

We should like to point out that in a number of patients we have observed a brief period of relatively effective but pathological identification with the dominant and usually sicker parent figure shortly before the outbreak of more overt psychotic manifestations. But whereas the parents may entertain abnormal beliefs or grandiose schemes in a contained fashion, the patient carries them out. Adele, Emil's sister, also shared with their mother and with the patient the bizarre, grandiose religious beliefs; but both women had maintained sufficient reality adaptation and social presence to exercise great reticence in discussing those ideas with others. In neither the mother nor the sister did these delusional beliefs interfere with productivity or social competence, in contrast to the devastating effect of these same beliefs upon the patient's life. One may surmise that Adele's sex and more distant relationship with the Fräulein facilitated greater and more effective utilization of the mother as a model. The patient, in a sense, could believe that to gain his mother's affection and approval, he should identify with his father and fill the gap in his mother's life by becoming a deity like his father. Under the stress of the father's death, his preoccupation and behavior became increasingly limited to the examples of which he saw the most, and which were reinforced and gratified by the entire family: his father as a demigod at home. In the face of his mother's expectation that he be the man of the house, incestuous proclivities also became rekindled, abetted by his nurse's earlier seductive manipulations.

Another important facet in this picture of *folie en famille* is the family use of clichés and the mislabeling of feelings and attitudes— for instance, the recurrent emphasis that this was an entirely happy family, superior to others. Nobody was permitted to show hostility, and if it appeared, it would have to be denied or rationalized. After hitting somebody, Emil always made up with handshakes and embraces. Transformation of such a pattern into behavioral skills tolerable to and effective with other persons would obviously involve a formidable task in relearning. Adele, who managed this belatedly with the help of analytic treatment, once remarked in discouragement when she began to understand the similarity between the patient's behavior in the hospital and her father's ideas and behavior, "Oh, the poor boy, how can he get over it, he is so right." Emil was right, in terms of the family's teachings.

But withdrawal, social isolation, and household-wide dereistic thinking are what we observe in this family, and when we consider Emil's learning opportunities in his family, it becomes clearer how the development and structuring of his personality must have suffered. What the patient knew and could learn of his father was not of the successful businessman and inventor, but the sour, cold, withdrawn, and formal authoritarian who was being babied and deified at the same time. What he saw mostly in his mother was stinginess, disinterest in the children, duplicity, and subservience to the megalomanic father. This must have been confusing to Emil, because her ambivalence together with the Fräulein's inconsistent alternation between harshness and seductiveness must have left him with incompatible part objects for identification. Moreover, the range and character of adaptive techniques that could be acquired in this skewed family structure were unsuited for living in the larger community.

Thus, we discern in the patient and related behavior and attitudes in the parents and in the family interaction all the characteristic primary and secondary schizophrenic manifestations as outlined by Bleuler (1911). The family as a whole was withdrawn from the community, thought deviantly from it, and there was ambivalence, lack of warmth and shared delusional thinking. The patient "learned" most of his symptoms from the parents' behavior; he caricatured and combined them, his basic personality organization lacked cohesiveness, and his behavior reflected the *folie en famille*.

If patients' difficulties and symptoms on which we base our diagnosis of schizophrenia can thus be identified as the product of faulty learning within the family, learning related to identification with deviant parental figures and their skewed or schismatic interaction, broader questions suggest themselves: does the trouble lie with the teaching process; with deficiencies in the "teachers"; with communication; with a learning disability in the child; or are all of these implicated? Here we have provided only a descriptive framework for the study and understanding of psychotic behavior as learned phenomena.

X

The Transmission of Irrationality

(1957)

One of the distinctive features of schizophrenia lies in the disturbed symbolic functioning—in the paralogic quality of the patient's thinking and communicating that alters his internal representation of reality. We are following the hypothesis that the schizophrenic patient escapes from an untenable world in which he is powerless to cope with insoluble conflicts by the device of imaginatively distorting his symbolization of reality. Such internalized maneuvers do not require action, or coming to terms with other persons, or altering their attitudes. The patient can regain the mastery that he once possessed in childhood, before his reality was firmly structured, and it could still give way before the power of his wishes. It can be an alluring way because it is self-contained. It is a bitter way because it is isolating.

The present study will focus on this critical characteristic of schizophrenia, and, therefore, must neglect many other aspects of the developmental forces active during the childhood and adolescence of schizophrenic patients, even though these other aspects can be separated from the forces distorting mentation only artificially.

The distortions of mentation, the core problem of schizophrenia, have been relatively neglected of late because of interest in "borderline cases" and in "pseudoneurotic schizophrenia" and in the similarities between the underlying psychopathology of certain psychosomatic conditions and that of schizophrenia. Patients suffering from these conditions are not clearly schizophrenic, because they remain

Theodore Lidz, Alice R. Cornelison, Dorothy Terry, and Stephen Fleck: Intrafamilial Environment of the Schizophrenic Patient: VI. The Transmission of Irrationality. A.M.A. Archives of Neurology and Psychiatry, *Vol. 79, 1958, pp. 305-316. Copyright © 1958, American Medical Association.*

sufficiently well integrated to permit a consensus between their think-ing and that of others, and effective social communication remains possible. Such patients are potentially psychotic, and when their com-munication breaks down and becomes instrumentally ineffective, they are psychotic. Some never need this solution, but others may be un-able to utilize it. It is possible for many persons to break under ex-treme conditions and achieve flight into irrationality, sacrificing re-ality to the demands of id impulses or to preserve some semblance of ego structure or self-esteem. A theory of schizophrenia must explain not only the patient's need to abandon reality testing but also his ability to do so. We must seek to understand why some persons can escape through withdrawal into unshared ways of experiencing the world around them more readily than others.

The thinking disorder in schizophrenia has been taken by some, and perhaps classically, to indicate dysfunction of the brain—dysfunc-tion caused by lesions, deficiency, or metabolic disorder. The search for this brain dysfunction has been pursued for over 100 years. Each advance in physiology or neuroanatomy brings new hope; and each new form of physical therapy tantalizingly provokes prospects of leading to definitive knowledge of the malfunctioning of the brain. However, careful studies, and even casual observations, show that the thought disorder in schizophrenia differs markedly from any pro-duced by a known organic deficit or a toxic disturbance of the brain. This is not the place to enter upon the nature of such differences. Al-though it is true that schizophrenic patients tend to concretize, they are also obviously capable of high degrees of abstraction, and may tend to abstract all too readily. More pertinently, unless a patient is permitted to become dilapidated by social isolation, the irrationality either remains or becomes more or less circumscribed. This girl who writes violently invective letters filled with delusions to her parents will in the next minute write a letter to a friend without a trace of delusional material, and then sits in her room and correctly composes inordinately complex music. No defect of thinking due to dysfunc-tion of the brain permits such highly organized conceptualization.

There have been many approaches to the search for a genetic pre-disposition to schizophrenia. Our studies do not turn away from such consideration, but consider that a meaningful approach would focus upon a predisposition to symbolic distortion. Although our emphasis leads in another direction for theoretical reasons, which we shall seek to indicate briefly, we wish to point out that neither our theory nor our interpretations of data are of primary concern at present. We are attempting to present data derived from our study which we believe reliable and highly pertinent.

We consider that man is not naturally endowed with an inherent logic of causal relationships, but, rather, that the surroundings in which he is raised influence his ways of perceiving, thinking, and communicating. What makes "sense" at different periods of history and in different cultural settings (and, to a less extent, from one family to another) varies greatly. The Hindu way of regarding life in this world and life after death is irrational to us—and our way is just as meaningless and confused to the Hindu. Still, a trend toward a type of rationality exists in all cultures and in all groups. It is not that any of us has some particular ability to perceive reality as it is, for the actuality of reality—the *Ding an sich*—is never attainable by our senses. There is, however, a pragmatic meaning concerning what is fact— what is reality. It is measurable in terms of how our perceptions lead to effective action: if what we tell ourselves about events in the world around us leads to a degree of mastery over our environment and to workable interaction with the persons with whom we live. The effectiveness of reflective mentation is measured by how it helps the individual master his environment and achieve sufficient consensus with other persons to enable collaborative interaction. Communication, the outward manifestation of symbolic activity, measures the efficacy of mentation by the degree of consensus attained with others concerning what we perceive and what events mean. However, matters are not so simple. A large portion of mental activity is autistic rather than reflective; and autistic reverie is closer to primary-process thinking, and to a great extent in the service of the wish of instinctual drives. The permeation of reflective thought, by the autistic processes, provides a major key to the understanding of schizophrenic thinking. Then, too, schizophrenic regression can reintroduce elements of perceptions and thought processes of early childhood that interpenetrate with more mature reflective and autistic mentation. Further, not all shared ideas need be reasonable and effective for purposes of controlling the environment. Man's need for emotional security, while he lives in this world of contingency, leads to systematization of ideas that actually may run counter to experience. Such systems, based upon unproved and untestable axioms, can direct our perceptions and understanding. As they are culturally approved, they are termed "beliefs" rather than "delusions." They result in compartmentalization of experience into segments that are kept from conflicting and challenging one another. Adherence to an axiom into which the perception of experience must be fittted almost requires distortion of perception of the environment. The issue is raised because a similar situation may be found within the family. If a parent must protect his tenuous equilibrium by adhering to a rigidly held need or self-concept, and everything else must be subsidiary to this defense, distortions occur that affect the rest of the family.

The family is the primary teacher of social interaction and emotional reactivity. It teaches by means of its milieu and nonverbal communication more than by formal education. The child's sources of identification and self-esteem derive from the family and markedly influence the developing patterns of symbolic functioning. However, the child is also exposed to the parental interpretations of reality and the parents' ways of communicating. Parental interpretations may have limited instrumental utility when they primarily serve to maintain the parents' own precarious equilibrium. The topic is very complex, and this paper will deal only with some of the more obvious influences of parental instability upon the children's thought processes.

We shall pursue the hypothesis that the schizophrenic patient is more prone to withdraw through distortion of his symbolization of reality than other patients, because his foundation in reality testing is precarious, having been raised amidst irrationality and chronically exposed to intrafamilial communications that distort and deny what should be the obvious interpretation of the environment, including the recognition and understanding of impulses and the affective behavior of members of the family.

Primarily, we are seeking to describe these families and find common features among them, rather than compare them with other types of families. We are, so to speak, describing the terrain of a country we are exploring, not comparing it with the geography of other countries. We have been skeptical, holding aloof from accepting too readily many current and past theoretical formulations. In general, rather than focusing attention upon one phase of development or any single interpersonal relationship, we have been more interested in studying the forces that interfere with the emergence of a reasonably independent and integrated personality at the end of adolescence—the critical period in the development of schizophrenia, even if the onset is later in life.

We shall discuss in this chapter two closely interrelated aspects of the family environment—the rationality of the parents and the nature of the communication within the family.

Parental Irrationality

We shall first consider the rationality of the parents in the grossest terms. The findings are unexpectedly striking, when compared with data from larger statistical studies (Kallmann, 1953; Pollock et al., 1939). However, Terry and Rennie (1938) found comparable figures, though their data are difficult to evaluate clearly. None of the parents of our patients was ever hospitalized in a mental institution and thus probably would not have been indexed as psychotic in any broad epidemiological survey of psychoses in the parents of schizophrenic patients. Minimally, nine of the fifteen patients had at least one parent who could be called schizophrenic, or ambulatory schizophrenic, or clearly paranoid in behavior and attitudes. The finding is difficult to express explicitly, for the shading between what one terms schizophrenia and what bizarre behavior and ideation is arbitrary, and the line between psychosis and a paranoid outlook is equally fine. Although the proportion of families with more or less schizophrenic parents is very high, minimally 60 per cent of the families, it will become apparent that the cut-off point was quite arbitrary and other families could have been included. The classification is made difficult because of parents who maintain a reasonable degree of social presence and yet display seriously distorted thinking and motivation. Some of the mothers are seriously scattered and confused, particularly when anxious and under pressure. Fathers may be eminently successful but display behavior to their families that is pervaded and dominated by paranoid beliefs. Brief illustrations will clarify these statements.

We shall say little about the two mothers, Mrs. Narab and Mrs. Thomas, who were frankly schizophrenic except to say that despite delusions, hallucinations, and very confused reasoning they had continued to be the parent with the major responsibility for raising the children. The husband of one was somewhat grandiose, if not paranoid, and spent most of his time away from home, while the other couple was divorced. Although a third mother, Mrs. Schwartz, sounded frankly schizophrenic, she ran the family business after her husband had suffered a "nervous breakdown" (before the patient was born), after which he had become passive and subservient to her. She openly expressed beliefs that her telephone was tapped and that the neighbors might burn down the home.

There were two mothers, Mrs. Nebb and Mrs. Newcomb, who completely dominated the lives of their passive husbands and children. We consider these women typical "schizophrenogenic" mothers in needing and using their sons to complete their own frustrated lives. Their sons had to be geniuses, and any faults in them or anything that went wrong with their lives were consistently blamed on others—classmates, doctors, teachers, and society in general. They believed that only they understood their sons. We could never really understand these mothers, for their incessant talk was driven and mixed up, displaying unbelievable obtuseness to any ideas not their own. While we have hesitated to call these women schizophrenic, they are certainly not reality-oriented and are very close to being psychotic. Brief descriptions may convey the problem.

Two major private psychiatric hospitals had refused to keep Jack Newcomb, not because of his behavior but because they could not stand his mother's incessant interference. Such behavior had plagued the boy and his teachers throughout his school years. Mrs. Newcomb talked incessantly about some fixed idea of the cause of her son's illness. When her ideas were questioned, she counterattacked; and if forced to abandon a theme, she would relinquish it only temporarily, retreating to her next equally unreasonable idea. When the family had wished to build a home, she had exhausted four or five architects, and the house was never built. When the daughter eventually gave up attempting to inform her mother that she intended to get married and simply announced her engagement, Mrs. Newcomb steadfastly ignored the daughter's intent. While the girl was seeking an apartment, the mother would only talk about re-engaging her college room for the next academic year. The mother ignored the need to make plans for the wedding until the father, an unusually passive man, finally intervened shortly before the date that had been set for the wedding.

Mrs. Nebb's life was dominated by the idea that her twin sons were geniuses, whose development must not be hindered by setting any limits except in defense of her own extreme obsessiveness. Delinquent acts of the twins while they were still in grade school, such as breaking into and robbing a house and setting a barn on fire, were ignored and blamed upon other children. She insistently regarded a move from a mountain resort to the city, required because the twins were ostracized, and which disrupted her husband's business and social life, as a move to give her twins the superior education they required. Mrs. Nebb fell into violent rages because of trivia that interrupted her obsessive cleanliness but gave inordinate praise for acts that the twins knew were nonsense. The household under her domination was a crazy place, and description could not be attempted without provoking the charge of gross exaggeration. For example, both twins claim that for many years they thought that constipation meant disagreeing with mother. Whenever one of them would argue with her, she would say they were constipated and needed an enema; both boys were then placed prone on the bathroom floor naked while the mother, in her undergarments, inserted the nozzle in each boy, fostering a contest to see which could hold out longer—the loser having to dash down to the basement lavatory. The projective tests of these last two mothers were judged frankly schizophrenic.

Only one of the four or five fathers who were considered psychotic or paranoid was as disorganized as these mothers. Mr. Newberg, though a steady provider and a man with an ingenious turn of mind, was constantly engaged in working out one or another of his many inventions, which never materialized. He was vaguely suspicious and paranoid, fostering suspicion in his children; but it was his incessant talk, in which he jumped from one topic and one idea to another in driven fashion, that seemed most disturbing to the family. Like Mrs.

Newcomb, he would hammer away at a fixed idea, and an hour with Mr. Newberg thoroughly exhausted either of the two interviewers who tried to cope with him. The other fathers were more capable and less disorganized but more fixed in their paranoid ways. Mr. Dolfuss was also an inventor, but a successful one, for a single ingenious invention had made the family wealthy. He spent much of his time steeped in the mysteries of an esoteric Asiatic cult, believing that he and a friend who shared these beliefs were among the few select who would achieve salvation in reincarnation. Whether he believed in his divinity or it was his wife who deified him is not clear, but this family lived in what we have termed *folie en famille,* which centered about the father and his esoteric beliefs, and according to a social pattern that was widely divergent from the society in which they actually lived. Mr. Grau and Mr. Reading may be mentioned together as being competent business men who expressed many paranoid beliefs which did not interfere appreciably with their business activities but seriously upset family life. Among other things, Mr. Grau was paranoically bitter against all Catholics, not an unusual situation, but here the paranoid bigotry focused upon his wife who was a devout Catholic. At times he feared going to work because he felt people were against him. His wife, who has not been counted as psychotic, probably as a matter of relativity, was an extremely immature, scattered woman. Mr. Reading was so suspicious that people were taking advantage of him that the hospital staff could not establish any relationship with him over a six-month period. His major concern at all interviews was to prove to the staff that his wife, who was actually a seriously obsessive woman, had been a malignant influence and had ruined his daughters, and also to make certain that the hospital was not lying, misrepresenting, or somehow taking advantage of him. Both men were hostile and contemptuous of women, and both had only daughters. The material offered here concerning these parents has been sparse, but we have abundant information which permits us to be certain that all nine have been virtually psychotic or markedly paranoid at least from the time of the patient's birth until the onset of illness. We are more interested in scrutinizing the situations in the remaining six families, in which the parents cannot be labeled so readily.

We can extract some generalizations from the study of these more disturbed parents which seem to apply to most, if not all, of the remaining six families, as well as to parents of many other schizophrenic patients. The struggles of these parents to preserve their own integration led them to limit their environment markedly by rigid preconceptions of the way things must be. The parents' precarious equilibrium will tumble if the environment cannot be delimited or if the parents must shift from the one rigid role they can manage. Mrs. Nebb must see herself as the mother of twin geniuses. We understand something of how this came about. She, too, was a twin, but the deformed ugly duckling of the family, who dreamed of the phallus that would turn her into a swan. The birth of twins was her triumph, and their accomplishments were her means of outshining her dominant twin sister. Mrs. Narab had written of how she had given birth to a genius, or perhaps a Messiah. She kept a diary of the child's development for fifteen years, presenting an idyllic picture of the home life, which we learned from the sons and husband had little resemblance to reality. In a somewhat different sense, Mrs. Grau, the rejected Catholic wife, could only raise her daughters as Catholics, for she could not live according to any pattern except the one established for her by the Church. Mr. Reading had to dominate his household and maintain his narcissistic esteem through admiration from all of the females around him—his mother, wife, and two daughters. The slightest challenge to his imperious and unreasonable demands provoked a storm of fury. These people must retain the necessary picture of themselves and their family. Some will fight to retain it; but others adhere to their conceptualization which reality cannot alter or a new situation modify. They perceive and act in terms of their needed preconceptions, which they relinquish only under extreme pressures, and then with all sorts of maneuvers to explain through projection or ignore through isolation. We should like to take an example from outside the series of fifteen families—from a case in which the sibling of a schizophrenic patient was in analysis. The father had left home when the children were very young to gain justice and revenge against a rival firm that had ruined his business by publicly accusing him falsely. Nothing mattered to him except to re-establish his power and prestige and gain revenge. He pursued his course for over fifteen years without even visiting his family, though always writing that he would return home the following week. He was markedly grandiose and paranoid, however just his cause. Still, his attitude was scarcely more pathological than the mother's. All through the years of separation, she insisted that nothing was wrong with the marriage, maintaining a shallow, euphoric attitude and telling her children that their concerns were groundless—the father was just attending to his business and would be back next week. Penelope was finally rewarded, but she could not unravel the fabric she had woven. Her son became schizophrenic within a month of her husband's return.

THE NATURE OF THE PARENTAL COMMUNICATION

The parents' delimitation of the environment, and their perception of events to suit their needs, result in a strange family atmosphere into which the children must fit themselves and suit this dominant need or feel unwanted. Often the children must obliterate their own needs to support the defenses of the parent whom they need. They live in a Procrustean environment, in which events are distorted to fit the mold. The world as the child should come to perceive or feel it is denied. Their conceptualizations of the environment are neither instrumental in affording consistent understanding and mastery of events, feelings, or persons, nor in line with what persons in other families experience. Facts are constantly being altered to suit emotionally determined needs. The acceptance of mutually contradictory experiences requires paralogical thinking. The environment affords training in irrationality.

The domination of a parent's behavior and attitude by rigid defensive needs clarifies other traits often noted among these parents. "Impervious" is a word we find ourselves using frequently to connote a parent's inability to feel or hear the child's emotional needs. The parent may listen but does not seem to hear and, further, seems oblivious to unspoken communications. These parents cannot consider anything that does not fit in with their own self-protecting systems. Indeed, as Bowen and his coworkers (1957) have also noted, such parents may respond to the child only in terms of their own needs displaced to the child, thus building up an entire pattern of maladaptive interactions. Bateson et al. (1956) have recently studied a related aspect of parent-child interaction. The parent conveys the impression of being cold or rejecting, and, of course, may be, but imperviousness is not simply a consequence of rejection of the child, but more a rejection of anything that threatens the parent's equilibrium or self-image.

These parents often talk in clichés conveying a false impression of limited intelligence. Clichés and stereotypes serve to simplify the environment to enable the parents to cope with it in terms of their set needs. Such parents not only label a child as "the selfish one" or "the quiet one" but actually perceive the child only in terms of the stereotype. The fixed notions of an etiology of the illness, which may drive the psychiatrist to the verge of desperation, is a related phenomenon.

"Masking," which also confuses communication, refers to the ability of one or both parents to conceal some very disturbing situation within the family and to act as if it did not exist. "Masking" usually contains a large degree of self-deception as well as an effort to conceal from others; but it involves a conscious negation, as well as unconscious denial. The parent, unable either to accept or to alter the situation, ignores it and acts as though the family were a harmonious and homogeneous body which filled the needs of its members. Although some degree of masking may exist in all families, in some of our families the masking of serious problems dominated the entire family interaction. Problems which family members will not or cannot recognize are unlikely to be resolved. Children who grow up in such homes are aware that something is not right. They may become deeply resentful that the more intact parent takes no action to protect them from the situation. The children are puzzled, but may also learn to mask or ignore the obvious. Their efforts to explain away the situation, or to accept or convey pretense of affection and devotion, which has no resonance or real meaning, distorts their value systems.

The following two cases illustrate rather extreme degrees of imperviousness in which the parents appear severely rejecting.

The Ubanques impressed the hospital and research staff as strange people, but they were one of the few couples in our series who were reasonably happily married. The younger of two daughters was severely hebephrenic. Mrs. Ubanque sought to blame the sex talk of the girl's college roommates. However, both parents could convince themselves to an amazing degree that the daughter was not really ill but merely being contrary and refusing to behave normally. This tendency increased as their financial means for retaining the girl in the hospital diminished, bearing little relationship to her condition. However, after some months of intensive therapy, the patient improved considerably. She repeatedly expressed her hopelessness that her parents would ever listen and understand her unhappiness over her school and social problems. As the patient could not be kept in the hospital for a long period and as the psychiatrist who was interviewing the parents found it impossible to get them to focus upon any meaningful problems that might be upsetting, a therapeutic experiment was undertaken with great trepidation. The patient and the parents would meet together and, with the help of both psychiatrists, would try to speak frankly to one another. The daughter carefully prepared in advance what she wished to convey, and we tried to prepare the parents to listen carefully and to reply meaningfully. The patient, to the surprise of her psychiatrist, freely poured out her feelings to her parents and in heart-rending fashion told them of her bewilderment and pleaded for their understanding and help. During the height of her daughter's pleas, Mrs. Ubanque offhandedly turned to one of the psychiatrists, tugged at the waist of her dress and blandly remarked, "My dress is getting tight. I suppose I should go on a diet." The mother had fallen back upon her habitual pattern of blocking out anything that would upset her bland equanimity. The next day the patient relapsed into incoherent and silly behavior.

Mrs. Forel, a cold and highly narcissistic woman, has been the other mother who did not wish to visit her offspring in the hospital. She said, "Wouldn't it upset Billy too much to have his mother see him in a place like this?" This clearly meant: I couldn't stand visiting my son in a mental hospital. Mrs. Forel's intense dependency upon and attachment to her older sister, a very masculine woman, had contributed greatly to ruining her marriage. The sister had developed an intense dislike for the patient when he was still a small boy. After her husband's death, Mrs. Forel lived with her sister, but her twelve-year-old son was not allowed in the house and had to live in a boarding house nearby. One Christmas eve the mother stood by while the sister turned Billy away from the home and from spending the evening with them. Later, when they were all going to visit relatives in a distant city, the sister refused to take Billy along, and the mother remained blandly in the car while they passed the boy trying to hitchhike in a snowstorm. Mrs. Forel's dependency upon her sister took precedence over her son's needs.[1]

Another type of imperviousness existed in the cases of the Narabs and the Nebbs. The mothers were solicitous enough, but the vision of the genius child who would complete and justify their lives made them oblivious to the actual needs, abilities, and deficiencies of their children. Mrs. Schwartz was so caught up in a struggle with her eldest, psychopathic son that she scarcely noted anything that occurred in the life of the youngest son, who eventually became schizophrenic, even though she was very controlling of much of his life.

"Masking" also distorts the communication within the family severely. Mr. Lerner had been an eminent attorney who supported his family at a lavish level and basked in the light of his legal prestige and his associations with prominent persons. After his partner, the contact man for the firm, committed suicide, his income fell off disastrously. Mr. Lerner was an obsessive brief writer and researcher who could neither gain clients nor plead cases. Gradually, he withdrew into his office, and into his study at home, spending his time making scholarly analyses of legal matters, which earned him almost nothing. The need to consider himself a great legal mind and a prominent person took precedence over the needs of his family. He could not admit his failure to himself or anyone else, and could not alter his ways. His wife, who, fortunately, was a competent woman, went to work and, with the help of her relatives, managed to support the family as well as her husband's law office. For over ten years she helped maintain the pretense to the world and to her children and even managed to keep herself from recognizing the resentment she felt toward a husband who let her shoulder the entire burden of the family. She had to maintain the myth of a successful marriage to a strong father figure. The children could not help but know that it was all fraudulent. The situation required consistent falsification, and all the communications between

---

[1] Literary and dramatic illustrations of many features of these families which we seek to convey can be found in Eugene O'Neill's *Long Day's Journey Into Night*, Tennessee Williams's *The Glass Menagerie*, and August Strindberg's *Easter* and *The Father*.

members of this household had a high degree of pretense concerning the feelings they felt obligated to express in order to maintain the façade. The daughter, as a patient, kept protesting the expense of her hospitalization to her father, though she was well aware that he had earned nothing since her early childhood.

Mr. and Mrs. Lamb both strove to mask a situation they could not hide successfully. Mr. Lamb, a successful business man and once an athlete of renown, needed to be the center of considerable adulation. Mr. Lamb could not tolerate the rivalry of his son and required the help of alcohol and numerous affairs to maintain his feelings of masculinity. To alleviate his anxiety and to prevent open conflict, he pretended that he was not an alcoholic and that he spent most of his time traveling in order to provide well. His wife also tried to maintain the pretense that they were happily married. Unable to consider separation seriously, she strove to blind herself to the seriousness of his alcoholism; his noxious influence on their son, whom he constantly belittled; and his extramarital affairs, which were highly embarrassing to the family.

Mrs. Lamb appeared to accept her husband's obnoxious behavior but sought to establish altogether different standards in her son, in whom she fostered aesthetic interests. A son, in such situations, gains confused concepts of what his mother cherishes in a man. The many other problems that beset this family are outside the immediate interests of this chapter; but we should note that the highly sensitive mother often became impervious to her son's needs because she had to center her attention on her husband and support his infantile needs.

Habitual masking may then be viewed as an irrational form of communication, but another feature that often affects the child's mental functioning is complete breakdown of communication between parents, especially when the child is caught between different value systems and attitudes which cannot be integrated. Mrs. Nussbaum resented the daughter who was born after she and her husband had become emotionally estranged, whereas Mr. Nussbaum sought from his daughter the affection he could not receive from his wife. The parents had quarreled before the patient's birth over their respective attachments to their families, attachments which took precedence over the marital relationship. Mrs. Nussbaum's family had accused Mr. Nussbaum's oldest brother of ruining their father's business. When Mrs. Nussbaum had seemed to side with her family, her husband considered her disloyal and never forgave her. Indeed, they never spoke of the matter again, but never became reconciled and were openly hostile, though continuing to live together. Communication between them was largely vengeful and undermining. The father, for example, perhaps partly to punish his wife and partly to escape her vituperative temper, spent his evenings in his office reading, but, to conceal his own impotence, let his wife and family believe that he had a mistress with whom he spent much of his time. Many of the family quarrels centered on this nonexistent situation. In addition, the father's seductive use of the daughter to bolster his narcissism, while seeking to ignore his wife, further confused communication and meaning in this family.

We could properly place the Benjamins, the remaining family, in the large category of psychotic or borderline parents, even though the parents were not so clearly psychotically disturbed. Mrs. Benjamin, particularly when anxious, spoke incessantly and said very little, and even less that was pertinent to the situation. She asked questions endlessly, but constantly interrupted with another question before anyone could answer her. This woman might be termed obsessive, but her obsessiveness was extremely scattered and disorganized when she was anxious. In contrast, her husband's ritualized obsessiveness led to behavior that often seemed highly irrational. He would go into rages if a toothpaste cap was not replaced, throw his wife's entire wardrobe on the floor because her clothes were in disorder, or her fur coat into the bathtub because she had left the coat lying on the bed. Although he frequently complained and worried about money, he could not keep from making unnecessary purchases. When seriously concerned about meeting the cost of his son's hospitalization, he bought a third car and could not understand why his wife was angered by his fine present for her, even though his purchase of a second car just a month before had precipitated a violent quarrel. Mr. Benjamin saw nothing hostile in the purchase. We wish to call attention to the irrational atmosphere produced in a family when the parents are obsessive-compulsive, particularly when the two obsessive patterns are in direct conflict. The covert, hostile, and symptomatic behavior of each parent challenges the defensive pattern of the other. Neither makes sense, but both parents find rationalizations for their own behavior which neither the spouse nor the children can really understand. Though Mrs. Benjamin, along with Mrs. Ubanque, Mrs. Forel, Mrs. Grau, and Mrs. Reading could not be considered overtly psychotic, they all were strange, disturbed persons. The defensive structure of all these women led to a type of behavior that created great difficulty in communication within the family because what they said was more in defense of their fragile equilibrium than a communication pertinent to the given situation.

Before ending this initial survey of the irrationality present in the family environment in which schizophrenic patients grow up, we wish to direct attention to the conscious training of children to a paranoid orientation that takes place in some families. Both Mr. Grau and Mr. Reading sought not only to make their daughters distrustful and suspicious toward their mothers but to share their own paranoid suspiciousness of almost everyone. In a different vein, the Dolfuss parents inculcated a system of religious belief that was aberrant and virtually delusional in the society in which the family lived.

COMMENT

The study of the irrationality and defective communication in these families presents a complex task. A fairly complete picture of each family would be required to bring out the many frustrating problems involved. Here, we have merely sought to convey an impression of the broad sweep of the distorting influences present in all of the families studied, which have also been apparent in most, if not all, of the families of the many other schizophrenic patients treated in the Yale Psychiatric Institute during the past several years. Other less obvious and subtler influences also require attention; these will be considered in subsequent chapters.

Although our studies encompass only fifteen families, they form a good random sampling of middle- and upper-class families with schizophrenic offspring. The marked disturbances in instrumental utility of communications that can readily be noted in all of these families cannot be ignored in the search for reasons why these patients may be prone to withdraw from a reality orientation when unable to cope with their serious interpersonal problems.

We are not pointing to such defects in communication and the presence of an irrational milieu as a cause of schizophrenia. We are concerned with multiple factors distorting personality development rather than seeking a "cause." Here we simply, but significantly, indicate that our patients were not raised in families that adhered to culturally accepted ideas of causality and meanings, or respected the instrumental utility of their ideas and communications, because one or both parents were forced to abandon rationality to defend their own precarious ego structure. We are, therefore, concerned here with factors that may differentiate the genesis of schizophrenia from the genesis of other psychopathological syndromes, in that persons who grow up in such families, having had their symbolic roots nourished by irrationality in the family, are less confined by the restrictions of the demands of reality when means of escape and withdrawal are required.

Of course, the presence of poorly organized or disorganized parents can just as well be taken as evidence of a genetic strain that transmits schizophrenia. Indeed, we have probably found more evidence of mental illness among parents and in other relatives than any study of the genetic factors of schizophrenia. At this time we are describing what exists in the family rather than explaining how it came about. According to our concepts of human development, such distortions of reasoning are more explicable through extrabiological transmission of family characteristics than through genetic endowment. However, we need not seek a solution with an "either-or," for, as with many other conditions, both genetic and environmental factors may well be involved.

XI

The Prediction of Family Interaction from a Battery of Projective Tests

(1956)

This study represents an attempt to make systematic use of projective techniques in the study of family interaction. We shall present material from only one family, which necessarily precludes generalization. It is not our purpose to present the test results of this family as characteristic of other similar families but rather as an illustration of a method.

The data consist of the interpretations and inferences contained in a report of the family based only on psychological test materials with no further information except the age, occupation, and education of each member. The accuracy of this hypothesized picture of the family was then evaluated in terms of information obtained from interviews with the family members, and impressions based on these interviews.

The psychological report on this family was written from the following points of orientation: (1) Our primary interest was in the interaction among the family members. (2) We focused on resemblances between children and parents in their patterns of needs and conflicts and the way in which these were manifested. We hoped in doing this to find clues to the developmental reasons for at least gross differences in children of the same family; in particular, the development of mental illness in one child and not in the other. (3) We also

Dorothy Terry Sohler, Jules D. Holzberg, Stephen Fleck, Alice R. Cornelison, Eleanor Kay, and Theodore Lidz: The Prediction of Family Interaction from a Battery of Projective Tests. Journal of Projective Techniques, *Vol. 21, 1957, pp. 199-208. Copyright © 1957, Society of Projective Techniques and Rorschach Institute, Inc.*

were looking for factors which would characterize the family as a whole: relatively unique behavior which established a family climate. (4) Finally, we wondered whether study of the test material from an entire family would increase our understanding of the individual members.

This study of one family is not intended as a validation of projective techniques. Nevertheless, this type of approach, if carried out on a sufficient number of subjects, has much to recommend it as a method of validation. It avoids two important limitations found in many validation studies. The first of these has to do with the criterion for evaluating the test results. It does not require, for example, that the tests differentiate among nosological entities or between successful and unsuccessful employees. One may argue that it is doubtful that interview material and clinical impressions are more nearly accurate as criteria. This may very well be true, but as criteria they are appropriate and relevant to the purpose for which projective techniques were devised: to describe the individual.

The second difficulty in assessing the validity of projective techniques lies in finding appropriate units of measurement. Formal scoring categories are still of unknown validity, and it is argued that their use violates the significance of the test as a whole. Schafer (1949) in discussing this problem, has pointed out the advantage of using the test interpretation as the unit of measurement. By this procedure, it is possible to avoid the problem of losing the significance of the test as a whole. The interpreter is free to base his hypotheses on his total impression of a test or test battery. He also is free to analyze the data without being forced to adhere to any particular scoring procedure. We have adopted this method of evaluating predictions by comparing them with information derived from the interviews. We believe that only by an accumulation of this type of evidence from individual cases can we begin to understand which areas of human behavior can best be described by projective tests.

SUBJECTS

The Benjamin family consists of the parents, a daughter of nineteen, and a son, sixteen, who is a patient at the Yale Psychiatric Institute.

The father is a successful businessman, and the mother a housewife. The parents have a high school education. The daughter at the time of testing also had completed high school, and the patient was in his third year of high school when hospitalized.

PROCEDURE

Each family member was given a series of tests in two sessions. In the first period, fourteen Thematic Apperception Test cards[1] and the Rotter Sentence Completion Test were administered. The second period was given over to the Rorschach and the Draw-A-Person. The Rorschach was administered and scored according to Klopfer's method. The Draw-A-Person was administered according to Machover's procedure.

Two psychologists worked independently at first, writing up detailed interpretations of the tests for each individual. One had administered the tests. The other had had no contact with the family. They discussed their individual reports in order to resolve differences in interpretation and then considered each test, card by card and response by response, in order to assess the family as a whole and speculate on their interaction. The tests were considered in the following order: Rorschach, Thematic Apperception Test, Sentence Completion, Draw-A-Person.

After the test productions of the family as a whole were considered a general report was written, based on a previously devised outline. This was made up of seventy-two items under general headings. Only the general headings will be summarized here.

We described the factors which seemed to characterize the family as a whole. We were especially interested in any suggestion of tendencies to distort reality and the possible effects upon the children of such distortions.

The relationship between the parents was considered next, with re-

---

[1] The cards used were 2, 3BM, 3GF, 5, 6BM, 6GF, 7BM, 7GF, 9GF, 10, 12M, 13 MF, 18BM, 18GF. The same series was given to every subject, regardless of sex. This was done because the BM and GF cards, designed as alternates, do not appear to be really equivalent. It was thought too that giving a subject cards designed for the opposite sex might elicit important information about sexual identification.

gard to factors which drew them together initially, and changes in their attitudes toward each in the course of the marriage.

A number of the items referred to parent-child relationships. Did the parents seem to have conflicting roles for the child? Which was the preferred child of each parent? In what way did factors such as the sex of the child influence this preference? How did the child confide in the parents and how important was this to the parents? How did the parents react to the growing independence of the child and his movement away from the family ties?

The question of relationships outside the immediate family was also considered: the parents' strong ties to their parental homes or to individual interest, vocational or avocational.

After the report on the family had been written, it was analyzed into 333 discrete written interpretive statements, each of which was intended to represent only one interpretation. Two raters working independently disagreed in twenty-one instances as to what constituted a statement. The resulting agreement between raters, then, was 93 per cent.

These 333 interpretive statements were then judged for agreement with the interview material. The judgments were made independently by the two psychiatrists in the study. They had taken no part either in the test interpretation or the interviewing of the family, but were thoroughly familiar with the interview material. The amount and richness of this interview material requires comment. Both parents were seen once a week for almost two years, for a total of 110 interviews. The patient's sister had a total of twenty-nine interviews, and the patient had three or four therapeutic hours a week during this time.

The raters judged each interpretive statement to be in agreement with the interview material, in partial agreement, unknown, or in disagreement. The unknown rating was given when there was not enough pertinent information in the interview material to make a judgment.

It was necessary to assess the interjudge reliability. In rating any one statement it was possible for the judges to agree with each other completely or partially, or to disagree.

1. The judges were said to be in partial agreement on a statement

when one judge rated it partial agreement and the other rated it either agreement or disagreement.

2. The judges were said to be in disagreement on a statement when (a) one judge rated it agreement and the other rated it disagreement, or (b) one judge rated it unknown and the other rated it either agreement, partial agreement, or disagreement.

The judges agreed with each other on 62 per cent of the statements; they were in partial agreement on 11 per cent and they disagreed on 27 per cent. The per cent partial agreement was divided by two and the result (5.5%) was added to the per cent complete agreement (62%). In this way an over-all rater agreement of 67.5 per cent was obtained.

After both judges had made their ratings independently, they discussed their disagreement and arrived at a joint rating. We were interested to see whether one judge's ratings prevailed over the other's in the joint ratings. This was found not to be the case. One judge had only three more of his original ratings represented in the joint ratings than did the other judge.

Classification of Predictive Statements

The statements were classified in four different ways, independently of the comparison with the interview material. In each instance two raters worked independently. The agreement was then computed and the final ratings were decided after discussion of the disagreements.

General, Stereotyped, and Idiosyncratic Statements. An important factor to be considered in the evaluation of the interpretive statements is the extent to which the family and its members are differentiated from families and people in general. Therefore, an attempt was made to determine whether the statements in the write-up which were judged to be in agreement were only safe generalizations which could be made about anyone.

It appeared that there were at least two types of statements which would be relatively undifferentiating. The first concerns behavior which is universally characteristic. Statements of this type, which we call General, differentiate one individual from another only when a rather extreme degree of intensity is specified. Thus "He is seething with hostility" is more specific than "He has feelings of hostility." A statement such as "the mother has a strong need for affection" was called General since everyone needs affection. Even if the interview material gave no evidence of more than average need for affection, the judges might be less likely to rate this statement incorrect than they would an Idiosyncratic statement such as "The parents' sex life may be somewhat bizarre."

A statement was called a Stereotype if it could have been made solely on the basis of group identification of the individual: e.g., socioeconomic status, age or sex, without information from the test material. This is not to say that the tests were ignored when these statements were made. On the contrary, they indicated which of many possible stereotypes might be appropriate. The prediction "They (the family members) are undoubtedly strongly upwardly mobile" might have been made only from the knowledge that the family is upper-middle class, that the parents do not have college degrees, and that they are Jewish. However, the father in his Thematic Apperception Test stories made many references to the superiority of people with college degrees and the importance of reading the right books.

We made a larger number of Stereotyped statements than one ordinarily would in a psychological report because we were following an outline which forced us to attempt to answer questions about various activities for which there was often no direct evidence in the test material. These Stereotypes are not necessarily more likely to be in agreement with the interview material than other statements in the write-up, because they are not universally characteristic of members of the group from which the stereotype is drawn.

Two raters worked independently to classify the statements. Those which were not judged to be General or Stereotyped were called Idiosyncratic. The raters agreed on 238 or 71 per cent of the 333 statements. The final ratings included 32 General statements, 90 Stereotypes, and 211 Idiosyncratic statements.[2]

Statements about Overt and Covert Behavior. The problem of pre-

---

[2] The raters, who in this instance were also the authors of the report, may have been biased in the direction of making too few ratings of General and Stereotyped.

dicting overt behavior from projective test material is a difficult one, and we were interested in discovering whether there was any difference in the judged accuracy of our predictions in this area as opposed to predictions of covert behavior.

The Covert category includes statements about defense mechanisms, other theoretical formulations of personality dynamics, personality traits, needs, feelings, and attitudes toward the self. Statements rated Overt were any which specified behavior, discussion of roles played by the individual, and attitudes toward others. It was difficult to decide how to rate statements about attitudes, since they imply both overt and covert behavior. We decided rather arbitrarily to split in the manner indicated, since attitudes toward others imply a communication between two people, whereas attitudes toward the self may not always be communicated to others.

There was 83 per cent agreement between the raters. A total of 215 Overt and 118 Covert statements was decided on.

Group and Individual Statements. The next classification was into Group and Individual statements. Many of the predictions had to do with resemblances in the family, so that the same prediction was made for more than one family member. There was perfect agreement between the raters in this classification.

Personal and Interpersonal Statements. The fourth classification was into Personal and Interpersonal statements. The former refer to personality characteristics and the latter to some type of interaction between two or more people. The Interpersonal statements included, in addition to descriptions of behavioral interaction, statements concerning the attitude of one person toward another and reactions or feelings evoked by one person in another. This category also included statements about one person's feelings about the interaction of other members of the family, and descriptions of roles played by the individuals in the family. This classification became difficult when the predictions had to do with one person's attitudes toward other people in general. We became somewhat arbitrary about this. Such a statement as "He is essentially a hostile person" we classified as Personal since the emphasis is more on feeling than on interaction. Statements about a person expressing his feelings to someone else were classified as Interpersonal.

The two raters making the Personal-Interpersonal classifications disagreed on 24 per cent of the statements. There was a misunderstanding on one aspect of the definition of the Interpersonal category which resulted in a consistent error, making it difficult to evaluate the agreement. When the disagreements resulting from the consistent error are removed, the agreement on the remaining items is 257 out of 291, or 88 per cent.

The inter-judge agreement on these four classifications seemed high enough to make it worth while to use them in analyzing the data, since they might help clarify differences between the agreements and disagreements with the interview material.

RESULTS AND DISCUSSION

The results of the comparison with the interview material are summarized in Table I, for the statements as a whole and for the four classifications. Sixty-seven per cent of the total number of statements were found to be in agreement; 9 per cent in partial agreement; 8 per cent unknown; and 16 per cent in disagreement.

Neither the General nor Stereotyped statements differed in accuracy from the Idiosyncratic statements. The Stereotyped statements were the most likely to be judged correct, but the Chi Square comparing them with the rest of the statements fell short of significance at the .05 level of confidence.

There was no over-all tendency for the statements about Overt behavior to be any more or less in agreement than the statements about Covert behavior. When they were considered with the other two classifications, Group-Individual and Personal-Interpersonal, one difference appeared: the Overt statements in the Group category have a significantly large number of disagreements (Chi Square = 3.95, $P < .05$, df = 1). Most of these are Group-Interpersonal statements about attitudes of family members toward each other.

The Group and Individual statements differ significantly in the proportion of agreements and disagreements (Chi Square = 7.94, $P < .05$, df = 3). Sixty-three per cent of the Group statements were agreements as opposed to 70 per cent of the Individual statements. Twenty-two per cent of the Group statements were disagreements, and only 12 per cent of the Individual statements were disagreements.

The Personal and Interpersonal categories do not differ significantly from each other in terms of agreement with interview material.

The Individual-Personal statements have the smallest proportion of disagreements and the Group-Interpersonal statements the highest (Chi Square $= 4.00$, $P < .05$, $df = 1$). The Group-Interpersonal statements refer to family interaction, and thus represent a greater departure from the test data than do the Individual-Personal statements about personality make-up usually found in test reports. The tests, apparently, are better sources of information about the individual than about his relations with other specific individuals. Nevertheless, we had some success in describing the family interaction and it is of interest to examine the agreements and disagreements in this area.

Agreements

The Interpersonal areas will be summarized here. No attempt will be made to describe all of the agreements in these areas. The Personal categories will be considered later in the section on individual members of the family.

The interview material and the predictive statements both emphasized the intense need of both parents and the patient for closeness with others, approval, and affection. It was manifested primarily in an unusual lack of reticence and sense of personal privacy in the family.

The father's feeling of inadequacy as a man was quite apparent, and a number of predictions were made about the influence this would have on the other members of the family. We thought, for example, that the father would be at least tempted to prove his masculinity by having extramarital affairs, although we were not sure he would actually carry this out. He reported having several. It was predicted that the father would push the patient to prove his masculinity, encouraging and fostering sexual activities and athletic interests. This too was borne out in the interviews.

A basic distortion in the parental roles was hypothesized, on the basis of the father's impulsiveness and immaturity, which would not be likely to be counteracted by the passive mother. The parental attitudes of overindulgence and lack of dependable authoritative control we felt would lead to acting out in the children.

The father was seen apparently correctly as the focus of jealousy in the family. Destructive quarreling was correctly predicted. The father's need to be close to his children, to know what they were thinking, and the seductive interest of both parents were picked up. The patient had an unusually dependent relationship with his parents. The daughter appeared to be separating herself from the family, but was jealous of the attention her brother was receiving.

Partial Agreements

An example of partial agreement was the discussion of the expression of anger. Temper outbursts were correctly predicted for the father. They were also predicted to a lesser degree for the mother and the patient. The patient's therapist pointed out that the patient acted out in a hostile way, but denied angry feelings. When his parents came to visit him he sometimes left them, saying he wanted to watch television instead. Neither he nor his parents could see anything hostile in this. The mother expressed anger indirectly in a masochistic way, by talking so much that she incurred the irritation and anger of her family and outsiders as well. The extreme degree to which the whole family made use of denial was recognized, but it was difficult to predict how it would influence the expression of hostility.

Disagreements

The largest single group of disagreements could be attributed to a particular error in interpretation concerning the relationship between the parents. On the basis of the father's Sentence Completion test, which showed an unusual amount of concern with his wife and family, we hypothesized a relationship where the father took the more nurturant role, to his wife as well as his children. For support we noted a Rorschach response of the patient: "two butlers rolling out a red carpet for the Queen of Sheba," and the mother's intense need for affection and attention. It seems worth while to note in some detail the errors stemming from this hypothesis.

We stated that the father probably waited on the mother and paid her a great deal of attention. The actual situation during the patient's lifetime was one of constant quarreling, extreme lack of consideration by the father for the mother, open contempt, and occasional blows. The father at the time of the patient's hospitalization was painfully guilty about his behavior toward his wife and its effect on the patient. In the two years of weekly individual therapeutic interviews with the parents, there was striking improvement in the marriage. The father came to exhibit the interest in his wife which we had thought to be present at the time of testing, although he was not controlled by her as we had hypothesized. The father was always much involved with his children, and his guilt when his son was hospitalized was intense. Both parents were capable of change, and their son's illness provided motivation and opportunity.

Because of our assumption that the mother's role was one of demanding dependence, we hypothesized that she would be particularly unable to tolerate dependent behavior in the father, and we stated this as the quality in her husband which Mrs. Benjamin would like least. We had underestimated the degree of explosive temper and irritability in the father, which was, and still is to a lesser degree, the source of the mother's major difficulty with her husband. We also assumed, in discussing ways of disciplining the children, that the parents would insist on consideration for the mother.

One partial agreement is interesting in view of this misinterpretation. We felt that the father would find the mother's demands for attention a burden and that this would constitute the quality which he liked least in his wife. This seemed to be true, but not quite in the sense in which we conceived it: that is, the mother's demandingness was expressed indirectly by a flow of incessant talk, full of irrelevant detail, which Mr. Benjamin found extremely irritating.

Statements Which Could Not Be Evaluated

The predictions in the unknown category had to do with sexual activities of the family, family activities in the home, attitudes of one member toward another, predictions into the future, and formulations of personality dynamics. Only a few of the formulations of personality dynamics were judged unknown; they appeared in the other categories when there was sufficient evidence to evaluate them.

INDIVIDUAL FAMILY MEMBERS

When the family members are considered individually, there are some striking differences with respect to the four classifications of data.

The patient received a significantly large, and the father a significantly small proportion of General statements (Chi square = 16.37, $P < .001$, df = 3). There were no significant individual differences with respect to the Stereotyped items, nor were there any with respect to the Overt-Covert classification.

The individual family members differ significantly with respect to the Group-Individual and Personal-Interpersonal categories (Chi square = 41.48, $P < .001$, df = 9). The majority of the items referring to the patient are Individual-Personal (personality description) and Group-Interpersonal (family interaction). There are only two items referring to the patient in the Individual-Interpersonal category (interaction with specific family members). The significance of this seems to be that the patient was seen not as an individual interacting with other individuals, but as the dependent child of his parents, not yet separated and individuated from them.

The majority of the statements referring to the father fell in the Interpersonal (family interaction) categories. This reflects the degree to which the father was seen as the focus of the family, exerting an important influence on the development of the children.

The daughter was described in a very small number of statements in the Interpersonal (family interaction) categories. This reflects the impression (corroborated by the interviews) that she had separated herself from the family, while the parents and patient were still caught up in an excessively interdependent triangle.

The parents were given almost twice as much attention in the report as were the children. This apparently is due to the fact that the report was oriented toward explaining the effect of the parents on the personality make-up of the children.

Seventy per cent of the statements about the patient were agreements: a larger (but not significantly so) percentage than for any other family member. However, the qualitative impression is that the patient was the most poorly depicted as an individual. This is explained by the large number of General statements referring to the patient. Of all members of the family, the patient was the most difficult to understand as an individual. This is not surprising in view of the fact that he was psychotic, with a diagnosis of paranoid schizophrenia. His behavior during the tests was fairly well organized, and he managed to hide his more important delusions. The psychologists could conclude only that he was covering over a good deal of material. The degree of disorganization in the patient was undetermined, although it was apparent (particularly from his drawings) that he was in a state of acute turmoil.

The father emerged more clearly as an individual. The degree of compulsive behavior in this man was underestimated, however. More striking in the test material were his aggressiveness, volatile emotionality, and need to prove his masculinity. An implication of this need which perhaps might have been emphasized more was the degree to which he bragged and displayed his wealth in order to prove his competence as a man.

The description of the daughter proved more accurate as time went on and the social worker was able to establish a relationship with her. There had been disagreement between the psychologists as to whether she might have had sexual relations. We learned later that she had been involved in an affair in which she played a sadomasochistic role. There seemed sufficient evidence to corroborate the impression from the test material that she would be likely to act out in a self-destructive way.

SUMMARY AND CONCLUSIONS

A description of a family, based solely on projective tests given to all family members, has been reported and evaluated. The interpretation of the test material was focused on understanding the interaction between the family members with particular reference to the influence of the parents' personalities on the children, the general themes characterizing the family as a group, and the different developmental problems confronting each child. Similar work has been carried out with several families containing a schizophrenic child, and with three volunteer families in which there was no apparent mental disorder. Although this study was not undertaken as a validation of projective tests, the method could be used for this purpose.

Material from one family was presented to illustrate the procedure. The tests were administered and interpreted with no knowledge of the family except their ages, education, religion, the father's occupation, and the fact that the son was hospitalized at the Yale Psychiatric Institute. The interpretations based on the test material were compared for agreement with extensive material from all members of the family. The parents were seen weekly for almost two years, the daughter was interviewed twenty-nine times, and the patient was undergoing intensive psychotherapy during this time.

The collaboration of two psychologists was an especially valuable aspect of the procedure, since the scope of the predictions was both wider and more specific than is usual in psychological reports. Many implications for family interaction were not realized until the test material had been discussed thoroughly. There also were interpretations in the independent write-ups which were discarded in the combined report because they seemed incorrect and would have been at variance with the evidence in the interviews. There was little disagreement in the independent interpretations, but a definite tendency for each psychologist to concentrate on different aspects of the material. Thus the joint picture of the family was more comprehensive than either of the individual efforts.

Probably the majority of the hypotheses about family resemblances and partial identifications came from the Rorschach. Clues concerning overt behavior by which important needs were gratified were supplied by the more structured tests such as the Thematic Apperception Test and Sentence Completion. The Thematic Apperception Test seemed to be the best source of information about attitudes toward other members of the family. The Draw-A-Person was used primarily to supply evidence of attitudes toward the self and the opposite sex.

The interpretive statements derived from the tests were classified in four different ways independently of the comparison with the interview material. This was done in order to separate the general statements which could be ascribed to many people from the more specific statements, predictions of overt behavior from covert, and statements about individuals from those about family resemblance and interaction.

The raters did not feel in a position to judge with assurance the degree of congruence between the interpretive statements and interview material until the family had been seen in a semitherapeutic setting for almost two years. The length and intensity of contact with the family proved very important. A preliminary evaluation of the interpretive statements was made after the patient had been hospitalized for about six months. The parents had been seen regularly during that time, and the sister had been interviewed five times. In this preliminary evaluation, 31 per cent of the statements were put in the unknown category, whereas only 9 per cent remained in that category in the present evaluation. Furthermore, there were disagreements in the first evaluation which were corroborated in later interviews, and vice versa. It is clear that this kind of evaluation of test material cannot be done on the basis of a few interviews. Certainly many important questions about this family remain unanswered, even after almost two years of contact with them.

In the present evaluation, the agreements constituted two thirds of the total number of statements, 9 per cent were partial agreements, 8 per cent were undetermined, and 16 per cent were disagreements. The individual personality descriptions contained the highest proportion of agreements. The statements most likely to be in disagreement were predictions of attitude of one family member toward another, and statements about family interaction.

In considering the family members separately, it was found that the patient received a significantly large and the father a significantly small number of General (relatively undifferentiating) statements. Other significant differences in the relative number of individual and interactional statements appear to reflect at least gross differences in the roles played by the members of the family. The father was the most active influence in the family, while the mother played a more passive role. The daughter was separating herself, while the patient was the dependent child, not yet individuated from his family.

The Benjamin family does not represent one of the most successful productions of the interpreting psychologists because of the basic error in interpretation which brought a number of other misinterpretations in its wake. This was known before the present study was undertaken. The family was selected because there was extensive information about them, and because elaborate precautions had been taken to conceal the information from the psychologists. Furthermore, it proved important to study the misinterpretations, and to consider how they might have been avoided.

It has not been our customary procedure to make blind interpretations of the tests in the larger study of the families of schizophrenic patients. The test material can be put to better use when the information about the past and present functioning of the family is known. The blind interpretation of several families has helped us understand, however, what can be predicted about family interaction. They have, in fact, given us courage to venture farther in this area than at first seemed possible.

The study of all members of the family has implications for the understanding of the individual. Hypotheses about a person may be confirmed by the attitudes displayed toward him by the other members of his family. Furthermore, the individual's self-concept may differ in important respects from the ways in which the members of his family perceive him. The study of the family as a whole not only increases understanding of the family interaction, but also provides the opportutnity to see the individual through the eyes of his family.

TABLE I

DISTRIBUTION OF JUDGMENTS OF AGREEMENT ACCORDING TO FOUR
INDEPENDENT CLASSIFICATIONS

	Total		General		Stereotyped		Idiosyncratic		Overt		Covert		Group		Individual		Personal		Interpersonal	
	No.	%	No.	%	No.	%	No.	%	No.	%	No.	%	No.	%	No.	%	No.	%	No.	%
Agreement	224	67	21	66	66	73	137	65	145	67	79	67	83	63	141	70	70	71	154	66
Partial Agreement	27	8	6	19	4	4	17	8	14	7	13	11	11	9	16	8	6	6	21	9
Unknown	28	9	2	6	6	7	20	9	19	9	9	8	8	6	20	10	9	9	19	8
Disagreement	54	16	3	9	14	16	37	18	37	17	17	14	29	22	25	12	14	14	40	17
Total	333	100	32	100	90	100	211	100	215	100	118	100	131	100	202	100	99	100	234	100

XII

Ego Differentiation and Schizophrenic
Symptom Formation in Identical Twins

(1958)

Among the patients in the study was an identical twin whose co-twin became extremely disturbed immediately after the patient was hospitalized. The patient was treated in the Yale Psychiatric Institute and continued in analytically oriented psychotherapy after discharge, while his twin managed to remain at home receiving analytically oriented treatment from a therapist who kept detailed process notes of each session.[1] The study of these twins, together with all of the other members of the family, and the intrafamilial environment they created permitted a unique opportunity to examine the special problems of ego development confronting twins and the impact of the family dynamics in shaping the personalities and the pathology of these twins in particular. We believe that if we wish to use twin studies in exploring the genesis of schizophrenia (Kallmann, 1946; Kallmann and Bondy, 1952; Schlegel, 1955, 1957), we must understand and take into account the dynamic problems of twinship because the ego development and ego structure of twins is apt to differ markedly from those of nontwins. The specific problems of identical twins, however, contribute to the understanding of ego formation and inte-

Theodore Lidz, Sarah Schafer, Stephen Fleck, Alice R. Cornelison, and Dorothy Terry: Ego Differentiation and Schizophrenic Symptom Formation in Identical Twins. Journal of the American Psychoanalytic Association, *Vol. 10, 1962, pp. 74-90. Copyright © 1962, American Psychoanalytic Association. This paper was presented at the Midwinter meeting of the American Psychoanalytic Association, December, 1959.*

[1] We are greatly indebted to this psychiatrist who must remain anonymous to help conceal the identity of the family.

gration in general. In this chapter, we shall seek to focus on these matters while for the time being we neglect the intrafamilial conditions which seem to us to have particular pertinence to the development of schizophrenia.

The literature concerned with the personality development of twins, though sparse, calls attention to a group of problems highly relevant to our case. It reminds one of Aristophanes' poetic fable concerning the nature of love in Plato's *Symposium*. Originally, he tells us, humans were double with two heads and eight extremities and of three sexes, male, female, and androgynous. Because of their challenge to the power of the Olympians, Zeus split them in half. Since then, the halves wander the earth, unable to rest in their incomplete states, seeking their other halves. Identical twins were originally thus united. Kent (1949) in her study of a series of disturbed twins during their childhood remarked upon the frequent symbiotic relationship which she believed was fostered by the presence of a rigid, unloving mother. Most pairs divided into a dominant and a submissive twin, the twin with acting-out tendencies being the dominant one. Many mothers related to the twins as if they were one child, but at the same time treated them differently emotionally. In this setting, twins were intensely rivalrous for the mother's affection, and some reacted with extreme dependency upon the mother while others became aggressively rebellious. Such twins had great difficulty in establishing relationships with other children. Freud (1922) in considering normal and pathological jealousy commented upon the pattern in which early intense rivalry with and hostility toward a sibling turn into love and identification with the envied sibling, and can lead to one pattern of homosexuality. This developmental pattern may be particularly common among twins. Solomon and Bliss (1956), Weatherly and Deabler (1954), Hartmann (1934-1935), and others have reported homosexuality in schizophrenic identical twins, while Orr (1941) and Karpman (1953) both found homosexuality a major problem in the fraternal twins they reported. Karpman (1953) studied the passive member of the twinship who reported that he had been hostilely competitive for the mother but felt doomed to disappointment because his twin was more attractive and so transferred his love to the twin he had originally hated. When separated from his twin upon entering college, he had an upsurge of compulsive sexual urges as a defense against homosexuality. He struggled with his need for his brother and further felt he needed his brother as a protection against his incestuous impulses toward his mother. These problems can be seen clearly in the twins we are presenting. Orr's (1941) patient was also driven by a constant wish "to find a twin" after separation, and having feared to excel or be excelled, sought to be a mirror of his twin, sacrificing his individuality, and considering himself feminine and castrated. This man complained that his chronic dilemma was whether he was a half person or a whole person. Demarest and Winestine (1955) found the necessary focus of treatment in the five-year-old twins they reported to be the children's inability to differentiate themselves from each other and from the mother. Cronin (1933) describes adult identical twins in whom the lack of differentiation was outstanding. They experienced greater love for each other than for any other person. One was assertive and masculine, and the other passive and feminine. They had not only shared their mother, but had sexually shared the maid who had helped raise them, and then lived in a polyandrous relationship with a woman legally married to one of them. Joseph (1959) analyzed an identical twin who had a passive, feminine orientation but who took the initiative in performing fellatio on his brother. When he separated from his twin, he sought to assuage his loneliness by lying in bed and gazing in a mirror, imagining the image to be his twin.

CASE PRESENTATION

We can present only a small fragment of our data, and will seek to utilize illustrative examples symbolic of the family situation in lieu of completeness.

Peter Nebb was admitted to the hospital from college at the age of twenty. He had been unable to study, feeling incomplete and lost without his twin, being preoccupied with a ritualistic means of controlling himself, and expressing paranoid beliefs about a former homosexual partner. He was confused, and suffered from ill-defined states of "dissociation" when he would "become another person," dress as a bum and wander the streets. His younger identical twin, Philip, became intensely upset when Peter was hospitalized. Having been dependent upon Peter who was his ideal, he felt that he verged on becoming acutely psychotic. His talk was driven and disorganized, and his projective tests appeared schizophrenic in many respects. Transvestite homosexual activity had increased markedly following his brother's hospitalization. However, with the help of intensive psychotherapy Philip managed to avoid a clear-cut psychotic break, and was able to remain at home.

We must turn back to the preceding generation in our effort to understand these twins. The mother was also a twin, a fraternal twin who from birth had never matched her vigorous, attractive, and dominant sister, probably because a dysplastic habitus gave her a peculiar appearance. Although she had envied and hated her twin, she was nonetheless strongly attached to her and either saw her or spoke with her on the telephone almost every day throughout her life. Her sister had been openly favored by the parents. When their mother had become a chronic invalid, they had withdrawn Mrs. Nebb from school to take over the household chores and raise an infant brother named Philip, whereas they encouraged her sister to finish high school and gave her many advantages. Mrs. Nebb turned her energies toward grooming her brother to become a great man. She prided herself on his every achievement, enforcing strict and rigid discipline while prodding him onward—only to become bitterly disappointed when, after making a brilliant record in college, he became an alcoholic ne'er-do-well. The brother's failure was a serious blow to Mrs. Nebb which affected her conscious attitudes in rearing her twins.

Mrs. Nebb identified with her father who had kept a general store in a rather remote mountain community and dispensed patent medicines to the local inhabitants who came to him for medical advice. She became a practical nurse, and eventually a registered nurse. Her access to the homes of some wealthy families fanned a consuming determination to acquire higher social status for herself. She worked successfully as a nurse until she was almost forty years old, when her twin sister became engaged to a wealthy man. Mrs. Nebb, who had previously never considered marriage, now set about finding a husband for herself, and, according to her own statement, deliberately corralled her husband, five years younger than she, in order to have a double wedding with her twin sister. Although Mr. Nebb was a competent and friendly man, he was extremely shy and passive. He had never gone out with women before and, in general, behaved like a stepchild who must remain in the background and placate women. Indeed, his mother had died when he was born and he was raised by a foster mother whom his father later married. He became a reasonably successful real-estate broker, but never aspired to the renown of his father, a professor of literature, or to the eminence of his older brother in the business world.

Following the draw in finding husbands, competition now turned to efforts to produce twins. The sister "led two children to one" when Mrs. Nebb triumphed by giving birth to twins. From that moment on, the twins were her glory and the focus of her life and, because of her domination of the home, the focus of the family life. The story of the birth of the twins became a family legend: Peter had kicked Philip out of the way and into a breach position, which required a prolonged delivery for Philip. The story contained the implication that Peter, as a fetus, had deliberately displaced his twin to gain priority. Whatever the reasons that made Peter more aggressive, the birth set a pattern. Peter was preferred by his mother and from the start was more aggressive, more daring, and more charming—like Mrs. Nebb's sister. Philip, on the other hand, was more docile and passive like Mrs. Nebb herself. Whether Peter was selected because he was more aggressive, or became more aggressive because he was selected, cannot be determined.

The twins belonged exclusively to the mother, and the family was consequently divided into two groups: the father and oldest son, comprising the outgroup, were supposed to adjust to the primary purpose of raising the extraordinary twins to live out their full capacities. Mrs. Nebb let the twins know that because of her pain at their birth and her sacrifices for them, they must never leave her. They were her indirect means of surpassing her twin.

Mrs. Nebb insisted that the twins were geniuses whose activity must not be inhibited by any restrictions. She believed she had failed with her brother because she had been punitively controlling, and she would succeed with the twins by using obverse methods. She categorically eschewed any discipline, but she was nonetheless extremely controlling and intrusive in other areas, particularly in all matters that threatened her serious phobia concerning contamination. This applied to bowel habits, bathing, food fads, and abhorrence of animals, where any breach in the practices she dictated produced severe rebuff. She had banished her husband from her bedroom and bathroom when he had a mild transient fungus infection of the groin, and thereafter he could only use the basement lavatory. The older brother and father were labeled "dirty," and the brother "dirty-mind-ed" for refusing to let mother bathe him and examine his stools after he was fourteen.

The twins were raised as a unit. They were dressed identically until nine or ten, and they were practically indistinguishable in appearance. Often they were not differentiated by the parents, and both were punished or praised for the deeds of one. Further, Mrs. Nebb had trouble differentiating their needs from her own: the twins were part of her, and her relationship to them was shaped by her own problems which predisposed her to treat the twins as phallic extensions of herself. Often, when she was ill and received medicine, she also gave it to the twins. At one time, the boys could not keep awake in school, and learned that Mrs. Nebb had been placing the sedative she had received for herself in their breakfast food. They were both bowel trained starting at three months. Suppositories and enemas were liberally used, and enormous amounts of parental affect and energy were concentrated on bowel functions. Later, indeed until late adolescence, mother would give both twins enemas together, often because one was angry with her, which meant to her they were constipated. The enemas were administerd according to a ritual in which both boys lay naked on the floor, and mother lubricated their anuses with her finger and inserted the nozzles with water as hot as they could stand. The twin more dilatory in getting into position would have to dash to another floor to the toilet. She continued to bathe them and to wash their genitals until they were fifteen. The mother constantly praised the twins to her friends and strangers and asked them to perform for guests. Friends were often amazed to learn that Mrs. Nebb had another son.

Already in their preschool years, they gained the reputation of pint-sized terrors. They had to be withdrawn from kindergarten because Peter, in particular, was an exasperating behavior problem. They found that they could feign asthma (a disease from which they suffered intermittently after the age of three) to gain their way or be left alone; and before long they learned that mother would believe any story they made up to please or circumvent her. The twins were virtually always together, sharing thoughts, and had secret ways of jabbering that conveyed "I love you most," which they did not say outright. Mother discouraged other playmates, and later she frowned on girl friends. The twins shared interests, hobbies, and pranks. Together they dared much, for there were two of them. Still, there was a profound difference between them, for Peter was the leader and initiator of trouble, while Philip loyally followed his ideal. At six or seven, Philip stabbed a boy who had attacked Peter, thus proving his loyalty. Philip often felt intensely anxious and fearful of the dangers that Peter's behavior brought. He took to religion, praying that Peter would be good. During treatment he recalled that he had been frightened by thoughts of killing Peter and had changed "kill" to "kiss" in childhood obsessive rituals.

Each twin, then, related to his mother and co-twin in an interconnected manner. Peter was the phallic, acting-out aggressor identified with his mother's twin, and Philip was more identified with the mother's passive, feminine, and devalued castrated aspects, and they assumed similar roles with each other. They complemented each other, with Philip ceding the masculine role to Peter. They were rivalrous for mother, but sought to gratify different aspects of her needs. In accord with this role division, Peter concentrated on the task of carrying out action with a relative impoverishment of his inner life, while Philip specialized in internal elaboration of experience, both affective and ideational, and was inclined to be the passive spectator.

Mrs. Nebb not only systematically abjured setting controls and limits herself, but, in addition, undermined her husband's sporadic efforts at discipline. By her scorn of his actions and by her contempt for him, she let the twins know that they could disregard their father. Still, when they were young, he would occasionally fly into a fury and beat the boys who were then terrified. Even when the boys were in college she encouraged them to disregard their father and even her own authority. She would try to get her way in the home by having hysterical "fits" and spells of uncontrolled crying. When Philip was in college he took it upon himself to stop her outbursts by taking her over his knee and spanking her. Once, when Mr. Nebb tried to interfere with a spanking, Mrs. Nebb abruptly stopped shrieking, told him to mind his own business, and ordered Philip to continue to spank her and then started to scream again.

When the twins were nine, they precipitated a major family crisis. Peter, fascinated by fire since the age of four, started a fire in some hay and blocked Philip's attempts to extinguish it. The fire spread, burning down a nearby barn. Soon they were involved in more serious troubles. Peter broke into a boarding house vacated for the winter, and formed a gang which systematically ransacked and vandalized the place. Peter was incriminated by the police as ringleader, and although Mrs. Nebb continued to deny that her twins were involved despite their confessions, the boys were ostracized. The episode with the involvement with the police remained a serious trauma to the boys despite Mrs. Nebb's negation of it. These events at least contributed to the family's move from the mountain resort to a metropolis, though Mrs. Nebb still insists that they moved only to afford the twins the superior education they required. Mr. Nebb, for valid business and social reasons, refused to move, and arguments extended to threats of separation. However, it was Mr. Nebb's last stand, and after he finally capitulated, he ceased trying to assert himself concerning family decisions and the control of the twins.

In the city, the twins seemed to settle down. Their interests focused on scientific experiments. They were good students but had little to do with others, even refusing to eat lunch in school as was customary. During this period, Philip had his first sexual contact when he masturbated with another boy, which shocked Peter when Philip told him of it.

When, as small boys, they had first asked their mother about female genitalia, she answered as directly and openly as she could—by pulling up her skirt to illustrate her explanation. Still, Philip recalled, he continued to think that she had a penis hidden somewhere. The mother's overt seductiveness continued after the twins reached adolescence. She not only examined each bowel movement, continued the enema routine, bathed them, and often displayed herself naked before them, but she would get into bed with them until they were fifteen. When Peter made a visit home from the hospital and was trying to converse seriously with his father, which was a new interest and experience for him, Mrs. Nebb, unable to intrude and gain his attention despite various ruses, finally came into the living room naked in her effort to regain her son's favor.

The break in the twins' symbiotic existence came at fourteen when, sent to a boarding school, they were placed in widely separated dormitories. Peter's aggression toward Philip came to the surface in a shattering rejection of Philip as he sought to rid himself of his alter ego. Peter, using his charm and unbridled imagination, soon became the center of an admiring group from which he actively excluded his twin. When Philip also sought to gain prestige by fabricating stories, Peter exposed his lies and Philip was ridiculed. Philip who had always been loyal, felt betrayed and abandoned. Presently, he found a homosexual boy and became the passive partner of a pair who embraced and played with each other even in the presence of other boys. Philip was generally regarded as a "queer" and became an outcast. He was dropped from school at the end of two years ostensibly because of poor grades, but his overt homosexual behavior was, at least, equally important. Transferred to another school, Philip immediately formed a firm homosexual relationship with his new roommate and started to practice various perversions aside from mutual masturbation.

During their last summer vacation in boarding school, the twins went on a camping trip together with Philip's homosexual partner. Within a short time, Peter, who had not been overtly homosexual until then, sought to insert himself between his twin and his friend. His triumph became clear when he and the other boy went to bed together naked in Philip's presence. Philip cried inconsolably and the trip ended precipitously.

Peter's hostile acts did not disrupt their close relationship. Philip behaved like a rejected but adoring suitor, well aware that his homosexual attachments were substitutes for the relationship with Peter. The development of the homosexual defense against disorganization following the loss of his cardinal object relationship occurred relatively early in adolescence and was, in a sense, not ego-alien to Philip. Very early in childhood he had accepted the role of a passive partner who was incomplete without his twin, and, much as a wife might, lived to augment and complete Peter's life.

Philip did not gain admission to a select college as Peter did and he attended college in his home city. Without Peter around, the family found Philip to be pleasant, considerate, and quiet. He assumed a more parental role in the family, making decisions for his indecisive parents, and taking a firm hand with his mother. However, he began to dress himself as a girl and admire himself in the mirror, wishing and wondering whether he were developing breasts. He had thoughts that perhaps he might have female internal genitalia. He began to roam the streets dressed as a girl, or as a bum, to be picked up by men and willing "to do anything," to be kissed by them. When his twin became psychotic, such behavior not only became a dominating compulsion, but he insisted on telling his father (and as soon as possible, Peter) every sordid detail of his homosexual experiences. Several interesting motivations for these needs emerged in therapy.

While the twins' rivalry for their mother had been intense in early childhood, Philip had ceded her to Peter, needing and fearing Peter and identifying with him. As his father was a devalued and castrated figure whom the mother did not want as much as she did Peter, Philip's oedipal conflict revolved about his twin and mother as much or more than the parental relationship. With Peter away at college, the major figure that prevented recrudescence of his incestuous attachment was out of the way. He warded off his incestuous impulses and his castration fears by becoming a transvestite—a phallic woman and thereby denied the absence of a penis in the woman. Peter's collapse threatened his entire integration. When his mother now turned to Philip for completion, his fears heightened to verge upon panic. He not only feared Peter's wrath, but with Peter no longer mother's favorite, Peter no longer stood between him and fears of castration by the displaced father. He now had a great need to demonstrate to both his father and to Peter that he was a girl and had no designs upon his mother. The understanding of the transvestite, homosexual behavior also requires recognition of his wish to be a girl—in a continuing identification with his mother and as a complementary mate for Peter to retain their unity. During treatment he had a dream, which he interpreted as a wish to tell his twin: "You do not have to castrate me. I can hide my penis and be a wife to you." The failure to achieve a masculine identity was abetted because his father was a devalued figure, unwanted by the mother. The wish to be a girl led to fantasies of having female sexual organs that verged on the delusional.

Although Peter's difficulties and symptoms were similar to Philip's in many respects, they contained critical differences. Peter finished prep school with high academic and athletic honors and was fulfilling his mother's ambitions. He selected a college distant from home because of its prestige, but also to place distance between himself and his mother whose sexual seductiveness troubled him. He took with him to college a ventriloquist's dummy which he had learned to manipulate with unusual skill. He was a competent ventriloquist and amused his classmates by putting on "acts." The dummy was not consciously a substitute for Philip, but when it made him popular, as he had wished, he became jealous, destroyed it, and then grew lonely without it. He concentrated on gaining popularity, and his grades were poor. More serious difficulties started in his second year. With increasing frequency he suffered from "tension periods" which he sought to master by a system of ritualistic thinking combined with breathing and muscle control. He sought the correct mathematical formula for his system rather than questioning its validity. Masturbation became compulsive to gain relief from tension. He felt incomplete without Philip. At times he would sit in the library next to some boy who resembled Philip. While Philip had started his transvestite wandering, Peter, too, would wander about dressed as a bum—but he could never clarify this behavior and did not know why he pursued it. Some time during the year, he started a homosexual relationship with another boy named Peter.

During a school vacation Peter and his partner, Peter, took a long trip together with a third boy. In a striking repetition of the earlier vacation when Peter had stolen Philip's partner, the third boy took the homosexual partner away from him and now Peter was in Philip's position. He probably had been attempting to identify with Philip by selecting a partner named Peter, and loving the boy as he needed Philip's love, even as some homosexuals seek to love boys as they wish their mothers to love them. Following the rejection he now became paranoid toward his former boy friend, believing the boy was trying to destroy him. The classic pattern—I love him . . . I do not love him . . . I hate him because he persecuted me—was resounding against his own destructive behavior toward Philip, and his ambivalence toward his twin whom he was trying not to need and love (Freud, 1922).

We can discuss only certain critical problems confronting Peter. He emphasized his search for a substitute for his mother, his flight from her seductive wiles, and his terror of all women as overpowering and engulfing. Drawings made during his psychosis showed women with biting mouths and dentate vaginas, and intercourse as an anal-sadistic act. He felt lost with his twin at home pre-empting his mother's attention for the first time while he felt excluded and rejected by her admonitions that Philip was less selfish and self-centered. He was bitter toward his mother for basing her existence upon him, and he was contemptuous of his father. Heterosexuality was filled with terror for him, and homosexuality was not sufficiently ego syntonic with his previous dominant exhibitionistic and phallic trends. In contrast to Philip, Peter was not burdened by severe castration threats from his twin or his father. The greater danger remained preoedipal —of incorporation by the mother and loss of identity by remaining her phallus. The castration threat, one might say, came primarily from women—a fear that had strong roots in the reality of his relationship with his strange mother.

The twins' intrapsychic configuration differed at the time they became ill. Philip had attained a defensive equilibrium—albeit a highly tenuous, pathological, and dangerous one—through his feminine identification and transvestite role that neutralized the dangers from both parents and his twin, though it required compulsive acting out. Peter, however, struggled with a dilemma common in adolescents who become schizophrenic. He found himself a part of his mother, and the burden of achieving success to complete her life and her phallic strivings weighed heavily upon him. He was supposed to be a man and yet remain part of a woman. He was struggling for an identity discrete from her, and in this case from his twin as well. His mother's seductive behavior made him fearful of losing control of himself, and he feared being near her—and for similar reasons of being close to Philip. Now his mother's reversal in turning from him to Philip undermined the worth of his more masculine identity. He felt betrayed, and murderous impulses mingled with the incestuous, creating panic over loss of ego control. Needing constant admiration to support his failing narcissism, he regressively felt the need for his twin's adulation—and attempted to find a homosexual solution. The restitutive maneuver failed when he was rejected, even as he had rejected his twin. The rejection of his love was destroying him.

There were quite obviously many other important aspects in the family dynamics. Anality played an unusually prominent role in this family—but in this paper we cannot discuss the influence of the mother's sadistic and intrusive anal assaults on her twins upon their development of passive, homosexual, and masochistic fantasies.

While the basic problems of these twins are very much alike, we wish to emphasize the critical differences between them and how they seem to be clarified by the twins' positions in the family configuration. Raised as a unit and as rivals for their mother, they could not occupy the same space or role in the family, and established a complementarity by sharing the space. The nature of the pattern which evolved was greatly affected by the way in which mother identified them and reacted emotionally to them. Peter, because of birth priority, his greater constitutional vigor, or his phallic name, came to be preferred by the mother and identified with her aggressive, envied twin sister. Through him she would live out the dominant, aggressive role to which she had always aspired. Mother deliberately led both twins to be rebellious against authority, to consider themselves beyond rules, and to ignore their father. Without counteracting sources of a positive paternal identification, Peter was phallic, grandiose, antisocial, constantly needing admiration, and, when excluded by his twin and his mother, became homosexual in the pattern of seeking a boy to love as he wished to be loved. Philip, in contrast, identified by mother with herself, represented the passive and feminine aspects she despised in herself. In this role he could complement Peter, repress his own hostility, and lean upon him for leadership. He relinquished his mother to Peter and thus protected himself from her engulfment and Peter's hostility, and he could retain Peter as a love object. In his fantasies he was a girl, and his transvestite homosexuality was ego syntonic and protective. Philip's safety depended, however, upon having

Peter about as mother's favored object, and with Peter psychotic, Philip was in danger. Both twins, then, were still part of their mother, but each was identified with a different aspect of her, which, in turn, permitted a symbiotic ego structure between the twins.

We have, in this presentation, neglected the older brother of the twins. His situation was difficult and unenviable—rejected by his mother who wished to use him as she did the father as a pawn in preparing the way for her twin kings. He did not escape unscathed and had serious emotional problems, but his rejection by his mother made it easier for him to accept his hostility toward his obnoxious brothers and to differentiate from them and his bizarre mother. He was identified with the father who, despite the mother's opinion, had some positive values and at least a relatively stable integration.

DISCUSSION

Certain problems in ego development confronting identical twins, particularly those raised as a unit, noted in the review of the literature are clarified by this study. Perhaps, they stand in sharp relief because of the pathology of this family, including the mother's efforts to compensate for her own ego deficiencies arising from her own development as a twin.

1. Identical twins seem disposed to develop symbiotically without adequate ego boundaries between them. Initially, at least, each has difficulty in differentiating his own behavior, thoughts, and wishes from those of his twin. The developing ego also responds to needs and drives in the twin as well as within the self. Whereas every child must differentiate the self from the mother, such twins have the additional problem of differentiating from the co-twin.

2. A primary object relationship is established with a person who is not different but a mirror image and with whom most experiences are shared. Problems of narcissism become accentuated, and love of the object remains self-love. As the object reacts much the same as the self, it becomes more difficult to differentiate the internal motive from the external, and, in a sense, reality from fantasy. Relating to other persons less empathic than the twin is hindered or blocked. The narcissistic object choice imposed upon the child would seem to heighten homoerotic trends.

3. No matter what efforts are made to treat twins as one person, and this case forms a rather extreme example, they cannot be one, and differentiation and separation are inevitable, however painful or unwelcome they may be. In the effort to occupy a single place within the family and particularly with the mother, a complementarity develops. The twins divide roles. One is apt to become more dominant and the other more passive. In our example, we have indicated that the role relations established by the mother and with her also patterned the complementary roles of the twins with each other, and they each identified with different aspects of the same mother. Here, as in many other twins, the initial rivalry for the mother led to hostility between the twins, which was resolved by the passive twin ceding to the aggressive twin, thus gaining security by denying masculinity, but furthering the passive homosexual attachment and aborting resolution of the oedipal conflict. The hostility is repressed but reappears in jealous rivalries when either twin forms a new relationship, because the bond to the co-twin remains narcissistic and symbiotic. It does not become a true object relationship like the affectional bond between father and son that occurs in an ideal resolution of the oedipal situation.

4. Because of identical or complementary expectations from parents, the sharing of the resolution of the oedipal situation, and the division of roles between them, the superego structure of each twin tends to remain incomplete. Behavioral standards and expectations for the self depend upon response of the twin rather than being properly incorporated as a self-controlling structure. Ego ideals may be followed that fit the partial identity of the twin, and a pattern that requires complementing by another.

We believe that the use of twins to study the etiology and psychopathology of emotional disorders—which has focused largely upon genetic factors in the past—requires consideration of such special problems of ego development in twins and their ensuing vulnerabilities.

In closing, we wish to note that the problems of homosexuality and homosexual panic, linked with paranoid schizophrenia since Freud's study (1911) of the Schreber case, cannot be considered separately from problems of incest and incest panic, which often ushers in the schizophrenic break, or separately from the hypochondriacal delusions involving change in sex that Macalpine and Hunter (1953) stressed in their review of the Schreber case. Incest and homosexuality are often two sides of the same coin—narcissistic problems in which love of the self, love of someone undifferentiated from the self, and love of someone like the self are not clearly differentiated—but this interrelationship and its roots in the family interaction are the topic of another study (see Chapter XIII).

XIII

Incestuous and Homosexual Problems

(1958)

The critical import of incestuous problems in the onset, symptoms, and therapeutic management of youthful schizophrenic patients has become increasingly apparent. We have come to anticipate the patient's fear that incestuous impulses will overwhelm the ego leading to panic, further withdrawal or intensification of rigid defenses. Often the patient, particularly the male patient, will fluctuate between incestuous and homosexual concerns and fantasies. Several striking examples indicated that the patient's incestuous preoccupations were based upon tangible difficulties in their relationships with their parents. We therefore turned to the sixteen patients in our study to clarify the issue. In at least half of these patients, judging conservatively, incest problems were critical. When the patient's difficulties are viewed against the family setting rather than simply intrapsychically, these problems like many schizophrenic symptoms gain new meaning and a more tangible etiology.

We are not concerned here with actual incest which various authors have noted as an occasional traumatic factor in the lives of schizophrenic patients. However, the incidence of incest in schizophrenic patients, like that of other pathological events, rises when attention is focused upon it. In another series of seventeen consecutively admitted schizophrenic patients, pertinent inquiry only on admission disclosed that four of these patients had had incestuous

Stephen Fleck, Theodore Lidz, Alice R. Cornelison, Sarah Schafer, and Dorothy Terry: The Intrafamilial Environment of the Schizophrenic Patient: Incestuous and Homosexual Problems. In Individual and Familial Dynamics, *edited by Jules H. Masserman. Copyright © 1959, Grune & Stratton, New York. This paper was presented in part at the annual meeting of the Academy of Psychoanalysis, May, 1958.*

relations (Endicott, 1958). As far as we know, actual parent-child incest did not occur in any of our cases, but a social class variable may be involved here as almost all of our patients belong to the upper economic classes. On the other hand, we are not referring simply to personality distortions traceable to faulty resolution of oedipal problems. We are considering here the continuation of incestuous wishes or strivings in late adolescence and adult life, or the regressive reappearance of such wishes coming into conscious conflict with the intense incest taboo.

CASE ILLUSTRATIONS

The area of interest may perhaps best be clarified by an illustration. Bill Forel, a twenty-year-old schizophrenic youth with vagrant tendencies and grandiose delusions, had at the age of eleven lost his father who had been a maternal, affectionate figure to him. Bill tried to convey his dilemma about being near his mother to his therapist approximately as follows. When his mother drinks too heavily she becomes softhearted, affectionate, and unrestrained in contrast to her usual cold and preoccupied attitude. At these times Bill feels that she wants to engulf him, perhaps to eat him up, or she kisses him in a revolting sort of way. He becomes tight inside, experiences an unbearable tension, and must get away. He goes out for a walk, seeking relief. A feeling goes all through his body. He does not ejaculate, but it is a sexual feeling which like an orgasm reaches a pitch and becomes so unpleasant that it is unbearable. Still, it would be a pleasant feeling if directed toward a young and pretty girl. At such times he must exert extreme control because he feels that if he let himself go it would end in his having intercourse with his mother. When sober, his mother acts like a stranger. He prefers this for he can then feel comfortable in her presence, but when he gets those sexual feelings he cannot stay near her. He notes his comfort with his therapist because he feels that his therapist, in contrast to his mother, has control of himself and will not let anything happen if the patient should lose control.

The occurrence of such incestuous preoccupations in schizophrenic patients has long been recognized and understood in such terms as a concomitant of the regression to an intense preoedipal attachment to one parent or the other, or as evidence of the constitutional ego weakness with inability to cathect boundaries between the self and others (Szasz, 1957). We learn, however, from Bill's older brother who is not psychotic that he too became very uneasy around his mother because of her seductive fondling and unmotherly kissing, and that when he would seek to get away, or became angry with her because of her neglect of his invalided father, she would seek to woo him back and pacify him by becoming even more amorous. The brother had been disturbed to find shortly after he married that he would awaken from dreams uncertain whether he was in bed with his wife or his mother. And when, for example, during her first interview, the mother of another young man tells the social worker, "He is not just part of my life, he is all of my life. Why, when he became upset, I slept with him just like man and wife," there is reason to consider that the schizophrenic patient's concerns with incest are based on more than his own regressive propensities or his restitutive efforts.

Incestuous problems are not being presented as etiological of schizophrenia but as a focal issue in the patient's faulty ego structure and sexual identity which are related to the seriously disturbed family settings in which schizophrenic patients have grown up. Although incestuous problems are common among schizophrenic patients, we do not know whether they occur in all such patients, and, of course, conscious incestuous concerns can occur in other types of patients. However, Glueck (1957) studying sex delinquents in general found that those who had been involved in incest all belonged to the most disturbed group labeled "schizo-adaptive," and Weinberg (1955) who surveyed 203 court cases involving incest concluded that the problem cannot exist without serious family disorganization, and family disorganization also appears to be a prerequisite for the appearance of schizophrenia in an offspring.

These and still other issues are interrelated with the topic isolated for purposes of presentation here. Homosexuality in particular, implicated in the etiology of schizophrenia ever since Freud's (1911) study of the Schreber case, seems to be intimately related to the problem of incest; at times they seem almost like two sides of the same coin. A thorough discussion of the interrelationship would involve consideration of some fundamental psychoanalytic concepts and we shall here simply indicate the nature of the relationship by noting that both are narcissistic problems in which love of the self, love of someone like the self, and love of someone undifferentiated from the self are apt to be quite confused. This state is to be anticipated in a schizophrenic patient with poor ego boundaries between the self and a parent, often a parent who also has poor ego boundaries and an uncertain sexual identity (Chapter II).[1] While active seductive or incestuous interplay may be limited to one parent and one child, the other members and especially the other parent almost always participate, at least by their passivity or denial (Chapter XII; Parsons, 1954; Weinberg, 1955).

Flugel (1921) and Parsons (1954), Parsons and Bales (1955) have studied the family from a psychoanalytic orientation and both stress that a precarious balance exists between the erotic bonds essential to the cohesiveness of the nuclear family and the normal development of the children, as against incestuous impulses that are disorganizing for the family and its members. Thus, the de-erotization or at least desexualization of the child-parent attachment is one of the cardinal family functions. The fate of the oedipal situation holds its central position in psychiatry because it is here, in particular, that the developing child traverses a knife edge with potential disaster on both sides. On the one side, his development will be stunted and distorted unless he receives affectionate love—one might say, erotically motivated parental love—during the preoedipal periods. On the other side, the erotic quality of his attachment must gradually be frustrated and the child-parent love freed of sexuality in preparation for the latency period. We believe that this process depends not on biological subsidence of erotic drives, but on the child's finding a reasonably conflict-free place in the family, with his position in relation to both parents established and his identity as a childhood member of his sex accepted.

When a parent, particularly the mother, needs to gain affectional and erotic satisfaction predominantly from the parent-child relation-

[1] The re-evaluation of the Schreber case by Macalpine and Hunter (1953) with its emphasis upon hypochondriacal delusions related to ideas of physical transformation into the opposite sex does not contradict the homosexual hypothesis but rather places emphasis on another aspect of the patient's uncertainties concerning sexual identity.

ship rather than from the marital relationship and promotes uncontrolled erotization of the bond to the child, the essential frustration of the child required for satisfactory resolution of the oedipal relationships cannot occur. Other serious deficiencies in the essential family structure and in the filling of the paternal and maternal roles also open the way for incestuous tendencies. In particular, marked violations of the boundaries between the generations will disrupt the imperative structure that holds incestuous trends in check, as when one parent is more of a child than a spouse to the other parent, or a rival with a child, or when a child is used as an emotional substitute for a spouse as noted above. Other failures of parents to fill their essential roles can also court trouble, for instance, when the mother is cold and unyielding, thus pushing a daughter toward the father, or when the father is passive and ineffectual and so fails to strengthen the repression of the son's oedipal wishes. Schismatic differences between parents when each seeks to undercut the other and win the child away from the spouse can permit the child to feel that he is more important to one parent or the other than is the spouse. When one or both parents are psychotic or borderline schizophrenic, the parent may have difficulty in establishing clear ego boundaries between himself and the child, and the child's progression from narcissistic love to object love is impeded because of the difficulty in differentiating the parent's needs from his own. As all of these circumstances are prominent findings in families of schizophrenic patients, one might anticipate that failures of essentials for the resolution or the repression of oedipal strivings would lead to incestuous trends in schizophrenic patients. When incestuous impulses remain or become more or less conscious, they further upset the balance of the family; other distortions of the family life and of the personality structure of its members will follow upon the need to avoid infringement of the strong taboo.

How such family situations can foster incestuous ties and fears as well as homosexual proclivities was illustrated in Chapter XII concerned with the Nebb twins, both of whom were seriously troubled by fantasies of incest with their mother and by impulses toward homosexual incest with each other. Mrs. Nebb had clearly been unable to establish boundaries between herself and her twin sons, was flagrantly seductive with them, and taught them that they were all-important, whereas their father was a dull man who meant little to her. This mother, it will be recalled, often slept with her sons well into their adolescence, bathed them, and gave them enemas in a highly sexualized manner in which she was the intrusive aggressor. Mr. Nebb's inability to fill the roles of husband or father further opened the way for incestuous fantasies and strivings and for confusions of sexual identity in the twins.

Another clear example is provided by the family relationships of Dora Nussbaum. Dora had been hospitalized after lengthy analytically oriented therapy and an even longer period of increasing disorganization which included episodes of impulsive sexual acting out. She had shouted in public that her father wanted to rape her. Dora had conscious incestuous fantasies, and suffered periods of panicky concern that incest might occur. When, for example, her father had sat on her bed in the hospital when she had the flu, Dora had jumped up, fled from the room, and immediately had become more disorganized.

The Nussbaums' marriage had been marred from its inception by their discrepant personalities and by their intense conflicting loyalties to their respective parental families. Mr. Nussbaum was highly narcissistic, needing demonstrative affection and given to gregariousness and effeminate flashiness. His wife was aloof, penurious, and a rather misanthropic woman with a vituperative tongue and given to marked depressive mood swings. Her primary emotional attachments remained with her own family, especially one sister. She was proud of her oldest child, a boy, and very attentive to him. Before the birth of the patient, four years later, the Nussbaums became emotionally estranged because of a conflict between their families in which Mr. Nussbaum's brother was accused of business dealings that led to the suicide of Mrs. Nussbaum's father. The couple became deeply resentful toward each other, and though they continued to live together, the marriage became a hostile encounter in which constant open conflict was avoided by mutual withdrawal and silence. Mrs. Nussbaum suffered an injury to her neck when Dora was born, and the infant's care was left to a maid. Later, Mrs. Nussbaum attempted to be a good mother but became impatient with the child, and, as her own unhappiness increased, she became increasingly critical and hostile. When

Dora's behavior became very trying after the age of twelve, the mother expressed her frank hatred. When Dora left for college, her mother reputedly said, "I hope you come home in a coffin." In contrast, Mr. Nussbaum turned to his daughter and lavished affection upon her with much physical demonstrativeness, to his wife's great disgust. He would hug and kiss Dora excessively and often lie on her bed until she went to sleep. When Dora awakened at night frightened, she would get into her father's bed until she learned the facts of life and feared that she would become pregnant. As she became ill in adolescence, the father would frequently comfort her by holding her in his arms until she went to sleep.

Mr. Nussbaum was highly critical of his wife, letting his daughter know that he had little regard for her mother. He insisted for some years that there was nothing really wrong with Dora but only with his wife. Indeed, Mrs. Nussbaum must have been profoundly disturbed at times, expressing extreme hopelessness about Dora's behavior, telling the girl she wished she were dead and suggesting dual suicide. The family situation was further aggravated because Mr. Nussbaum avoided his family problems by spending most evenings in his office, encouraging his wife and daughter to think he was having an affair. However, as he was impotent, or said he was, the fictional mistress served not only to aggravate his wife but also to bolster his narcissism. Despite his intense feelings that his wife was rejecting and destructive to Dora, he assumed little real responsibility himself.

These are fairly typical illustrations of the intrafamilial environments of schizophrenic patients with incestuous problems in the research series of upper- and upper-middle-class families: the Nebb family on the bizarre side, and the Nussbaum family less dramatic than most; but both were among the more intact families and neither included overtly schizophrenic mothers or paranoid fathers as is the case in some of our other families. These families which raise an offspring who develops the most serious psychiatric illness fail to provide directives for repressing incestuous interests. Thus, they fail in one of the fundamental tasks of families. The taboo against parent-child incest is among the most intense and universal taboos. The Anlage for incest exists in every family in the erotically toned parent-child attachment, but its progression into an incestuous bond would not only disrupt the structure of societies based on kinship systems, it also would threaten the existence of the nuclear family in all societies, prevent the child from channeling energies into socializing activities, interfere with peer relationships, and block his emergence as an adult. The prevention of incest does not, however, ordinarily rest on conscious evocation of the taboo. The family structure and distribution of essential roles contain the requisites which normally keep incestuous trends from invading consciousness. When conscious avoidance of incest becomes necessary because of defective family structure and role confusion, the personalities of the family members become further distorted because spontaneity becomes impossible and role conflict inevitable. We do not believe that we have fallen into a circular argument. When we examine Talcott Parson's (1954) analysis of factors essential in family structure for the preservation of the incest taboo, we find them to be notably lacking in these families. We shall concentrate, therefore, on these deficiencies of family structure and interaction rather than on the intrapersonal pathology of its members.

DISCUSSION

The family is a special type of small group; it is an organic unity with certain structural requisites and imperative functions which, if distorted, will seriously affect the functioning of its members and the personalities of the emergent generation. The family is also a unit in that the action of any member affects all members. Unless all find reciprocally interrelating roles within the unit, role conflict ensues. Its structure and functions are dictated in part by biological imperatives and in part by social mores and needs. Two biological givens establish the family's framework. It is divided into two generations and into two sexes.The parents, having grown up in two different families, seek to merge themselves and their backgrounds into a new unit which satisfies both their needs and completes their personalities. They serve as leaders, educators, and models for their offspring who gain the essentials of group living by learning how to fit into this family. Yet, in contrast to the parental generation, the children must learn to live within the family and yet become capable of emerging from it. The parents subserve different family functions according to sex and transmit these sexually linked roles to their offspring through their behavior. In a general way, the father's functions are more instrumental (i.e., concerned with the family's well-being in society) and the mother's more expressive (i.e., concerned with intrafamilial interaction and the affectional relationships of its members). However, the parents must act in coalition, united by their marital attachments and needs for complementarity in providing for themselves and their offspring. Deficiencies or aberrations in the sex-linked roles of parents, or in the parents' sexual identities, can sometimes be absorbed by role shifts as far as the parents are concerned, but gross distortions jeopardize the sexual identity of the offspring.

We have mentioned only a few of the requisites of family functions and organization. We shall now focus on the severe deficiencies in the maintenance of essential boundaries between generations, in the parental coalition, in the fulfillment of maternal and paternal roles, in the parents' basic sexual identities, and in effecting sociocultural integration of the family unit. All these deficiencies have been important findings in the families we have studied. They are often so interrelated that they cannot be kept isolated even for purposes of discussion.

The Generation Boundaries

The obvious and chronic sexual seductiveness of a parent that was apparent in the illustrative cases was just as flagrant in several other instances. Here a parent's need for affectional and erotic gratification was being served rather than the child's need for a close and erotic bond to the parents during the preoedipal period. The child's erotic attachment was fostered and continued into adolescence rather than being frustrated to permit the child to enter the latency phase. Even in the two cases involving female patients where frank sexual seductiveness was not overt, the basic family configuration was the same as in the Nussbaum case. Their mothers had been aloof from the patients and husbands. They were highly neurotic or borderline psychotic women and were also very restricting and controlling. The fathers were clearly narcissistic, requiring constant bolstering of their masculinity in the form of admiration and implicit obedience from their wives. The marriages were highly schismatic almost from inception with each spouse derogating the other to the children. The father wooed the daughter to his side of the conflict, and sought in her the admiring woman he needed but could not find in his wife. The patient learned early that she was more important to the father than his wife, and sensed his need for erotic gratification from her. She was aware that she could widen the breach between her parents and gain the father for herself. One of these patients suggested that the solution to her problems and those of the family was to split up. She would live with her father and her sister with her mother. When the father of the other patient suggested an identical solution, the patient emerged briefly from her catatonic muteness to state, "I'll do anything my father wants, but he can't have me that way." Such use of a child to replace a spouse by a parent whose own affectional and erotic needs are poorly controlled constitutes a most flagrant violation of the boundaries between generations and courts disaster.

The parents are supposed to be guides and educators who both foster growth and set limits. They must serve as objects for identification and as models of love objects who can be relinquished as the child grows from the family into society. Further, when there is confusion between the generations, it inevitably fosters conflict in the role relationships between the family because no two persons can simultaneously occupy the same position. As can be noted in the illustrative cases, there were other breaches in the boundaries between the two generations as well: Rivalry of a parent with a child, one parent behaving as a child of the spouse rather than as a parent, abdication of decision-making for the family to a child, etc.; all contributed to the difficulties in one family or the other. However, the use of the child to complete the life of a parent, particularly the erotic needs of the parent, disrupts the entire familial pattern of a generation that leads and one that follows, one that educates and one that is educated, one that gives from maturity to enable the child to grow and the other that assimilates in order to mature.

The Parental Coalition

There were various reasons why parents sought gratification and fulfillment through a child, including the serious psychopathology of a parent such as Mrs. Nebb, who could not establish boundaries between herself and her twins. Mrs. Narab, the schizophrenic mother of a schizophrenic youth with severe incestuous fears, resumed her artistic pursuits at our suggestion. She became upset when she recognized her painting of a mother caring for her sick son turning into a picture of a mother having intercourse with her son. However, in every case the parental coalition and the parents' mutuality in relation to the child who became ill were not simply deficient, but had degenerated into disregard, contempt or overt hatred, with one parent undermining the worth and authority of the other. Each parent was left without emotional support in carrying out role functions, and without a source of erotic gratification from the marital relationship. Thus deprived, such parents are prone to turn to the relationship with a child for fulfillment. Then, too, the child who should be confronted with the fact that each parent's primary emotional and erotic attachment is to the other parent can instead seek to widen the gulf between the parents rather than learn frustration of erotic attachments and cede one parent to the other. Cessation of the child's sexualized attachment need not occur under these circumstances. When it does, the motivation is conscious fear of revenge or the child's projected hostility rather than through experiencing the necessary frustration ameliorated by affection which can lead to early identification with the parent of the same sex and strengthen the child's superego and sexual identity. But when the child is used to gratify a parent's needs, a symbiotic relationship can develop in which the child continues in an object relationship that is essentially narcissistic for both. The child feels undifferentiated from the parent and the sexual strivings are incestuous, not moving toward another discrete person but remaining, in infantile fashion, bound to the parent who is part of him.

The Parental Roles

The family equilibrium was also disturbed in every instance because the fathers of the schizophrenic sons and the mothers of schizophrenic daughters failed in their paternal or maternal roles either because of severe psychiatric illness, or because they were the devalued partner in the marriage, or sometimes both. When the father fails to fill the instrumental leadership role and is instead another child to the mother or acts the part of a defeated castrated husband, as did Mr. Nebb, the son can disregard him as a rival for the mother. Here, the fear of retaliative castration from the father does not operate to repress the oedipal strivings. Rather, observation of the father's plight can lead to fear of castration or engulfment by the mother which increases trends toward homosexuality. When, as with the Nussbaum family, the mother is cold and unyielding and a rival to the daughter, a girl has little reason to appease the mother to retain her as a love object. She is pushed by the mother to the more femininely oriented father. Another type of parental role failure occurred in some families in that the center of gravity lay outside the nuclear family because the parents' primary attachments and the center of their interests lay in their own parental families. The parents' dependence on their siblings, particularly the homoerotically tinged attachment of a mother to her sister, as occurred in the Nebb family, the Nussbaum family and others, deprived the spouse and in some instances the child as well of these parents' primary attention and affection.

The Sexual Identity of the Parents

Related to role failure but more difficult to establish and discuss briefly is the matter of a parent's insecurity in his or her sexual identity. A satisfactory identification as a member of one's own sex in a parent seems essential in order to serve as an adequate model of a primary love object or an identification model to a child. We have a distinct impression that in all the families in which clear-cut incestuous problems existed, either the father had strong feminine or homosexual tendencies, or the mother sought phallic completion from a son and had little interest in a daughter. The parents' respective homoerotic tendencies may well have contributed to the choice of a marital partner. The child is caught in a serious dilemma when needed to redress the imbalance created in the family organization by the defective sexual identity of a parent. Such parents are apt to gain satisfaction by identifying with a child of the opposite sex, as seemed to be the case with Mrs. Nebb and with Mr. Nussbaum. The parent may then also gain vicarious pleasure from the sexual behavior of the child.

Such considerations are also pertinent to the problem of homosexuality. Mr. Benjamin, for example, the father of a boy with intense fears of incest, seemed to identify with his son homosexually. Relatively impotent and unable to gratify his wife, Mr. Benjamin often spoke as if the boy should sleep with his mother. He would suggest, for example, that the boy would be helped by sleeping with a movie star and then specifically named an actress whom he had repeatedly said resembled his wife. He had also shown homosexual seductiveness toward the son by taking showers with him, comparing genitalia, massaging him in his bath, etc. When one of his friends who he knew was a homosexual visited over week ends, Mr. Benjamin permitted him to share a room with his adolescent son, and he took no stand when this man made advances to the boy. In this case, the father's faulty sexual identity had many other repercussions including the failure to maintain the separation between the generations, a confusion in the assumption of a parental role, the father's primary attachment to an older sister who dominated this family, constant quarrels between the couple with mutual disparagement, as well as many other problems not immediately germane to this paper such as the construction of highly irrational defenses by the father to protect his pseudo masculinity.[2]

Sociocultural Isolation of the Family

Because the children must emerge from the family into the larger society, the family milieu must in many ways reflect the cultural setting. Stated another way, the family must be sufficiently in harmony with its social environment to enable the child to emancipate himself. Our families often fall short of this prerequisite, although the parents may as individuals function adequately and even successfully in jobs and in the community. However, as a family group, they remain

[2] Such problems are not uncommon in these families. The Nebb twins, Narab sons, and Daryl Lamb all considered their fathers to have homosexual tendencies, and our attention has been drawn to the homosexual interests of some mothers of schizophrenic daughters.

relatively isolated from other groups, and this is particularly true of the eight families with the most severe incest problems.

It is possible that we are faced with a circular situation: sociocultural isolation may promote incestuous trends in a quasi-closed system whose inner shaky equilibrium would be disturbed intolerably if the family group were to interact with other groups. On the other hand, the existence of incestuous problems together with the family's other prestige-endangering vicissitudes could lead to their encapsulation. So far our material seems to point to the marital problems between two disturbed partners (how ever well they may function outside the family as individuals) as the primary link in a chain of events which gets further complicated by the arrival of children who become enmeshed in the pathological parental interaction. Incest is only one facet in the development of this drama.

This condensed presentation of an extremely complex topic can offer only an impression of our approach and thinking about the subject. It is hoped that at least three points have been conveyed: (1) that problems of incest are extremely important to the understanding and treatment of many, if not most, schizophrenic patients; (2) that incestuous impulses cannot be understood simply as a symptom of schizophrenia—as a symptom of regression, restitution, or of blurring of ego boundaries due to constitutional ego weakness. The material indicates the continuing interactional nature of the incestuous tie to a parent; (3) the incestuous problems indicate serious family deviations as well as individual psychopathology. These families which produce schizophrenic offspring suffer flaws in family structure conducive to the provocation of incestuous trends which are so alien to the functioning of the nuclear family and to the socialization of children that they are banned by the most widespread and intense taboo of mankind.

In closing we wish to indicate the importance of incestuous problems in the development or onset of schizophrenic reactions.

1. The patient does not become a distinctive individual with needs and impulses clearly differentiated from those of the parent. He instead subserves the needs of a parent, and the establishment of clear ego boundaries is hindered.

2. The patient's emergence from the primary object relationships

is blocked, with energies tied to the parent rather than freed for extrafamilial socialization and for learning processes.

3. The schizophrenic patient's tendency to sexualize all object relationships may well rest on the absence of experiences where he is being forced to desexualize his primary object relationship to a parent, be it the parent of the same or of the opposite sex.

4. The incestuous concerns can lead to panic because of fear of being overwhelmed by the forbidden incestuous urge with ensuing punishment by the self and others for infraction of this basic taboo.

5. The patient cannot regain security by regression to a dependent position on the parents because it is proximity to the parents that is feared. The regression must either be profound to the earliest pre-oedipal periods or be accompanied by withdrawal maneuvers.

XIV

Schizophrenic Patients and Their Siblings

(1961)

The question has been raised repeatedly: If the family milieu is critical for the production of schizophrenia in a particular offspring, if it exerts a serious pathogenic influence upon this child, what about the siblings? Why are they not affected?

We designed our entire intensive study of the families of patients around this question, selecting only families in which the schizophrenic child had at least one sibling who could be studied. This permitted a comparison of the patients with persons who were not schizophrenic but who had been raised by the same parents and exposed to many similar intrafamilial influences. The siblings rather than some other arbitrarily selected persons form a comparative group—and we are pointedly avoiding the term *controls*, since we do not believe that a true control series can be established in this type of study.

Of course, we do not aspire to a definitive answer, for if the question of why one child in a family rather than another becomes schizophrenic could be answered, the cause of schizophrenia would be virtually found. Genetic investigations, despite the impressive findings of twin studies, have thus far failed to produce evidence for either a dominant or a recessive trait. Their failure may be due to primary reliance upon hospital records and the incidence of overt and flagrant schizophrenia. The contribution of the various genetic studies has recently been reviewed by Jackson (1960), and currently Rosenthal (1959, 1960) is carefully examining their methodologies and findings.

Theodore Lidz, Stephen Fleck, Yrjö O. Alanen, and Alice R. Cornelison: Schizophrenic Patients and Their Siblings. Psychiatry, *Vol. 26, 1963, pp. 1-18.* Copyright © *1963, The William Alanson White Psychiatric Foundation, Inc.*

The evidence indicates that extragenetic influences play a very significant role. The scrutiny of our data can help clarify the problem, particularly along two lines: (1) by noting the incidence of serious psychopathological conditions among the siblings; (2) by examining the differences in the intrafamilial influences impinging upon the siblings within a family with particular reference to (a) the changes in family circumstances and intrafamilial role relationships that alter the conditions under which siblings are raised; (b) the mother's capacities to provide affectionate nurturant care to the various siblings during infancy; (c) the different role allocations and role assumptions of the children in the family dynamics; (d) how the parental personalities and the configuration of their relationship lead children of one sex to be confronted by greater developmental problems than children of the opposite sex; (e) idiosyncratic problems; and (f) the influence of the siblings upon one another.

Comparing the intrafamilial factors influencing the schizophrenic patient with those affecting his siblings obviously presents difficulties. The investigators are aware of the bias that can arise from the knowledge that one sibling is schizophrenic and another is not. As the difficulty is inherent in the study, nothing could be done except to take it into account. Another problem is that an intensive study including all family members could not encompass a large sample, and unless the study was intensive, it could not expect to gain meaningful answers. In the sixteen families the various combinations and sequences of brothers and sisters were limited, and some factors of potential pertinence require study of various permutations of gender and sequential placement within the family. Another limitation arises in presenting the material. It is difficult to compare the developmental situations of the siblings briefly, for the material is inordinately complex and properly would require a thorough exposition of each family.

The "Normal" Sibling

Any intent to compare the development of the schizophrenic patient with that of "normal" siblings had to be modified greatly for the simple but incontrovertible reason that only a small minority of the siblings could be considered reasonably well adjusted. While normality cannot be readily defined, everyone who has examined the material has been struck by the serious personality problems of the siblings as a group. The sixteen patients have a total of twenty-four siblings. Only five or six of the siblings are making reasonably adequate adjustments, and of these only three are considered well adjusted, even if the assessments are slanted favorably.[1] Examining the siblings for the presence of serious psychopathology, we find that three are clinically schizophrenic and another six or seven, including one who is a severe psychopathic personality, are making borderline and very tenuous adjustments. The remaining eight or nine siblings suffer from a variety of clinical neuroses, acting-out tendencies, and psychosomatic ailments, alone or in combination, for which four had required psychiatric treatment prior to the time of study (see Figure 1).

FIGURE 1

RANGE OF ADJUSTMENT OF 24 SIBLINGS OF SCHIZOPHRENIC PATIENTS

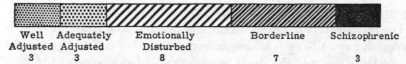

Well Adjusted	Adequately Adjusted	Emotionally Disturbed	Borderline	Schizophrenic
3	3	8	7	3

The listing of psychiatric diagnoses for the siblings would serve little. The range and severity of their problems can be illustrated by citing the problems of the children in the two families with the largest number of siblings. By chance, one contained four sons and the other four daughters. In the Schwartz family, the youngest son was the patient, a paranoid schizophrenic with delusions that people were against him, accusing him of homosexuality. His oldest brother was a severe sociopath, an embezzler, forger, and gambler. The second son had been disturbed in adolescence and may have been transiently delusional in early adult life, but had become a successful mathematician and had moved far away from the family and its problems. The third son was seriously phobic, suffered from anxiety, and was unable to practice his profession, although he managed to hold a routine job and to marry, living with his wife in the parental home.

[1] Margaret Thaler Singer, in an unpublished investigation, estimated the stability of fourteen siblings of eleven schizophrenic patients through a study of their projective tests. She considered four to be constricted normals, five as moderately or severely neurotic, and five as clearly schizoid or latently schizophrenic.

The second daughter in the Thomas family had been schizophrenic for many years, the most chronic and withdrawn patient in the series. Her older sister had been in analysis for several years because of serious and diffuse emotional and marital difficulties. The third daughter, who also was in psychiatric treatment, had severe marital problems, had a violent temper, and felt chronically frustrated, tending to be highly suspicious of the motives of others. The youngest sister had withdrawn from the family and had married. She refused to use her inherited wealth, tying herself down to her housework and children in a bizarre, obsessive manner, maintaining a very precarious balance. She is a borderline or ambulatory schizophrenic.

While the nonschizophrenic personality disorders of the siblings may be of little interest to those who consider schizophrenia to be a clearly circumscribed disease entity, or to those seeking a predominantly genetic etiology, these disorders have pertinence to psychiatrists who entertain the hypothesis that schizophrenia is related to deviant personality development. If the intrafamilial transactions play a major role in shaping the personality of the offspring raised within the family, each child in these seriously disturbed families may well be affected in different ways and to differing degrees, and not all need reach the extreme of a schizophrenic reaction.

The personality problems of the siblings will receive further scrutiny during the discussion of the influences affecting their development within their families. However, two defensive maneuvers, marked constriction and flight from the family, require special comment because they were strikingly characteristic, particularly of the siblings who had made reasonably good adaptations.

Of the four best adjusted siblings, only one, a girl who had two psychotic brothers, seemed reasonably free and imaginative. The other three, as well as many of the more disturbed siblings, suffered from marked constriction of their personalities with notable limitations in their range of emotional maturity, their perceptiveness, and the use of their intellectual resources.[2] A sibling may, for example,

[2] Margaret Thaler Singer has also emphasized personality constriction as a major defense of siblings of schizophrenic patients from her unpublished study of the projective tests of a series investigated at the National Institute of Mental Health by Lyman Wynne and his coworkers.

successfully pursue a scientific career that requires minimal interpersonal awareness and remain relatively impoverished in other areas. The constricted personality usually utilizes the defense of isolation to prevent recognition of the extent of the intrafamilial difficulties, for facing the total situation would be shattering. In some, whole periods of the past have been completely repressed and particularly traumatic experiences have produced amnesias. In the investigation, where intensive therapy could not be offered the siblings, such defenses had to be respected as essential to the sibling's ego integrity.

A sister of a young schizophrenic woman had managed to avoid involvement in the parental conflict in which her sister had been enmeshed, carefully placating both parents.[3] She was a relatively poor informant about the family, insisting that she could remember very little about her childhood, or even about many recent occurrences. She went on to explain that life in her family had been so painful that she had taught herself very early in childhood to think as little as possible about the family's quarrels, never letting herself review a day's happenings. She tried to concentrate upon avoiding trouble, pleasing her parents, and doing well at school until she could leave for college and lead her own life. She did not consciously know how she felt about her strange and difficult parents. While we have counted this young woman among the more stable siblings—indeed the most stable sibling of the same sex as the patient—Margaret Thaler Singer, who interpreted the projective tests of the members of this family without any knowledge about them, wrote the following excerpt:

To coin a phrase, this girl is "her parents' child." One can see the impact of their communication styles upon her. She uses fragmented remarks, tells a story [on the TAT], then takes it back saying that she didn't find a meaning! Nothing gets validated and confirmed. She often describes interactions as rather pointless, fragmented affairs which she then denies. . . . people are not responsible for their own wrongdoings . . . children might need their attention brought back to concrete realities—they are seen as inattentive and drifting—people in general are not good, and interactions hardly ever lead to anything pleasant. She is more than willing to leave crazily incompatible acts hanging together as if they made sense or were

[3] More detailed data concerning this young woman can be found in Chapter VIII.

sequitors. . . . Men are seen in very poor light. . . . Mother is not seen in a positive way at all. On one card she told no story at all where a mother is usually seen. In another two stories the wife poisons the husband. . . .

Thus the projective tests bore out the clinical impression that this woman had managed to deal with potentially serious disturbance by constriction, isolation, and denial.

One of the most successful siblings, the brother of a schizophrenic girl, had knowingly or unknowingly gratified his parents' ambitions for him by choosing a wealthy spouse and becoming a capable physician. He was pleasant and affable, but communicated little of pertinence. Singer, again without knowledge of the subject, stated, on the basis of the projective tests:

He is obsessive. He has learned from his father to take an intellectual position and try to seem detached. On the Sentence Completion Test he talks of viruses, chemistry, Beethoven, pharmaceutics, and politics. He senses he is nonrevealing and unimaginative. . . . He is repudiating imagination and fantasy . . . particularly on the TAT where he says things are a . . . matter of course . . . innocuous . . . status quo . . . nothing drastic . . . just a passing thing . . . no outcome . . . just simply another thing, etc. He has learned the Pollyanna-like style both his parents have. . . .

Although personality constriction was prominent in the siblings in this study, we know that some siblings of schizophrenic patients are reasonably stable and also highly sensitive and productive. A number of outstanding authors have had schizophrenic siblings, and some have apparently abreacted their traumatic lives in their artistic productions. Psychiatrists with schizophrenic siblings have sensitively used the insights gained within their own families to understand and treat schizophrenic patients.

Some siblings realize that they must flee from the disturbing family environment as soon as possible in order not to be overwhelmed. Several of them recounted how they had maintained an emotional aloofness for several years until they could get away; in others, the predicament of the schizophrenic sibling became so intolerable and frightening that they impulsively left home, as did a character in Tennessee Williams's *The Glass Menagerie*. In leaving the home, they are apt to try to block out the past and disengage themselves from their families. Of course, these siblings are often more able to leave

the parents and survive on their own than are the patients, in whom
such attempts at disengagement may precipitate an acute psychotic
break. The sister whose constriction has just been noted had no intention of returning home after finishing college and married prompt-
ly upon being graduated. In another instance, a college girl became
bedridden soon after her brother was hospitalized, and then with
the support of her psychiatrist moved away from the home and severed contact with her mother; even many years later she continued
to avoid her parents, and she visited her brother, who was hospitalized very close to her home, only two or three times in four years.
The brother of a male patient kept away from his mother—who was
schizophrenic, divorced, and pathetically lonely—because, in his
frenzy at her engulfing ways, he found himself planning ways of
murdering her. The most stable of the four Schwartz brothers was
the only one who had left the family; he lived at a great distance and
kept himself absorbed in his mathematics. One sister in the Thomas
family, but not the best adjusted, had made a complete break with
her family, not only avoiding contact with them but also consciously
seeking to lead a totally different type of life.

DIVERGENT INFLUENCES UPON THE
OFFSPRING WITHIN A FAMILY

The Effects of Changing Family Circumstances

The family is not static but is an organization with a dynamic
configuration in which role relationships change constantly. Time is
a factor in these changes, as children enter new developmental phases
and parents grow older. Sometimes marked shifts in the family occur,
leading to a loss of equilibrium or to deleterious defensive measures
to maintain a semblance of role reciprocity between members. In
some instances the family situation and the parental attitudes altered
so markedly that the patient was raised altogether differently from his
siblings, and a similar outcome of the developmental process could
not be expected. The Forel family offers a clear example.

The Forel marriage had never been compatible. The father, a weak
man, had struggled ineffectually against the domination of the family
by his wife, who was abetted by her two older sisters. All three sis-

ters were contemptuous of men, and the oldest was a virago who despised and sought to control men. Mrs. Forel was cold, highly narcissistic, and a teasing flirt. She refused to move away from the neighborhood where her mother and sisters lived, and each summer abandoned her husband to vacation with them for two months. The marriage became increasingly schismatic, with Mr. Forel feeling himself an outcast in his own home, his opinions devalued, and his wishes ignored. His frequent tantrums increased his wife's contempt for him.

There were three children; the patient, a boy, was the youngest child, with a sister thirteen years older and a brother eleven years older. All of the children suffered from the family atmosphere. The older brother considered his childhood to have been abysmal, but far better than the patient's. For the two older children the parental influences had been modified by close contact with the extended families of both parents. The older son had been a favorite of his grandparents and aunts, gaining their admiration and praise by ingratiating himself in an obsequious fashion that enraged his father. He became highly neurotic, terrified of male authorities. He believed that he had escaped very serious disorganization by, first, his attachment to a male teacher, identifying himself with him and trying to follow in his footsteps, and then by developing a psychogenic dermatitis that led him into intensive psychotherapy. The sister became a seriously constricted and anxious woman.

Shortly before the conception of the patient, the parents had verged upon the separation they had often considered. Mr. Forel had been offered an opportunity to establish a business in another state, but his wife refused to move away from her sisters. When Mr. Forel issued an ultimatum and threatened divorce, his wife capitulated and agreed to move, and also agreed to resume the sexual relationship she had terminated eleven years before. The patient was a product of the brief reconciliation. Finding herself pregnant, Mrs. Forel became enraged at her husband and sought unsuccessfully to terminate the pregnancy. After the child was born, she paid little attention to him, and, feeling lost without her sisters, upon whom she had always been dependent, she began to drink heavily and to entertain male friends. During the patient's childhood, both parents were frequently intoxicated, and the older children reported that the father often carried his wife home dead drunk. The older siblings and the father tried to fill a mothering role toward the patient. Then, when the patient was six, Mrs. Forel was seriously disfigured in an auto accident which occurred when her husband fell asleep while driving. She became depressed and refused to leave her room until her appearance could be restored surgically, more than a year later. Feeling guilty, the father sought to make amends by becoming subservient to her, and was treated more contemptuously than ever. Then in rapid succession, the brother left for college, the sister married, and the father failed in his business. The family moved again, and shortly thereafter the father developed a malignancy. As he went downhill, his wife totally neglected him, fearing that she might catch cancer from him. The father died when the patient was eleven, and from then on the boy never had a real home. They lived with his married sister for a time; and then his mother moved in with her oldest sister. This aunt hated the patient, who was defiant toward her, and refused to permit him to live in her house. He boarded in the neighborhood, visiting his mother when his aunt was not at home.

In at least half of the families, the sequential position of the off-spring formed a significant differentiating influence because of changing family circumstances, although the changes were less dramatic in the other cases than in the one described above. The children's position in a family can, however, make considerable difference in the parents' attitudes toward them even when they are of the same sex and closely proximate in age because of the places they fill in the dynamic equilibrium of the family. We have considered two of the most difficult problems of differentiation in our series in previous papers: the differing role and identity assignments of a set of identical twins (Chapter XII); and the very different situations confronting two sisters born less than two years apart, the older of whom is schizophrenic and the younger reasonably well adjusted (Chapter VIII). The mother of the twins had selected the older twin to live out her masculine fantasies of the life denied her because she was a woman and was herself a less favored younger twin, while she identified the younger of the twins with her feminine, passive, and masochistic self. In the other case, the older of the sisters had become the focal point and scapegoat in a conflict between her parents that had antedated her birth and had been brought to a crisis by her conception, whereas the younger sister had remained relatively peripheral to the continuing parental quarrel.

The Mother's Capacity to Provide Nurturant
Care During the Patient's Infancy

In half of the cases studied, a clear disturbance was found to have existed in the relationship of the mother with the patient as an infant —a disturbance that was not present, or at least not to the same degree, in her relationship with her other children. This is in keeping with theories of the importance of infantile deprivation and maternal rejection in the genesis of schizophrenia. Three mothers had been physically incapacitated for many months following the patient's birth, disabilities that had been aggravated by their emotional problems at the time. One mother had been fearful of handling her oldest child, particularly of bathing him, a task which the father had to carry out. The mother of the two schizophrenic Robb sisters had been too insecure to take care of her oldest daughter and had turned her care, as an infant and small child, over to a nurse; when her son was born, three years later, she had cared for him herself; but when the younger daughter was born, she paid little attention to her, for she was preoccupied with hostility toward her unfaithful husband, and was considering divorce. Mrs. Ubanque, another mother of two daughters, had suffered "gloomy thoughts" following the birth of the younger girl, who became the patient, whereas the birth of the older child had been a joyous occasion—and a clear preference for the older child continued during the ensuing years. Mrs. Forel, already referred to, had sought to abort her youngest child, who became the patient, and had been emotionally withdrawn from him during his infancy as well as during his later years. At least one other mother's efforts at mothering were seriously impeded by her husband's extreme jealousy of any attention she sought to give her son, a situation that did not recur after the birth of a daughter. In several other instances, the mother had difficulty in providing proper nurturant care for her children as infants, but notable differences in the care provided the patient and the siblings were not apparent.

It is difficult properly to assess such influences in the first year of the patient's life. The problem is partly one of retrospective assessment, but even more one of sorting out what is pertinent and decisive in families where serious difficulties had existed prior to the patient's birth and then continued throughout his developmental years. Two things are apparent: that these difficulties in nurturing the infant did not occur in all cases, and that this problem was but one among many parent-child difficulties. However, such deprivation may be important in predisposing the child to schizophrenia. It may also indicate the start of a chronically faulty mother-child relationship, and such unsatisfactory parent-infant interaction may set a pattern aggravated by constant feedback from child to mother, mother to child, and one parent to the other, involving the sibling relationships as well.

The Child's Role in the Family Dynamics

The Child and Parental Conflicts.—In those families that we have designated as "schismatic," the parents were in open conflict, trying to coerce each other, each encountering from the other either defiance or, at best, a temporary hostile and resentful submission. Each undercut the worth and self-esteem of the other and divided the family, the mother wooing the children to side with her, and the father wooing them to side with him in the conflict, each parent fostering distrust and devaluation of the other. In many cases a constant threat of family dissolution hung over the children. The parents were preoccupied with their marital problems, and, in the absence of affection and support from each other, turned to a child to fill their emotional needs. In our experience, the child who becomes schizophrenic is caught in the schism to a greater degree than are the others in a variety of ways. First, he may fill the role of the "scapegoat" whose difficulties preoccupy the parents and mask their basic unhappiness with one another. Second, he may insert himself into the split, seeking to widen the gap between them to gain one parent for himself. Third, he may devote his energies and attention to bridging the gap between the parents. He straddles issues, divides his loyalties, and seeks to become a different person for each parent in order to fill the emotional needs of both, consuming his energies in preserving the parents' marriage and in salvaging their lives, rather than in the interests of his own independent ego development. Fourth, he may be caught in a bind in which loyalty to one parent means rejection by the other; because of their opposing standards and needs, he cannot satisfy and feel accepted by one without arousing dissatisfaction or hostility in the other. The widely discrepant attitudes and directives of the parents cannot be integrated within the single child—the irreconcilable parents become irreconcilable introjects.

The reasons why one offspring rather than another becomes most intensively involved are diverse: the sequential position, the child's sex, changes in the family situation, childhood illnesses, and others not so readily categorized. However, the patient's involvement commonly relieves the other children of much of the burden.

The case of Dora Nussbaum (Chapter XIII) illustrates how one child became more caught up in a family schism than her sibling. Her parents, preoccupied with their own problems and their feud could invest little in their baby daughter, resenting her birth that blocked consideration of divorce. The baby became irritable and difficult, filling the role of a scapegoat and diverting attention from more basic sources of dissension in the home; eventually she widened the gulf between her parents by displacing her mother to the extent of near-incestuous involvement with her father.

In contrast, Mrs. Nussbaum had been delighted by the birth of Dora's older brother who was born before the chronic dissension with her husband had started. She continued to take pride in her son, whereas she was never able to act warmly toward her daughter. Although Mr. Nussbaum gained gratification from having an admiring daughter, he also used her in his conflict with his wife, spiting the latter by the alliance with Dora. Because of the alignments within the family of mother and son as against father and daughter, the situations in which the two children grew up were very different. Mrs. Nussbaum because of her behavior toward Dora and because of her husband's devaluation of her and hostility toward her could not form a model for Dora to follow into womanhood; and her hostility toward Dora posed a realistic danger. The son, in contrast, received affection from both parents, for his father was very much interested in him. Although he, too, was affected by the parental conflict, he was never the center of it, or made to feel that he was the cause of it —and he was two years old before it started. Further, his father provided an excellent career model for him to follow even in his mother's eyes.

The older of the two daughters in the Grau family was caught in a particularly difficult bind because of the parents' dissensions that antedated her birth and their irreconcilable ideas about religion, which focused upon how the child should be raised.[4] Her Protestant father refused to permit her to be baptized into Catholicism despite his written promise, he constantly condemned Catholicism and all Catholics, and he later refused to permit her to go with Catholic boys. Her Catholic mother fought back, sought to woo the girl to Catholicism, and secretly circumvented her husband. She was constantly anxious about her unbaptized child, and eventually had her baptized without her husband's knowledge. The parents' religious quarrels were but symptomatic of many areas of discord.

The patient struggled with these irreconcilable introjects until she finally defiantly sided with her paranoid father and sought to win him away from her mother. The younger daughter, while also subjected to the conflict, never became the focus of it. To some extent, the father relinquished her to his wife; since the older sister preempted the father's attention and affection, the younger could form an alliance with her mother. As we have noted previously, the sister learned at an early age to sidestep the difficulties in which the patient became involved.

In the Benjamin family the son who became schizophrenic sought to satisfy the disparate ambitions his parents held for him, to fill their unmet needs, and to keep them from separating. When they were at odds, he would become frightened by their seductiveness toward him; yet he would become jealous and more disturbed whenever they became more compatible. Both parents used the son's indications of affection and his criticisms of the other parent as a vindication of themselves, wooing him as an ally. At the same time, the father could not permit his son to gain a better education than he himself had obtained, and he unconsciously sabotaged his wife's hopes and the boy's ambitions. The confusions in the sexual sphere were even greater, with both parents behaving seductively toward their son. The pa-

[4] See Chapter VIII.

tient's older sister could simply side with her father and did not seek to hold the parents together. She was not threatened by seduction from the mother, and her father was less physically seductive toward her than toward his son. Less involved in the parents' difficulties and hence less burdened by guilt, she could also exploit the parents' disagreements to gain goals of her own, which her brother could not do.

The Child's Role in "Skewed" Families.—Not all of the parents were in overt conflict. In the families that we have termed "skewed" —predominantly families with male schizophrenic offspring—the serious personality problems and deviant ways of the dominant parent were not countered by the spouse. The patient, in contrast to his siblings, is the object of a particular intrusiveness by the dominant parent, usually the mother, which blurs the ego boundaries between parent and child and ties the patient to satisfying the parent's needs and to continuing a primary relatedness with her. The boy's differentiation from the initial symbiotic bond to his mother and the development of identification with his passive father are impeded. The symbiotic attachment leads to confusion of sexual identity, incestuous concerns, and a greater assimilation of the disturbed parent's deviant and paralogical ways. The siblings may resent the patient's special relationship with the mother, but they are freer to develop into independent persons. The oldest child may be selected as the object of this intrusive relationship, but in some instances the mother holds on to the youngest child as the older children grow away from her.

In the family with the identical twins (see Chapter XII), the mother never established ego boundaries between herself and her twins. From the time of their birth, her entire life was wrapped up in these phallic extensions of herself. The older brother of the twins, together with the father, became outcasts. The mother banished the father from her room and bed, and she considered the older son to be uncouth and unimportant. The older brother hated the twins, envied them, and suffered; and he became accident-prone, seriously unstable, and tended to act out. Yet he could identify with his father, who, despite his wife's contempt and ridicule, was a far more stable person than she. The older brother did not need to struggle to differentiate himself from his mother or to escape her bizarre demands; and eventually he felt very free to leave home and seek fulfillment elsewhere.

The Siblings' Gender

While most of the siblings were emotionally unstable, our data indicate that the most generalized and consistent factor related to the severity of the disturbance was the sex of the sibling. This factor is complex; since it is a function of the parental personalities and their interrelationships, its origins can antedate the birth of any of the children. The significant finding is that siblings of the same sex as the schizophrenic patients were, as a group, clearly more disturbed than siblings of the opposite sex. The developmental tasks confronting children of opposite sexes in a particular family were very different. While the sample in this series is small and unsuited for statistical analysis, the finding is in accord with the studies of concordance rates for schizophrenia in dizygotic twins, with studies of *folie à deux*,[5] and with the findings of Penrose (1945) and others concerning concordance rates for schizophrenia in siblings of schizophrenic patients. Such findings have led to the consideration of a sex-linked genetic factor, but Rosenthal's (1960) analysis of the collective data from

FIGURE 2

ESTIMATED ADJUSTMENT OF MALE PATIENTS AND THEIR SIBLINGS

Each vertical column represents a child in the order of his birth in the family. The patient is identified by "Pt" above the column. Symbols for males and females are shown above.

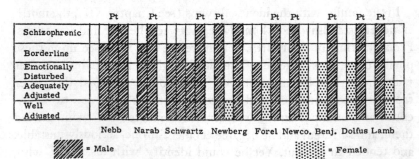

[5] For concordance rates in siblings, see Greenberg (1956) and Kallmann (1953).

FIGURE 3

ESTIMATED ADJUSTMENTS OF FEMALE PATIENTS AND THEIR SIBLINGS

Each vertical column represents a child in the order of his birth in the family. The patient is identified by "Pt" above the column. Symbols for males and females are shown above.

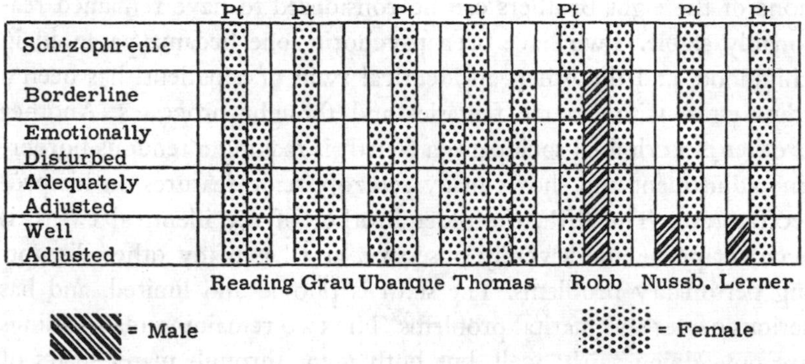

= Male   = Female

the various studies shows that the gender-linkage within the more extended family does not appear to follow genetic lines.

As shown in Figure 2, the nine male patients in our series had fourteen siblings—eight brothers and six sisters. Three had only brothers, two had a brother and a sister, and four only a sister.

Figure 3 shows the female patients and their siblings. The seven female patients had a total of ten siblings—seven sisters and three brothers. The paucity of brothers is unfortunate and limits the usefulness of the data. Four of the female patients had only sisters; one had a brother and a sister; and two had only a brother.

The Sisters of Male Schizophrenics.—The only sibling of a male schizophrenic who could be considered emotionally healthy and well adjusted is a sister. One other sister, now a young adolescent, may attain reasonable stability despite some acting-out tendencies. Two other sisters of male schizophrenics are living reasonably satisfying lives despite fairly serious personality problems; one is seriously constricted and insecure in her marital relationship, and the other has psychopathic traits that have thus far not led to serious difficulties. The remaining two women, the sisters of the most chronic male patients, were both seriously disturbed at one time, and both sought psychotherapeutic help; one is now pursuing a profession effectively, and the other has married and is raising a family, but is seriously constricted and insecure and is making a tenuous adjustment.

The Brothers of Male Schizophrenics.—In contrast to the sisters, none of the eight brothers can be considered to have remained reasonably stable. Two have been psychotic; one became paranoid in childhood, and the other, an identical twin of a patient, has been a transvestite with bizarre fantasies and thought processes. Another brother is a criminal sociopath; a fourth is making a tenuous borderline adjustment and shows many schizophrenic features on his projective tests. The fifth, the older brother of the identical twins, is accident-prone and severely obsessive, and has many other disrupting personality problems. The sixth is phobic and limited, and has serious career and marital problems. The two remaining male siblings are now doing fairly well, but both went through many years of serious turmoil. One may have been transiently delusional in adolescence, and the other suffered from a severe neurodermatitis, had serious concerns over his masculinity, and at times was incapacitated by anxiety, but he worked out his major problems in psychotherapy.

The Brothers of Female Schizophrenics.—Two of the three brothers have successfully pursued professions and have remained emotionally stable, although they are both limited by constriction of their personalities. The third brother, a man with two chronically schizophrenic sisters, has had considerable difficulty in both work and marriage and is rather schizoid.

The Sisters of Female Schizophrenics.—Only one of the seven sisters of the female patients has made a reasonably stable adjustment, and her limitations have already been mentioned. Her skillful avoidance of crippling involvement in a very bad family situation has been discussed in detail in Chapter VIII. One sister is chronically schizophrenic, and another, who completely withdrew from her family, is making a borderline schizophrenic adjustment. The remaining four sisters are rather seriously unstable, but the extent of the disabilities of two could not be clearly determined because of their fear of involvement and avoidance of frequent contact with the investigators.

One of them had left home precipitately soon after her sister was hospitalized.[6]

Two Illustrations of the Factor of Gender.—The indications that certain family constellations and interaction patterns create greater vulnerability to the development of schizophrenia for offspring of one sex than for the opposite sex (Chapter XV) are highlighted by the two families with alternate gender sequence of their three chil-dren. In one, two sons were separated by a daughter, and, in the other, two daughters were separated by a son. In both families the oldest and youngest children were schizophrenic, while the middle child of the opposite sex was not. While this finding probably is partly a matter of chance, the family situations will be presented briefly to illustrate how the family configurations created very different devel-opmental tasks for the boys and girls within these families.

In the Newberg family the oldest son became acutely schizophrenic at the age of fifteen. The daughter, who was thirteen at the time, has remained well and is probably the most stable and adaptable of any of the siblings in our series. The third child, a boy who was then nine years old, suffered from night terrors and paralyzing separation prob-lems, and soon after his brother's hospitalization developed delusional beliefs about his teachers and schoolmates.

The Newberg marriage had been filled with mutual recrimination and frequent threats of separation almost from its inception, with most of the quarrels focusing on the intense attachment of both spouses to their natal families. Mr. Newberg was the most poorly or-ganized father of any of the male patients. Raised in a disorganized family abandoned by the father, he had at an early age assumed re-sponsibility for the support of his mother. He remained intensely attached to her, was jealous of his brothers, and spent much of his spare time in his mother's home. He was equally rivalrous with his sons, behaving in many ways like another child in the family. He talked incessantly, in a driven way that the interviewers found dif-

[6] Data concerning the seventeenth patient and her family are not included in this paper. The patient had only one sibling, a sister who is emotionally disturbed and suffers from ulcerative colitis. The parental relationship is schismatic, and the mother is incapable of closeness or of acting warmly toward her daughters.

ficult to endure for even an hour at a time. He was scattered, pursuing one fixed idea after another. Although a steady provider, he was caught between his ambitions and his needs for security, and he constantly threatened to leave his job to pursue some hairbrained scheme. In his free time he worked upon a sequence of inventions that never materialized or a succession of hobbies each of which he was going to turn into a business. He talked constantly of his great abilities but accomplished little, and he created great confusion when at home.

Mrs. Newberg, in contrast, was one of the most stable mothers in our series. She depended greatly upon her older son, and sought compensation for her unhappy marriage in her children. Although she was oversolicitous, she maintained a reserve that probably impeded her relationships with them. She was firmly attached to her three sisters and refused to move away from the street on which they all lived, which caused her husband great inconvenience. While she justified this, in part correctly, by her husband's unreliability and her need for companionship and help in raising the children, her husband resented her lack of confidence in him. Mrs. Newberg's sisters intruded themselves into the affairs of the Newberg household, and one in particular was openly hostile and contemptuous of Mr. Newberg, constantly belittling him even in the presence of his children.

In this family, the sons had a very faulty paternal model in a man who boasted much and achieved little, who was highly inconsistent and given to suspiciousness, and who was more of a rival to them than a father. The mother and her sisters constantly denigrated him and placed little trust in him, conveying to the boys that they must not resemble him. They lived in an atmosphere where women dominated the extended family and were highly critical of men. For a son to become like the father meant becoming virtually psychotic, subject to constant hostile criticism and contempt, and almost intolerable to the mother whose love they sought.

The daughter's situation was very different. Surrounded by women who were mutually supportive, she had a number of positive feminine models. Although her father was frequently angry with her mother, he also expressed considerable admiration for her. The daughter was clearly her father's favorite, and her mother was not jealous or rivalrous. Further, the daughter did not need to fill the place in her mother's life, that her father had left unsatisfied; she did not have to achieve as a man in a world in which her grandiose father could accomplish little; nor did she have to face the issue, which confronted her brothers, of how a man could satisfy and be lovable to a woman when the father was so unsatisfactory to their mother and aunts.

The Robb family, in which two chronically schizophrenic daughters were separated by a son who, despite serious difficulties and several bad starts, has managed to achieve a career and marry, presents an analogous situation. Mr. Robb, a professor of education, married a troubled heiress who was seriously lacking in self-esteem. The couple had very different ideas of family life, child rearing, and the types of people with whom they wished to associate. Mrs. Robb accepted her dominating husband's decisions and choice of friends and quietly suffered in associating with people whom she despised. When, however, her husband started a series of sexual liaisons, she followed suit to vent her anger and gain quiet vengeance. Then Mr. Robb invited female exchange students from abroad to live with the family, ignoring his wife's protests. Soon he was spending evenings talking with them and ignoring his wife, and he turned to one of these, who was a teacher doing advanced study, for guidance in raising the children. For many years Mrs. Robb had had little authority in her own home, but now her inadequate self-esteem and confidence fell markedly as her opinions were pointedly ignored and belittled. Deeply resentful and preoccupied with her unhappiness, she could invest little in her children.

The oldest daughter was cared for by a nursemaid during her infancy, but when the son was born the nurse was discharged, and the mother gained considerable satisfaction from caring for him. However, it was soon after the second daughter was born that the mother discovered that her husband was having affairs. From then on she gave little thought or attention to her children. Even though the situation has been presented only in barest outline, one can note that the daughters were uncherished by their mother and that they gained a strange view of the worth and role of a woman, since she was unempathic as a mother, and consistently devalued and held in contempt as a wife. The girls could readily feel that they could not satisfy or gain the affection of their oversolicitous and seductive father by growing up to resemble their mother. The son, who also developed rather serious problems, had at least received maternal affection and attention during his infancy and early childhood; and he had a successful and renowned father who provided a model—and whose example he eventually followed by marrying a wealthy woman from an unstable family.

When the families with schizophrenic sons and those with schizophrenic daughters were examined as separate series, notable differences in their configurations became apparent. Because of the parental personalities and the nature of their interactions, the families with schizophrenic sons presented more serious impediments to the integrated ego development of boys than of girls, and the opposite was true for the families with schizophrenic daughters, although a few families were probably equally noxious to children of both sexes.

The parent of the same sex as the patient—the fathers of sons and the mothers of daughters—formed a very poor model for the patient to internalize in order to gain identity as a man or woman because of the parent's serious psychopathology, because of the parent's attitudes toward the child, or because of the spouse's derogatory and undermining behavior toward this parent, and commonly for all three reasons. To maintain the approval and affection of the parent of the opposite sex, the child sought to differentiate himself from, rather than identify himself with, the parent of the same sex, and thus lacked a positive sex-linked model to follow in order to gain maturity as a man or a woman. The situation was aggravated because the parent of the opposite sex from the child seductively used the child as a replacement for the unsatisfactory spouse in filling his own emotional needs and thus interfered with the child's development into an independent person. Although the case illustrations have emphasized the child's difficulty in achieving identity as a member of his own sex, the problems created for his development go far beyond this. The resolution of the oedipal ties is impeded, and incestuous wishes remain conscious into adolescence; fears of vindictiveness by the parent of the same sex are heightened by the realistic rivalries existing in the family; and narcissistic and homosexual proclivities are fostered by the confused and confusing sexual identities of the parents.

The case material reveals that with but rare exception the mother of the male patient is engulfing of the son, seeking to maintain a symbiotic closeness with him, while the father is distant and rivalrous toward the son or is himself but a weak, emasculated appendage of his wife. In contrast, the mother of the female patient is aloof and distant from her, either because she is unable to accept in a daughter the femininity she rejects in herself or because she seeks to ward off homosexual impulsions, while the father tends to be derogatory of women in general but seductive with the daughter, whose admiration he needs to bolster his insecure masculinity and narcissism. A more detailed examination of these differences suggests that satisfactory ego development and integration in boys and girls depend upon different requisites in the family structure and interaction (Chapter XV). A boy's ego development will be injured more seriously than a girl's by a mother who cannot establish clear ego boundaries between herself and the child, since to achieve a firm masculine identity he must break away from the initial mother-child symbiosis more completely than a daughter needs to. In addition, a father who fails to fill a masculine instrumental role in the family will be more detrimental to a boy, who needs to learn this role, than to a girl. Conversely, a girl will be harmed more seriously by a cold and aloof mother, for the attainment of maternal affectional characteristics through empathic absorption of maternal feelings is more critical to a girl's development than to a boy's; and a father who dominates and derogates the mother and tends to be antagonistic and belittling toward all women will affect a girl's development more deleteriously than a boy's. The exposition of the different developmental tasks confronting boys and girls and how they are furthered or impeded by the family configuration goes beyond the purposes of this paper; here we are seeking only to indicate why a child of one sex may be more vulnerable to personality disorganization within a given family than a child of the opposite sex.

Idiosyncratic Problems in the Parents'
Relationship to the Schizophrenic Offspring

The comparison of some of the patients with their siblings must take into account certain special problems related to unique circumstances. Expectations before birth as well as many circumstances at and following confinement can set the stage for certain interaction patterns in the family or certain attitudes toward a particular infant. For example, differences in temperament present at birth may influence the ensuing child-parent relationship and interaction, although this, like many other such influences, is difficult to assess retrospectively.

The Nebb twins, one of whom was overtly schizophrenic and the other a transvestite who might also be considered schizophrenic, were, in contrast to their older brother, placed at birth in a special and unusual situation because their mother had been competing with her own twin sister to see which of them could produce twins. The birth of the twin sons was a major triumph for Mrs. Nebb, who had been the deformed and neglected member of her family, and they were to be her means of achieving prestige and dominance.

In another family, the daughter who became the patient had manifested artistic talent to an unusual degree by the age of three. Two relatives in the maternal line who had been similarly gifted from earliest childhood had become psychotic. The patient's mother had been directed away from developing a similar talent lest it lead to insanity, but the patient's unusual ability could not be suppressed. The mother was naturally ambivalent about the patient's dominant activity and vacillated between encouraging it and seeking to guide the girl into more conventional channels. The bright but untalented older brother had not been subjected to such ambivalent guidance or to an *a priori* expectation of great vulnerability to psychosis.

It must be noted, however, that there were other problems in both families that were just as serious as in the other families in the series.

The Interaction Between the Siblings

In our scrutiny of the divergent influences upon the siblings within a family, we must also note the effects of the interaction between the siblings themselves, although this topic extends beyond the limits and purposes of this paper. In the Narab family, the overtly schizophrenic mother considered both of her sons to be geniuses—even, at times, Messiahs—and her extreme intrusiveness into the lives of both was not countered by the father. The younger son became schizophrenic while the older traversed a narrow path, skirting overt psychosis. He was filled with venom toward his mother and feared that he might act out his homicidal fantasies about her if he remained near her; and, at times, he was almost equally hostile toward his younger brother. While *ex post facto* analysis is particularly hazardous in this instance, several factors seem important. Mrs. Narab had been smotheringly dominant of her first-born, but with the birth of the second son she turned her major energies toward him; and as the older son began to move away from her, she clung all the more tenaciously to the younger. The first-born could express his jealousy and anger toward his brother, dominating him and forcing him into a passive and masochistic position—one might say into developing a more Messiah-like personality and possibly emulating his father, whom both sons considered homosexual. The absorption of the mother's needs by the younger son appears to have provided greater freedom for the older.

Illness in one offspring—whether the schizophrenic patient or the nonschizophrenic sibling—affects the siblings differentially. At least three of our patients experienced comparative neglect when the prolonged illness of older siblings—rheumatic fever in one instance—required a great deal of the mother's attention. In the Schwartz family, the severe psychopathy of the oldest brother pre-empted the economic and emotional resources, as has already been noted. It was the youngest son who became psychotic. Not only had his father become ineffectual as a husband and father shortly after his birth, but his mother's attention had become absorbed by the oldest son's markedly antisocial and delinquent behavior. The family lived in a "tough" neighborhood, and the next older brother had protected the patient, as the baby of the family, and fought his battles for him—abetting his development as a passive, dependent child who was very insecure of his masculinity.

In the Grau family, the patient's difficulties throughout her childhood had had a very different impact on the younger sister. She explained that her older sister had borne the brunt of her mother's insecurity in raising children; the mother had relied on books with her first child but raised the second daughter according to less rigid directions. Moreover, the second daughter had avoided involvement in the parental conflicts by noting how her sister became embroiled with one or the other parent at each phase of development, and her major guide in life had been sidestepping situations that had caused difficulties for her sister. It also became clear that her antagonism to her older sister who created so much difficulty had led her to side with her mother rather than to seek the affection of her paranoid father.

The influences of the siblings upon one another may be diverse, but the child who becomes schizophrenic often lessens the impact of the parental pathology upon the siblings by serving as a target of the parents' intrusiveness, as a scapegoat, or as an example for the siblings of what not to do.

COMMENT

This comparison of sixteen schizophrenic patients with their twenty-four siblings, in an effort to clarify why the patient rather than his siblings became schizophrenic, has presented only a general survey of the problems, for any careful scrutiny from a genetic-dynamic orientation would require a separate article, if not a monograph, for each family. Several general findings that warrant attention have emerged from the study. One of these is that the question of why one child within a family becomes schizophrenic while the others remain "well" or "normal" requires restatement. As many siblings were psychotic as reasonably well integrated, and all except five or six of the twenty-four siblings suffered from serious personality disorders.

A definite gender-linkage was found in the occurrence and severity of the psychiatric disturbances in the siblings. The brothers of the male schizophrenic patients were clearly more disturbed than the sisters; and the sisters of schizophrenic females were sicker than the brothers, although the value of this finding is limited by the paucity of brothers of female patients in our series. Only one sibling of the same sex as the patient was considered to be reasonably stable; and no sibling of the opposite sex from the patient was overtly psychotic.

The influence of the parents and of their interaction with each other upon sons and daughters differed. In general, different configurations and parental personalities existed in the families with male and female schizophrenic offspring (Chapter XV).

Other differentiating influences upon the development of the children occurred with varying frequencies and in various combinations. In half of the cases, the mother had been either physically incapacitated, too intensely preoccupied with her marital problems, or too anxious and insecure to provide nurturant mothering care during the patient's infancy, while such conditions did not apply during the infancy of the siblings. In half of the families the patient was raised under conditions that were different from those under which the siblings were brought up; in a few families the difference was very marked.

When the siblings were close in age—and even when they were identical twins—they were also subjected to very different intrafamilial influences. The child who becomes schizophrenic may become a pawn or scapegoat in the parental conflict; he may be caught in a bind between the conflicting needs and wishes of the parents, who become irreconcilable introjects; he may invest his energies in seeking to salvage the parents' marriage and to satisfy the needs of both; he may insert himself into the split between the parents, and become a needed complement to one parent. The patients' energies during their developmental years were deflected from developing an integrated independent ego, and failure of closure of their oedipal attachments left them prone to incestuous conflicts during adolescence. The influence of the siblings upon one another may create more or less precarious circumstances and greater or lesser vulnerability.

We have not, of course, included all of the factors that may have been conducive to the production of schizophrenia. Little attention has been given to family characteristics that were reasonably similar for all of the siblings, particularly the paralogic modes of thinking and communicating of one or both parents that were present in all the families.

Although any reconstruction of the intrafamilial circumstances that influenced the development of these patients and their siblings cannot be fully satisfactory, the material offers clear and reasonable grounds for the understanding of why one child rather than another in a family becomes schizophrenic. The data support rather than refute the hypothesis that the intrafamilial environment plays a critical role in the etiology of schizophrenia.

XV

Comparison of Parent-Child Relationships of Male and Female Schizophrenic Patients

(1962)

Having drawn attention to the serious disturbances that permeate virtually every area of interaction in these families, we wish to focus upon the differences between families containing schizophrenic sons and those with schizophrenic daughters. Scrutiny of these differences serves to clarify many of the apparent inconsistencies in the literature concerning characteristics of the parental personalities and their ways of relating to their schizophrenic offspring. Mothers of such patients have been designated variously—as rejecting, aloof, unempathic, cold (Abrahams and Varon, 1953; L. Hill, 1955; Tietze, 1949), overprotective, intrusive, or symbiotic in their relationships with the patient (Alanen, 1958; Mark, 1953; Prout and White, 1950). Fathers have been observed and studied less frequently but have been described as distant, aloof, passive, neglecting (Frazee, 1953; Gerard and Siegel, 1950; Hajdu-Gimes, 1940), seductively close, hostile, or brutal (Alanen, 1958; Reichard and Tillman, 1950).

When we examined the seventeen core families in our study according to the sex of the schizophrenic child, certain parental characteristics and abnormalities of family interaction fell into definite clusters for male and female patients respectively. Alanen (1958) in his study of the mothers of schizophrenic patients had noted some differences between the parents of male and female patients. The moth-

Stephen Fleck, Theodore Lidz, and Alice R. Cornelison: Comparison of Parent-Child Relationships of Male and Female Schizophrenic Patients. Archives of General Psychiatry, *Vol. 8, 1963, pp. 1-7. Copyright © 1963, American Medical Association.*

er with a schizophrenic son tended to be closer to the patient than to her other children, and was "possessively protective" of him, whereas mothers of schizophrenic daughters were apt to be aloof and "inimically protective" of the patients. Although Alanen did not study the fathers, he gained an impression that fathers of schizophrenic sons provide poor models of masculinity because of their passivity and their submissiveness to their wives. Having gained similar impressions, we were led to focus upon the problem because we noted that the siblings who are of the same sex as the patient are, as a group, clearly more disturbed than the siblings of the opposite sex (Chapter XIV). It is clear that different tasks in achieving maturity and identity formation confront boys and girls, and there are strong indications that some family environments are more conducive to the development of schizophrenia in male offspring, and others to the development of schizophrenia in female children; or in less definitive terms, that some families are more deleterious to integrating ego development of sons than of daughters, and vice versa.

Amidst the complexities of the interaction patterns three issues appear critical and help to unify the findings. These are (1) the faulty model for identification provided by the parent of the same sex as the patient; (2) the impediments to proper resolution of the patient's oedipal attachments created by the disturbed parental interaction; and (3) the failure of the parents to maintain proper generation boundaries between themselves and the patient, either by being seductive with a child or by being more like a rivalrous sibling than a parent, with both patterns sometimes occurring in the same family.

The configurations that we shall outline are abstractions that fit some families very precisely and others less distinctly. One or two families have patterns more commonly seen when the patient is of the other sex, and a few families seem equally detrimental to offspring of both sexes, but the trend is clear and serves to clarify the dynamics of the parent-child relationships in all but a very few of our cases.

Female Patients

A greater consistency could be noted in the configuration of the families containing female schizophrenic offspring than in the families with male patients. Strikingly similar dynamics could be abstracted from the families of six of the eight female patients—and only one differed markedly, bearing a greater resemblance to the pattern discerned in families with male patients.

The mothers of the schizophrenic daughters formed very poor models of a woman both because of their own characteristics and because of their husbands' contemptuous and derogatory attitudes toward them. These were highly schismatic marriages with but two exceptions. The parents were in open conflict, each undercutting the worth of the other to the children, and commonly both sought to win the daughter to side with them in the conflict. The mother's insecurity and deficient self-esteem as a woman further declined in a marriage in which the husband constantly derogated her worth as a wife and mother. Usually she struggles against her husband but cannot maintain her ground against a dominating man who may be grandiose, if not overtly paranoid, a man who is embittered because the wife does not bolster his narcissism by constant admiration. The mother becomes the defeated and devalued parent, particularly in the eyes of the patient. Anxious about raising a daughter, unable fully to accept her or be at ease with her, possibly because of homosexual concerns, the mother remains aloof, and fails to invest the relationship emotionally and erotically as required for the proper nurturance of the infant and small child. However, we cannot designate these mothers by the catch-all term "rejecting." Most of them were very attentive to their daughters and aspired to be maternal. Their efforts were impeded by their insecurities, their marital unhappiness, and at times, by their jealousy of their husbands' greater interest in their daughters. The mother's aloofness prevents the daughter from establishing a proper preoedipal attachment and impedes identification with the mother, and directs the female child to the father for affectionate nurturant responsivity. While some of these mothers were seriously disturbed, only one was definitely psychotic, the remainder tending toward resentful depression, perplexing vagueness, and imperviousness to the daughter's feelings and needs.

In contrast, three fathers of schizophrenic daughters had clear-cut paranoid tendencies, and a fourth had a depressive psychosis with paranoid trends. With perhaps one exception, they were highly narcissistic men who needed constant admiration because of their concerns about masculinity. As one father stated, "When I married I was only half a man and could only marry half a woman." Failing to gain the obedience, loyalty, and admiration they required from their wives, they turned to a daughter in a seductive manner that in some instances verged upon physical incestuousness, and used the girl to fill the place unsatisfied by the wife. These daughters in seeking their fathers' love must attempt to differentiate themselves from their mothers who are so unsatisfactory to the fathers instead of endeavoring to emulate a woman whom father loves. With the mother-daughter relationship poor from the start, early identification with the mother is impaired; later, instead of following her mother into womanhood, the girl has a negative directive in trying to become different from the devalued mother. The absence of an acceptable role model in the mother greatly complicates the developmental process, especially if the daughter's desire to gain her father's love is fostered by his seductiveness and his clear indications that she is more important to him than his wife. The oedipal attachment is not resolved or adequately repressed even at puberty, and the girl moves into adolescence disturbed by an incestuous entanglement that eventually terrifies her, if not the father. The girl's ego development is further impaired because in so far as she finds herself resembling her mother, she despises herself and lacks self-esteem as a woman; a situation that can be aggravated because most of the fathers have little respect for any woman.

Because of the parental schism, the girl is usually caught in a bind of the type in which satisfying either parent means rejection by the other (Weakland, 1960). The situation is further complicated when the daughter, in search for warmth, trust, and affection, turns from her aloof mother to become involved with a father whose needs cannot be satisfied by a woman, and is subjected to the father's confusing combination of seductiveness and his disparagement of women.

There are, of course, variants of this generalized and abstract description of the daughter's position in the family. However, only one mother who was also overtly schizophrenic demonstrated maternal closeness to her daughter, and all of the fathers of female patients with the exception of the one who had been seriously depressed had been seductive. There are one or two families in the series in which the mother avoids open conflict by giving in to the dominant father, leading to a marriage that is more skewed than schismatic. In some such instances—more apparent outside of our series—the mother remains emotionally withdrawn from her husband and virtually hands the daughter over to the father as a substitute for herself, thus fostering a sexualized relationship between the father and the daughter.

Male Patients

Maternal aloofness was also prominent in the early histories of male patients, but the most striking findings concern the very poor masculine model provided the son by his father, and the mother's dependency upon this son for her own emotional satisfaction and completion, often with failure to set ego boundaries between herself and the boy.

Deficiencies of the father in furnishing an adequate role model of a man, husband, and father with which the son can identify and gain guidance into adulthood derive both from the characteristics and behavior of the father, and also from the mother's condescending or hostile attitudes toward her husband. Five or six of the nine fathers behaved more like sons to their wives than husbands, and several of these were unusually passive adjuncts to their dominant but seriously disturbed wives, nonentities in the home who never countered their wives' eccentric ideas of family life and child rearing. Other fathers, feeling excluded from the mother-son coalition, filled rivalrous rather than paternal roles toward their sons. Two were extremely distant men who were away from the home for long periods. Three of the nine fathers were psychotic, and one was an alcoholic who created grave difficulties for the family whenever he was at home, while three others disrupted the home life by their emotional instability and frequent outbursts. For a son to become a man like his father meant either to be psychotic, or a passive castrated figure belittled by a woman, or a highly inconsistent figure who created confusion and suffering for the family. With but three exceptions, these men were less aggressive than the fathers of schizophrenic daughters, providing little if any instrumental leadership within the family even when adequately effective in their occupations. The children of two of these three fathers considered these men to be homosexual, while the patient-son of the third was seriously perturbed by his father's homosexual seductiveness. Somewhat paradoxically of all the fathers of schizophrenic sons these three were among the four who were most competent in their occupations. The other fathers were all passive men who were insecure in their masculinity.

The mothers made it clear to their sons that they were dissatisfied with their husbands, and even the one mother who admired her husband as a deity and shared his grandiose delusions was condescending toward him as a man. The mothers clearly conveyed to their sons that they must grow up to be different from their fathers. Some mothers sought to have the son who became schizophrenic live out the life she would have liked had she been a man. For the son to grow up in his father's image would not gain him a love object like his mother.

All of the mothers of schizophrenic sons were also very insecure in their marital and maternal roles. Although they had difficulty in being close and maternal to a son as an infant, they soon became oversolicitous and overprotective and unable to differentiate their own anxieties from those of the child—which in a few cases reached the extreme of almost total failure of the mother to differentiate herself from the child. Some mothers, because of their insecurities in child rearing and their awe of a male child, were unable to set limits for their sons. In contrast to the aloof and distant mothers of daughters, the mothers of sons tended to be engulfing and, at times, highly seductive. Even the one mother who openly rejected her son could be extremely sexually seductive with him when she was intoxicated. One other mother was distant from her son, but the nurse who raised him filled the role of the intrusive, adulating, and seductive mother, sleeping with him and perhaps stimulating him sexually throughout his childhood.

One might venture to say that in contrast to the early relationship between mothers and schizophrenic daughters, the original mother-son symbiosis with its erotic components and the initial identification of the boy with his mother were never properly surmounted. Then, as the son found himself more important than the father to his mother, the oedipal attachments were never properly repressed. Retaining a stronger identification with the mother and, in a sense, remaining a part of the mother rather than seeking to identify with the father, the boy was left with a predominantly feminine superego and without proper ego boundaries between himself and his mother. In such situations, particularly when the father was highly rivalrous, the son had realistic grounds to fear both the father and the engulfing mother who was turning him into an adjunctive castrated figure like his father.

COMMENT

These male and female patterns are basically similar in many respects, almost mirror images rotating about the sex reversals in the oedipal configuration. The child who becomes schizophrenic has a poor relationship with the parent of the same sex who is aloof and often rivalrous, and who provides a very poor model for the child's identification. Such a child then seeks to be different from this parent to gain the love and approval of the parent of the opposite sex who tends to be engulfing or seductive, using the child to gain completion or gratification. In both constellations the patient's image of the parent of the same sex as a model to follow into maturity is damaged in two ways: (1) by that parent's conflicts and deficiencies concerning sexual identity and parental functions; (2) by the interaction with the other parent who accentuates the poor image either by acquiescing in the aberrant modes of child nurturing, or by actively devaluating and undermining the spouse.

However, this characterization of the similarities in the configurations in the families of male and female patients is an oversimplification because the developmental tasks in respect to the oedipal situation are not mirror images. In a hypothetical normal developmental pattern, the girl can retain much of her primary identification with her mother, and optimally can seek to gain a love object like her father by growing into a woman like the mother. In contrast, the boy must be able to rescind his early identification with the mother and gain security as a male, optimally by becoming a man like his father who can gain a love object like his mother, and be able to provide for a woman rather than remain dependent upon her.[1]

[1] These models differ from classic analytic theory which has emphasized the difficulties confronting a girl because of her need to shift her love object from the mother to the father, as well as the differences resulting from castration anxiety and penis envy. These theoretical differences are important, but their thorough consideration is not germane to the immediate topic.

In the skewed family configurations of our male schizophrenics the patient retains his primary tie with the mother and is not guided into a masculine role by having an effective father or a father admired by his mother. Furthermore, without a clear division in these families into two generations, the son cannot find a secure and separate position as a child, since his father may be rivalrous instead of parental and his mother may rear him to extend and complete her life.

The female patient, however, because of the mother's lack of empathy, attains neither the essential primary mutuality with her mother nor a solid identification with her. Seeking affection and nurturant care from the father, she develops an ego ideal based upon what she believes father needs and wishes from a woman instead of taking on attributes of the devalued mother.

While it must remain a matter for conjecture, it seems to us that a boy's ego development will be injured more seriously than a girl's by having a mother who cannot establish ego boundaries between herself and a child, because a daughter need not break away from the initial mother-child symbiosis as completely as the boy, who must gain a masculine identity. In addition, a father who fails to fill an instrumental role in the family will be more detrimental to a son who needs to learn a masculine role than to a daughter.

Conversely, a girl will be harmed more seriously than a boy by a father who dominates and derogates the mother and who tends to be antagonistic and belittling of all women. While a boy will certainly be affected deleteriously by an aloof and cold mother, the attainment of an "affectional-expressive role" (Parsons and Bales, 1955) through the empathic absorption of maternal feelings is more critical to the girl's development than it is to the boy's.

These gender-linked differences in the issues confronting children in the families of schizophrenic patients appear to be borne out by our study of the patients' siblings, where we noted that the siblings of the same sex as the patient were more seriously disturbed than the siblings of the opposite sex. Our findings also suggest that the seemingly contradictory descriptions of the parents of schizophrenics may be reconcilable if the patient's sex is taken into account instead of correlating parental personality profiles with a patient's diagnosis regardless of sex. While it is beyond the confines of this report, we wish to record that the differential examination of the patients' psychosexual development according to his sex also helps to clarify and establish more definite patterns of family dynamics pertaining to sociopathic patients and in other emotional disorders.

We wish to re-emphasize, however, that one must look beyond individual parental characteristics and study the nature of parental interaction and the entire family behavior in order to trace pathological developments in an offspring. Furthermore, we do not consider that such family patterns are in themselves specific to the production of schizophrenia in an offspring, but that other factors enter into the etiology of schizophrenia, in particular the disturbed thought processes and paralogic ways of one or both parents that provide faulty training in reality testing and distrust in the validity and utility of verbal communications (Chapter XXI).

XVI

Psychiatric Hospitalization as a Family Experience

(1962)

Clinical and research experiences in social psychiatry during the past ten to fifteen years have involved three broad areas. One has been the epidemiological approach seeking rather gross and topical data related to mental illness; a second focus has been on the patient's immediate environment in the hospital; the third area has been the investigation of the patient's family and its role in the development and clinical course of psychiatric illness.

We have stated previously that our intensive long-range investigation of the family background of schizophrenic patients made it necessary to examine closely and therefore also control the hospital in which these patients resided because the impact of the hospital environment and of staff behavior on families became an essential area for study. We described and discussed in an earlier paper the interaction between families and hospital staff (Fleck, 1962). In this chapter we wish to examine and illustrate more systematically the involvement of the family in the hospitalization of one of its members.

This presentation will be subdivided for the sake of clarity according to the various phases of a patient's hospitalization, but the processes to be described are in reality continuous. We shall focus in turn on the family's role in the events leading to hospitalization and on the impact on the family of the hospital admission; upon subsequent family involvement in the therapeutic program; and finally,

Stephen Fleck: Psychiatric Hospitalization as a Family Experience. Special Treatment Situations, *Vol. 1, 1962, pp. 29-37. Copyright © 1962, Forest Hospital Publications, Forest Hospital, Des Plaines, Illinois. Also reprinted in abridged and modified form in* Acta Psychiatrica Scandinavica, *Supplementum 169, Vol. 39, pp. 1-24, 1963.*

upon discharge and aftercare. In the final sections of the chapter a few of the broader implications of these studies which point to important considerations for the organization of psychiatric inpatient services and for psychiatric training will be discussed.

BACKGROUND

Because this paper deals not only with data from our study of the family environment of schizophrenic patients but also with material derived from studies concerning the hospital environment of psychiatric patients, we shall briefly describe our approach to the organization of psychiatric services which is derived from our own experiences and those of many others. We shall in this discussion go beyond material from the seventeen families and draw upon experiences with other families, including those of patients hospitalized on our unit in the general hospital (Detre et al., 1961).[1]

We believe with Bauer (1961) that the first function of a clinical university service as a teaching instrument is to provide good patient care and that this must take precedence over specific research projects and fixed models for residency training. Therefore, we established services designed to meet the problems of the patients and their families, seeking solutions of crucial problems instead of imposing the design of either a traditional medical or mental hospital. In the endeavor to understand and meet patients' needs we have sought and continually seek not only professional opinions and advice on all staff levels but also patients' ideas and observations concerning their existence in the hospital. Research projects conducted earlier at the Yale Psychiatric Institute by Caudill, Gilmore, Redlich, and Stainbrook (Caudill, 1958) and other similar studies provided important data and impetus in reorganizing the hospital into a therapeutic community type of operation (Stanton and Schwartz, 1954; Greenblatt et al., 1957). Like others, we have striven to overcome the classic flaws in the functions of a hospital community, such as poor communication due to hierarchical barriers between staff levels, separate and opposed

[1] A twenty-four bed Yale teaching service in the Yale New Haven Hospital directed by Dr. Thomas Detre. See Fleck (1962) for description of the Yale Psychiatric Institute.

camps of patients and staff, the transmission of staff anxiety and covert disagreements to patients in ways that abet disturbed behavior if not produce it, etc.

To promote adequate staff and staff-patient communication and to eliminate the traditional hierarchical staff division, the purely dyadic psychoanalytic therapy model was supplemented by more generally shared types of psychotherapy in the form of various group processes. In order to render all community life throughout the day as therapeutic as possible for the patients, we introduced group activities, group therapy, and group meetings. In addition to traditional group therapy with six or seven patients, we instituted meetings of all patients and staff two or three times a week, various activity committees run by the patients, patient government, and a patient-staff advisory committee.

The success of these groups in improving the atmosphere of the hospital, in furthering teamwork, and in elucidating much of the patients' pathological behavior resulted in the extension of group work to patients' families, quite aside from the purposes of studying family group behavior for our research. Previously, relatives of patients had been seen individually by social workers or occasionally by one of the residents or other staff members, a practice that was intensified and regularized for the patients and their families involved in the study (Tennant, 1954). However, certain areas could not be observed or studied unless the family was also seen as a group. In addition, regular meetings of groups of patients' parents and home visits offered informational and therapeutic advantages. When our twenty-four bed general hospital unit was opened, designed to serve community patients by providing brief hospitalization, emphasis was placed on continuing therapeutic involvement of the family, and families have been involved routinely in various group meetings and activities throughout each patient's stay. On both services there are now: (1) individual contacts with family members; (2) "four-way meetings" including at least one key relative, the patient, his therapist, and the social worker; and (3) group meetings for several families with or without the patients present. These family programs supplement but do not replace any other treatment modalities (Fleck, 1963).

These services then represent practical application of data derived from researches in the hospital milieu of psychiatric patients, and from the more recent investigations of patients' families. At the same time, these services are suited for and are being used for the further investigation of treatment efficacy, and of family involvement in patients' illness and treatment.

ADMISSION PHASE

Resistance to Hospitalization

Investigations have shown that admission to an institution tends to be determined not by a change in the patient's intrinsic pathological condition or process but rather by a shift in the family equilibrium or perhaps in the patient's extrafamilial environment. Such changes either render the patient more disturbed or make it necessary for the family to institutionalize him because they can no longer care for him even if there has been no fundamental change in his condition. Examples of such crises are the sickness or the death of another family member or economic vicissitudes (Wood et al., 1962). In general, such family crises are similar to those described and analyzed in the reports from the Wellesley Project (Klein and Lindemann, 1961) for families without major emotional illnesses. However, a family may postpone recognition of the patient as the sickest member until family distress has reached intolerable intensity and only then seek assistance. Although hospitalization may then be recommended and carried out, family members may continue to deny the existence of mental illness, and even criticize the physician or agency for hospitalizing their relative. This occurs in families that can maintain an equilibrium only if the pathology of that member who is ultimately hospitalized operates as an important balancing element in the family dynamics.

Families suffer distress in either case, whether they attempt to maintain a semblance of balance by continued inclusion of the disturbed and disturbing patient in the family circle or whether they are trying to regain some equilibrium by excluding the patient through hospitalization. While family distress may be equally severe, whether it rises to a crescendo preceding institutionalization or afterwards, very different remedial or therapeutic measures may be required. As is so often the case in medicine, it is easier to distinguish and diagnose these two types of family situations in their extremes or in the abstract than at the time of admission when it is most important to do so. The family which is thrown out of balance by institutionalization of a member is easier to recognize after several hospitals have failed to meet their needs. We then see a repetition of removal against advice of the patient from a hospital either to his home or to another institution, only to be followed by further change of institutions or intermittent trials at having the patient live at home. This may continue until emotional or financial resources are exhausted, or until some hospital staff achieves enough understanding of the family's needs to clarify and respond to their distress. Their distress may be aggravated by faulty notions of familial etiology in mental illness and attendant guilt concepts which a hospital staff can reinforce inadvertently instead of correcting.

For our first example of a family intensely disturbed by a son's hospitalization we refer to the Newberg family already described in detail in Chapter VI. It may be recalled that the fifteen-year-old son became psychotic during a period of threatening parental separation, that the father was erratic and derogated by Mrs. Newberg's relatives, and that the mother leaned upon her elder son as well as upon her sisters. Also, we described in detail how Mr. Newberg made life difficult for his family and the staff by his frantic schemes to ensure his son's speedy recovery after the hospitalization, when he could no longer deny that his son was ill as he had done earlier. Mr. Newberg's behavior could be understood in part as his desperate effort to counteract his own guilt feelings and the blame being placed upon him by his wife and in-laws, and also to reunite his family and thereby deny or undo the marital schism. However, the "need" for a psychotic member in the family equilibrium while the basic discord between the Newbergs persisted was demonstrated subsequently. Later, when the patient had improved and the parents had accepted his hospitalization, the younger son developed paranoid and phobic symptoms necessitating his interrupting school and obtaining emergency treatment. He also improved eventually, but not until more fundamental improvement in the marital relationship had been achieved.

Our second example will demonstrate that even colleagues, who would know better if one of their patients were concerned, succumb to the strong need to deny the presence of serious mental illness in their families. They may be quite ready to send their offspring to an analyst or child psychiatrist, but resist recognizing psychosis or the need for institutionalization. A seventeen-year-old girl was admitted to our Institute obviously catatonic with some hebephrenic features. The colleague-parent insisted she was not psychotic but only suffered a "brief decompensation from an obsessional neurosis." The psychotic decompensation followed the parents' divorce a year earlier. Both parents complained that it was unfair to leave their child secluded with patients who were all so very sick, although their child was clearly the most disturbed patient in the hospital, the concern of other patients and staff alike because of her extremely bizarre and inaccessible behavior.

Here the mother's guilt over the divorce and possibly over having prolonged a very unsatisfactory marriage with a disturbed spouse whom she considered a pathogenic influence on the child led to very irrational criticisms of the hospital and accusations that the staff mistreated her. Our interaction with the parents remained tense, replete with recriminations by the mother. She repeatedly sought to transfer the patient to another hospital, which was avoided only because one consultant after another insisted that the patient was improving satisfactorily in our institution and refused to recommend interruption of the treatment.

Family Exclusion of Patients

In a private institution it is rather difficult to encounter clear-cut examples of families who not only need to exclude the patient but also behave accordingly. Exclusion is probably always masked to some extent, and we shall later present examples of severe masking which were not easily discernible early in the hospital course.

Soon after fifteen-year-old John Cord was admitted to our ward following surgical revision of an amputation stump of his left index finger, his repeated overt rejection by his family became obvious. He was the third son in a lower-middle-class family, unplanned, and unwanted as a boy. Mr. and Mrs. Cord quarreled a great deal, with the son's many misdemeanors which had begun at the age of twelve being a frequent topic for mutual recrimination. Although his antisocial behavior was relatively mild, mostly chronic truancy, the parents insisted that his problems could be resolved only if he were removed from their home. Their wish was realized after outpatient care in two different agencies failed. Although the patient related well to his therapist, the family would not cooperate. When John was finally suspended from school, he was remanded to a residential center. After commitment, he made a series of suicidal attempts, all of which directly followed failures of attempts to reinstate himself with his parents. He ran away many times, always returning home. At the institution he formed good relationships only with adults. The "accidental" amputation of his finger with a meat axe occurred when his parents, instead of visiting him as they had promised, sent his brothers in their place. In the operating room he remarked, while his stump was being sutured, "Wait until my old man hears about this."

Although euphoric on admission to the psychiatric ward, he soon became depressed and then angry when he learned that he would have to return to the treatment center. His parents were embarrassed to have a child on the psychiatric service, avoided any discussion of his self-mutilation, and consistently refused to consider his difficulties. In the formal meetings they blamed each other—Mrs. Cord called the father cold, ambitious, and punitive; whereas Mr. Cord pointed to his wife's inconsistencies, her desire to work, and her anger with her wayward son. In view of the previous failures to influence the parents and because of their need to preserve a shaky marriage by excluding John, we concentrated our therapeutic efforts on helping John face the reality of his parents' abandonment of him and the necessity of returning to the institution from which he had come.

FAMILY INVOLVEMENT AFTER ADMISSION

Diagnostic assessment of the family situation upon admission is important but often extremely difficult. Often an early decision is required about which family members should be involved in treatment, and whether members should be treated individually, as a group, or both. Sometimes the solution is dictated by circumstances beyond the hospital staff's control, as when families live at a distance that permits only weekly or monthly contacts, or when the family is broken, or when the patient has already left parents or spouse. Staff shortage can lead to family treatment instead of individual contacts either before contraindications to group meetings are appreciated or even despite such recognition.

The management of the Wiley family in which the patient was a sixteen-year-old schizophrenic boy provides an example of ill-timed family group meetings. On admission the patient was overtly paranoid and grandiose. His parents had been divorced six years earlier. The parents had recognized that the patient was withdrawn for some time. His school performance had started to deteriorate two years before admission, approximately at the time of his mother's second marriage. Then violent quarrels with his stepfather became a serious problem.

Noting the mother's seductive behavior with the patient during the admission interview, as well as indications that she abetted the quarrelsome interaction between son and stepfather while claiming to protect the patient from her husband, the therapist decided to bring these issues into the open through conjoint family sessions. The results were catastrophic—the mother grew angry, the patient regressed markedly, and Mr. Wiley felt that his abusive behavior toward the patient had been vindicated. With hindsight we could appreciate that these family members should have been treated separately, and if this had not been possible, only the patient should have been engaged in psychotherapy immediately. He could not tolerate the incestuous proximity to his mother, one of the factors that led to his admission, but he could only express his intense hate toward the stepfather. Mrs. Wiley needed preparation through individual casework or therapy before being able to consider her role in the patient's agitation, let alone that the patient's anger was in part directed at her.

This is an example of intense family interaction, but the abuse and noise served more to obscure issues than to enlighten any of the participants. Essentially, the Wiley family was continuing an ineffectual struggle with issues beyond their comprehension, such as the patient's continued oedipal involvement that had to be clarified with each member on an individual basis. In this case the psychiatrist was misled by their behavior, assuming wrongly that the family was airing long-standing conflicts that the members had feared to bring out in the open. Such ventilation and emotional release are often desired and encouraged in family sessions because they may serve to clarify difficult issues and provide corrective emotional experiences. Such family interaction must be differentiated from family meetings filled with hostile, noisy, and vituperative exchanges which are only a sample of the customary family behavior.

It may seem paradoxical that the noisy family should calm down and that the quiet family may have to become noisy. It puts the psychiatrist in a position for which he is often reproached, namely, that he sees everything differently from the way it seems to "ordinary" people. But, by and large, psychiatrists must understand and deal with what lies underneath the surface behavior, no matter how paradoxical it may seem to the untrained. Family behavior, even more than individual behavior, is multiply determined, and whenever the need to hospitalize a member arises, we must assume that habitual coping devices of the family somehow failed, no matter how noisy and "frank" the family dialogue seems to be, as the next example will illustrate.

A thirty-seven-year-old pregnant woman in a psychotic depression was referred from the obstetrical service to the psychiatric unit. Mrs. Map had many complaints about her husband who seemed to be overly dependent and who drank heavily on occasion. We soon learned of considerable marital conflict with repeated separations, but we considered it significant that they had survived many crises successfully without outside help. After their two children were born, eighteen and fourteen years before, Mrs. Map had had several abortions. The current pregnancy was unwanted, as had been most of the earlier ones. Mrs. Map worked full-time to supplement the family income in addition to running the household. At first, and especially during her psychotic phase, Mrs. Map exaggerated her husband's irresponsibility and alcoholism. Mr. Map, in turn, derogatingly described how his wife ate wood. Mrs. Map improved on the psychiatric service where she also aborted spontaneously toward the end of the third month.

After Mr. Map had developed a trusting relationship with his caseworker, and after the patient had recovered from her acute psychotic state, family conferences were instituted which included the eighteen-year-old son. In these sessions it was possible to point up the spouses' mutual dependency and to correct the wife's distorted view of her husband as a very immature and irresponsible man, which his faithful work record and the fact that he had built their home by himself did not warrant. Mrs. Map was able to recognize her intense dependency needs, which she had denied during the eleven years that she had worked but which came to the fore with each pregnancy. The couple decided to continue with family therapy after the hospitalization and later were referred to a family service agency. They have continued to do well.

This vignette illustrates the importance of not responding to the "noise," the arguing and the recriminations, but to search for and identify the underlying problems, such as Mrs. Map's tendency to overcompensate for her dependency strivings, and to discern the constructive and cohesive forces in the family.

We have found it useful to be able to provide various therapeutic experiences to families. We have already indicated that there were certain parallels between the development of group treatment for patients and the evolution of work with families. In our schizophrenia research we used mostly, although not exclusively, separate casework contact with individual family members, usually both parents and at least one sibling. As this research progressed paralleling changes in hospital practices, we increasingly introduced various group procedures for the family unit. In addition, on the acute general hospital service individual family members other than the patient are often treated quite actively and a few have even been hospitalized.

Our experience with the Daniel family will illustrate the failure of various efforts to find an effective approach to a family, as well as the extreme degree of the parents' masking of their need to exclude the patient from the family. The Daniels were first seen individually by the caseworker, and a good working relationship developed with the mother during several weeks when the father was away from home. When the father returned, both parents began to advance many complaints about the hospital. Later, in a family session (which included the eighteen-year-old adopted patient, the social worker, and the therapist) the parents' displacement of their dissatisfaction with the patient onto the hospital could be clearly observed. The parents attacked their daughter as soon as she entered the room because of her sloppy appearance and for wearing the wrong type of shoes; they shifted to blaming the hospital for allowing her to buy orthopedically unsound shoes. In actuality, the patient had no orthopedic abnormality and did not need special shoes. There was also no basis for the parents' subsequent concentration on an alleged metabolic dysfunction. Although clinical and laboratory examinations had revealed no abnormalities at our hospital, or at another institution a few months earlier, the parents were outraged because we could not tell them the exact results of the tests but only that they were all within normal limits. The ease with which blame and criticism were shifted from the patient to a staff member, or to the hospital as a whole, could be observed readily during group interviews, but might not have been noted without such opportunity for direct observation.

The possibility of an idiosyncratic personality clash between these parents and a staff member had to be considered, but similar impasses developed with four different staff members. A quote from Mrs. Daniel about a social worker who was present during the conference illustrates how she could provoke hostility from the staff: "I do not like her training; I do not like her personality; and I do not like her culture!"

Although when seen individually each parent seemed more tractable, they insisted on being seen together, perhaps because each spouse feared what the other might reveal about the family. This may have been related to earlier disputes over their children's upbringing. Mr. and Mrs. Daniel had to prove that the patient had a congenital or acquired organic ailment, arguing that they both had been approved as parents at the time of the child's adoption. Moreover, the mother viewed herself as particularly well-versed in mental health matters, having had considerable training in one of the behavioral sciences. Thus their prestige and worth as parents were at stake, and their need to be rid of the patient as an unsuccessful experiment in child rearing had to be covered up. The daughter misbehaved and abetted their rejection prior to hospitalization. Her threats of injuring her mother were akin to the parents' aggressive and irrational attacks on the hospital. Although we thought the patient was improving in the hospital, they claimed that she had only "deteriorated horribly" because she seemed sloppier and had gained some weight. She was finally removed against advice.

With such families it is not difficult to decide how to proceed; family treatment is contraindicated, if not impossible. Patient and parents should be treated separately at least until significant changes in the parents' attitudes toward the patient have been achieved. Aside from illustrating the need for a hospital staff to work patiently with families who invite rejection in order to cover up their guilt feelings, this couple illustrates the discrepancy between parents' behavior within the family circle and outside in the community. Both parents were respected in their home town, Mrs. Daniel prominent in community agencies, and Mr. Daniel successful in his profession.

It is noteworthy how similar the behavior of the rejecting or excluding family is to that of the families which cannot tolerate the separation from the patient. Both conflicts may result in removal from the hospital to the patient's disadvantage. Both the overly attached colleague-mother and the Daniels attacked the hospital staff mercilessly; both felt very guilty in connection with their children's illnesses. But the physician-mother basically sought reunification with her daughter; the Daniels seemed to mask aggressively their basic rejection of an unsuccessful experiment in child rearing. However, families seeking to exclude the patient also have been noted to resent and even fear the patient's improvement. During visits with the patient they may provoke hostility in their interaction with him precipitating setbacks, thereby putting the hospital on notice that rehabilitation into the home and reintegration with the family are contraindicated. If visiting is interdicted, however, the family again may blame the staff for their dearth of understanding and uncooperative policies, and threaten to remove the patient. It is important to remember that such crises can also be instigated by the patient.

When family meetings were begun only after prolonged hospitalization, as has been the case with several Institute patients and their relatives, the reason for introducing such sessions was often the need for new and additional information about family dynamics. In some instances, an additional motive has been to help the patient gain emotional distance from his parents when this could not be effected adequately through individual and group therapy. The Lerners were not seen conjointly until the fifth year of the patient's hospital stay, and only then did it become clear how the parents instigated the patient's excited and paranoid behavior which served to help them mask their own feelings and conflicts to an extraordinary degree.

Eve Lerner was one of our most resistant patients, a paranoid schizophrenic in her thirties who first began to make significant progress after she was given a female therapist and conjoint family therapy was instituted. After prolonged individual sessions with the parents, mostly with Mrs. Lerner, it had gradually become clear that the patient had been subtly excluded by the family long before hospitalization. The mother, a professional woman, had ignored the daughter's paranoid symptomatology for almost a decade. Eve had been excluded through an atmosphere of secrecy and outright deceit concerning family matters, as has been described earlier in this volume (Chapters IV and V). None of these matters had ever been explained to the patient.

After it eventually became clear to us that the parents had not only reconciled themselves to the patient's institutionalization but also had begun to function better and more comfortably with the patient out of the home, we found it impossible to induce either parent to state the situation clearly and frankly to the patient. She expected to return home as soon as possible, and when with her the parents reinforced this hope, although they feared even an occasional house visit from Eve. In addition, the mother suffered from a psychosomatic illness with flare-ups that often coincided with periods of improvement in the patient. The home was supposedly open to the patient for week-end visits, but frequent misunderstandings and futile negotiations about mutually convenient week ends resulted in long periods without visits home. Although it was therapeutically not very important how often this patient went home, it was important that the parents could not work through their ambivalence and arrive at a consistent attitude and position as to whether or not the patient could ever live at home again. It was easier for them to focus on the patient's pathology than enter into discussions of arrangements for a visit home. For instance, if transporting her by car was inconvenient, they would state this without suggesting alternatives, doing so in a way that made Eve appear too rigid to think of alternatives. The patient would then allude to some paranoid delusion as if to justify the parents' reluctance to have her home. Family meetings resulted in clarification of the parents' behavior for the patient and for us, but produced no noteworthy change in the parents. However, the sessions greatly helped the patient free herself from the rigid limitation to perceiving, thinking, and feeling prescribed by the parents' paranoid need to cover up unacceptable realities. Although imperfections in either parent or in the family relationship could not be discussed in family sessions, the patient could begin to recognize them in discussing the family therapy meetings with her therapist. It helped her accept the parents' limitations, reduced her fear of knowing their imperfections and weaknesses, and permitted her to trust her own perceptions. A comment on how family studies have aided individual psychotherapy with psychotic patients may be in order here in connection with Eve's difficult and prolonged treatment.

The patient recovering from a psychosis encounters great difficulty in achieving a more rational and realistic view of a parent, spouse, or some other significant figure if he does not have the opportunity to re-evaluate and correct for himself earlier more distorted views and assessments of the other significant persons' attitudes and motivations. In classical analytic treatment with neurotic patients, this is usually accomplished through the transference. But this is possible only if the parents' personalities have been assimilated and incorporated by the patient in such a way that the therapist can gain a reasonably accurate and realistic picture of the patient's early familial experience through grasping the nature and quality of the transference. Unlike neurotic patients, young schizophrenics often cannot do this, because many have never had a reasonably realistic view of their family or of the world. Therefore, the therapist must appreciate that the patient, far from distorting reality, may be trying to grasp it when he paints a picture of a grossly disturbed parent. For the uninitiated it is often extraordinarily difficult to fathom how a very successful person, sometimes a well-known public figure whom we may even have admired from a distance, can behave as a parent in such bizarre and disorganizing ways.

Another form of work with families we have instituted is regular treatment groups of relatives without patients. They have consisted mostly of parents of patients because of our youthful population, but there have also been some spouses of patients. These family group meetings have become an integral part of the treatment regimen. In addition, group members are also seen individually each week. Such family groups have been effective in helping relatives with common feelings of guilt, stigma, anger, and their sense of failure brought on or intensified by the hospitalization of a disturbed child or spouse. The empathy felt among the members enables them to give one another support and lessen feelings of isolation. For many reasons these families are usually isolated from neighbors and their extended families, so that the family group may be the first place where a relative can expose his feelings without fear of rejection or other social disadvantage. The groups have been effective in enabling most families to resume social activities, suspended because of the patient's illness and their need to keep it secret. The more experienced group members, whose relatives have been hospitalized longer, lead and support the more inexperienced through the "initiation rites," i.e., how to cope with a patient's pressure to remove him from the hospital within a few days of admission or sift stories of mistreatment which patients always seem to have ready during early visits of their relatives. These groups deal with such issues more easily and effectively than can staff members. Later on the group meets issues such as the fantasy of hospital omnipotence, which is as clearly observable as the period of positive transference and overdependence on the group leader. So far, most new members have tried to sway the group in the direction of hostility toward the leader representing hospital authority; an attitude that then shifts to an unrealistic dependence on and faith in this authority before more individual and idiosyncratic problems are communicated and considered.

Family groups help parents work out various painful problems, especially the emotional separation that often must take place between parent and child. Most of our parents share this problem and they support one another in trying to free their children and "neutralize" the involvement between themselves and the patients. The family group has been particularly effective in reducing parents' "acting out," e.g., allowing patients to set up a battle between hospital and parents, removing the patient from the hospital against advice or covertly encouraging the patient to run away. When indicated, we arrange for relatives to continue in their group or with their case-worker, after the patient's discharge, to consolidate emotional gains or to work out further problems.

DISPOSITION

It is an old adage that plans for disposition should begin with the admission of a patient. Certain treatment decisions need to be made with plausible discharge plans in mind. If, for instance, treatment with the referring psychiatrist is to be resumed, how and to what extent should the psychiatrist be included in the hospital program? Whether or not to include the patient in the family group sessions may be determined, in part, by whether reunification with or separation from his family is envisioned upon his discharge. Various such considerations germane to disposition have already been touched upon, and this section will therefore be confined to some more general observations with emphasis on the difficulties and pitfalls besetting hospitals, patients, and families in accomplishing a smooth transition to outpatient treatment and life in the community. In fact, treatment discontinuity and inflexibility in providing for the discharged patient have been among the most common deficiencies of all medical care, including psychiatric treatment (Greenblatt et al., 1957; Freeman and Simmons, 1959; Linn, 1959; Eldred et al., 1962). Adequate reha-bilitation has been one of the stepchildren of most general hospitals, and is even more neglected in psychiatric hospitals, where rehabili-tation is often more complicated than physical restoration because of the greater importance of the social parameters. To whatever sur-rounding the mental patient returns, the people around him—family, coworkers, or others—usually require some therapeutic guidance. If, for instance, the patient is a housewife, she should in most instances resume her responsibilities gradually rather than all at once. Too often the patient has to resume many responsibilities just at a time when therapeutic contact and support are diminished or even lost because the inpatient staff cannot continue therapy after discharge. "Reintegration" into the family has often consisted of no more than discharging the patient to the care of some family member with the hope that the acceptable behavior the patient showed in the hospital will continue at home. In contrast, a satisfactory procedure requires some understanding of the family dynamics involved and consideration of the wisdom of such reintegration. To be satisfied simply if the patient gets three meals a day within his family without any heed to his emotional and social diet is no longer acceptable psychiatric "aftercare." An up-to-date hospital must not only identify family problems but also undertake their amelioration or resolution in so far as possible, so that the stresses which may have contributed to hospitalization will not recur.

If good psychiatric inpatient care demands therapeutic involvement of the family, abrupt cessation of these treatment measures upon the patient's discharge must be avoided. We must surmount in particular the obstacles to treatment continuity dictated by administrative convenience and traditions. The patient should be provided continuity of care, and his family must be helped to cooperate with all phases of the treatment program.

Private institutions or services in general hospitals where practicing psychiatrists can participate in the hospital treatment can most readily provide continuity of care. In other situations the hospital staff must continue to treat their patients and their families after discharge. This is routinely done on our general hospital service where weekly family group sessions are held for discharged patients and their families.

However, our experience with young schizophrenic patients indicates that they are usually better served through plans which, as in the case of Eve Lerner, do not aim at returning them home; not only because the family may be pathogenic for them but also because in our present cultural milieu the adolescent and young adult should be engaged in the process of emancipating from the family. To return the patient to the family, therefore, very often would mean the imposition of ambivalent dependency upon the patient instead of furthering his independence. In general, disposition can be sound only if the family, whether reunited or not, is being helped to cope better with the problems which precipitated hospitalization.

COMMENT

Our main thesis derived from the two research areas of family studies and investigations of the psychiatric hospital milieu has been that good psychiatric inpatient care must provide a therapeutic experience for the patient's family. Patients whose families forsake them to the hospital or whose families are ignored or rejected by the hospital have less chance of recovering than patients whose families remain actively involved with them during hospitalization. We have documented our thesis with illustrative case examples which permitted discernment of the pertinent underlying psycho- and sociodynamic forces. Families who seek reunification with the patient after admission must be differentiated from families which basically strive to be rid of the patient, although their overt behavior and interaction with the staff may be quite similar.

Family therapy as such and its techniques have not been discussed here, and the topic is vast and complex. Most of our family group sessions in the hospital are initially investigative and diagnostic, but as in individual psychotherapy, it would be very difficult to decide when a sequence of sessions turns from the more diagnostic to the more therapeutic. In particular, we do not consider family treatment in the hospital environment a therapy in itself, but only one of many essential treatment modalities to be employed as indicated.

The procedures we have described also have important implications for the training of residents and other professional personnel. We have already emphasized the importance of teamwork with interprofessional role flexibility for the purpose of establishing an around-the-clock therapeutic environment and for appropriate family involvement procedures. However, inexperienced staff members are liable to overidentify with patients and become hostile and overcritical of parents or spouses, sometimes sharing one side of the patient's ambivalence. Therapists-in-training may feel overwhelmed by the psychological cruelties they learn about from patients or observe during family visits or conjoint conferences. It is, therefore, particularly important in a training setting to have other personnel in addition to the patient's therapist deal with families. On a short-term service it is particularly important that teamwork mean not only the sharing of information, but the sharing of therapeutic tasks in family group sessions.

To do their job adequately in terms of present-day knowledge, psychiatrists will have to become proficient in family psychiatry; that is, they will have to be willing and competent to deal with family members. How to select the proper procedure for a particular family, whether conjoint family therapy or some casework type of treatment with individual family members or combinations of these, is by no means certain and requires additional study. Without using family therapy as an exclusive treatment modality, we have demonstrated how it can be a prerequisite of successful psychotherapy of schizophrenic and other patients, although other psychiatrists have shown that family therapy can be successful by itself, especially in the management of childhood disturbances (Ackerman, 1958b).

Finally, I wish to comment about the trend toward brief hospitalization for schizophrenic patients. Because so-called "continued treatment services" in many mental hospitals in reality foster inactivity, isolation, and social impoverishment, lengthy hospitalization is often considered deleterious. As a result patients are often discharged to the more active family environment, even though it may be a distorted and pathogenic setting. A good hospital will have a therapeutic program and a milieu which are specifically designed to counteract unnecessary dependency and to foster progressive achievement of autonomy, even as it will also involve the family with the purpose of lessening its pathogenic influence.

XVII

The Mothers of Schizophrenic Patients

(1964)

Despite the obvious importance of the mother in creating the intra-familial environment and her crucial moment in the personality development of the schizophrenic patient, we have deferred surveying and analyzing the mothers as a group until the end of our study. Considerable attention had been paid to the personalities of mothers of schizophrenic patients and their ways of relating to the offspring before the start of our project though the descriptions are often contradictory (Abrahams and Varon, 1953; Gerard and Siegel, 1950; Kasanin et al., 1934; Prout and White, 1950; Reichard and Tillman, 1950; Sullivan, 1925-1926; Tietze, 1949; Chapter II). Then Hill (1955) provided a remarkably insightful though somewhat inconsistent portrayal and discussion of mothers of schizophrenic patients. His concepts of the devastatingly overpossessive love that was not rejecting but unrealistic and conditional stood in direct contrast to J. Rosen's (1953) convictions that maternal rejection during the first year of life formed the significant causative factor of schizophrenia. Alanen's (1958) excellent monograph provided a careful review of all prior studies and some significant new findings that were in accord with our own emerging data. As our studies were uncovering serious difficulties in all areas of the transactions in these families, we preferred to bring balance to the topic by directing attention to the total situation before focusing upon the mother. Our various papers contain numerous references to the deficiencies of these women as mothers and wives, but we required a more coherent theory concerning the

Theodore Lidz, Alice R. Cornelison, Margaret T. Singer, Sarah Schafer, and Stephen Fleck. This paper has not been previously published.

importance of the family upon the development and maldevelopment of its children before we could seek to assay the mother's place and role in the genesis of schizophrenia.

The task presented greater difficulties than some other aspects of our study because the mother was both a cardinal informant and a central object of study in each family, and we were confronted by a mass of data which were extremely complex and which seemed, at times, paradoxical. We wished to evaluate, as far as possible, how often and to what extent the mother's difficulties arose in response to an abnormal child and whether or not they antedated the marriage and the birth of the child. The influences of spouses on each other are particularly difficult to assess. It appeared that in some families the mother's behavioral pattern had been well established prior to the marriage and more or less dictated the selection of a spouse, whereas in others the influence of the husband brought certain traits of the mother to the fore, crystallizing, so to speak, a configuration in a personality that had been more fluid prior to the marriage. In any case, it was apparent that the interaction of many of these women with their children was affected adversely by their efforts to cope with extremely difficult, disturbed, or inadequate husbands. Nevertheless, whatever the reasons, all but two or three of the seventeen mothers studied were seriously disturbed and strange women. Any study of the family milieu in which these patients grew up must pay particular attention to the mothers.

Describing these seventeen mothers and their impact upon their families and offspring presents difficulties. They cannot be categorized into a single group according to personality or way of relating to the schizophrenic offspring. Some fitted readily the description of the "schizophrenogenic" mother found in the literature (Hill, 1955; Chapter II)—the mother with nebulous ego boundaries who treats the child as an extension of herself, intruding but impervious to the child's needs and wishes as a separate individual. Other mothers fitted the category of the "rejecting" mother who did not want and could not cathect the child, a factor which has been described as causative of schizophrenia. The boundaries of such groupings, of course, are not fast—and merge into less clear-cut types of mothers whose difficulties and those they create for their children are recognized and understood through appreciation of similarities to the more extreme types. Several seemed to possess reasonable potential as mothers, but their husbands' serious psychopathology dominated the family life and thus affected the children directly and impaired the mothers' relationships with their offspring. There were mothers who could relate reasonably well to a son but not to a daughter, and an occasional mother who could interact more salubriously with a daughter. Some mothers had extremely little to do with the patient during the first years of his life as the nurturant functions were given over to nursemaids, and yet these were very disturbed mothers who clearly had a profoundly deleterious influence on their offspring. Consideration of the mother's influence could not be confined to the first year or two of life. We cannot describe *the* mother of the schizophrenic patient. An adequate survey of these mothers and their influence upon their children presented the problem of understanding some very different types of women and their effect upon their families as well as the patient over many years. We shall seek to convey some understanding of these women—all of whom were seriously handicapped by their own faulty upbringing and usually by the unfortunate marriages in which they had become enmeshed—and how they contributed to an offspring's failure to achieve a workable integration.

Before turning to a scrutiny of these mothers, it will be useful to recall some of the complexities of the task of being a mother. Motherhood is not an entity. It is not a quality that can be instilled into a woman by prenatal classes, natural childbirth, rooming-in or breast feeding. The functions of a mother extend over many years and are a compound of various emotions and attitudes, a series of interrelated skills, ways of communicating, etc., and involve the woman's relationships with her own parents and siblings, with her husband and her other children as well as with the specific child under study. Too often, particularly in studies pertaining to schizophrenia, the functions of a mother have been considered primarily in terms of her nurturant and empathic qualities during the first year or two of the child's life, as if her major function, if not her sole task, were to provide her offspring with a wholesome start by supplying his oral needs and thus inculcating a basic and lasting trust in the world and the people who inhabit it.

COMPONENTS OF MOTHERING

We cannot here attempt to review the many functions of a mother and the many capacities she is expected to possess. We believe that the process of mothering includes at least three major components. We can seek to convey something of the complexity and the inter-relationships of these tasks, and then scrutinize how the mothers of the patients managed these functions.

The Maternal Nurturant Relationships

In providing nurturance for the infant, the mother requires a number of skills and a sense of security in her own ability to handle the helpless and frangible baby. To meet the child's demands upon her, she needs properly to cathect the infant almost as an extension of herself. The investment contains narcissistic components but also includes derivatives from her affection for her husband. The investment of the infant demands a priority over her other relationships but should not exclude, or be excluded by, attachments to her husband and her other children. The ability to feel warmly nurturant may well depend upon having experienced such nurturant care in her own early childhood. It involves her feelings of worth and capabilities as a woman. For some, only a male child will bring a sense of completion, whereas others can only feel close to a girl with whom they can empathize. Most mothers in giving of themselves to an infant require replenishment from sources of affection and esteem—usually from the husband. Then as the child moves into the second half of infancy, he requires an increasing responsivity to his smiles, babbling, reaching out, etc., from the mother who becomes important as a specific individual. A particularly difficult transition occurs for many mothers when the child begins to ambulate, express initiative, and get into things. Some women, who can feel secure as long as they can control their babies completely, cannot allow them to separate. They find it difficult to tolerate the disorder the child creates, or to cope with the almost inevitable anxiety that he will hurt himself. Efforts to limit and control the noncomprehending child can limit the child's initiative, direct toward undue passivity, and foster distrust in his own abilities. If there is conflict over control, it commonly focuses upon bowel training or feeding, areas in which the child can assert himself through negativism. Such struggles foster ambivalences in both mother and child, and at this time the mother's frustrations with her marriage, loss of a career, etc., are particularly likely to influence her handling of her child.

Such considerations of the first eighteen months of life can obviously be greatly amplified, and similar issues arise with each new phase of development requiring different capacities from the mother and arousing attitudes from her past that are influenced by her current life situation. The child's feeling of worth as a member of his or her sex is influenced by the mother's acceptance of the child's sex, her own feelings of worth as a woman, by how her husband fosters such feelings, and by her attitudes toward her husband. The consistency of the mother's responses to the child and the reliability of what she says affects the child's trust in the validity and usefulness of verbal communication. With the child's progression through the oedipal phase the mother needs to frustrate gradually the eroticized and sensuous components of the child's attachment and yet permit temporary regressions when the child becomes insecure or frustrated in his increasing independence. The child's security in venturing into peer groups and starting school depends upon having a firm base at home from which he can move outwards, and a mother who will expect the child to have disappointments and difficulties but who can encourage him to surmount them rather than convey her anxieties or her own distrust of the larger world. The child's transformation at puberty with increasing movement into the extrafamilial world, and his interests in members of the opposite sex can accentuate old problems in the mother-child relationship as well as create many new ones involving the mother's abilities to cope with the erotic components of her attachments to the child, the recrudescence of problems of her own adolescence, her concerns over aging, over being left isolated with her husband, etc.

This sketchy perusal of the mother's role in the child's developmental process with indications of the many factors that enter into her capacities to relate to her child salubriously at each phase of development should suffice to indicate the complexity of the simple task of providing adequate "mothering." Yet the mother exerts important influences in still other ways.

The Mother and the Family Structure

The mother-child interaction transpires within a family social system which it influences and by which it is influenced. The dynamic structure of the family, particularly of the isolated nuclear family characteristic of contemporary American life, depends primarily upon the nature of the marital relationship of the parents. The family must achieve certain structural requisites to direct the child's development into an integrated pattern. The development of a family social system suited for adequate child rearing rests upon the abilities of the parents to form a parental coalition, to maintain boundaries between the generations, and to adhere to their respective sex-linked roles. We have discussed the effects of the parents' marital relationship upon their children's personality development elsewhere. The mother's capacities as a wife and her ways of relating as a wife clearly influence the structuring and integration of her children's personalities. Thus, a woman who cannot achieve a coalition with her husband and find reciprocally interrelating roles with him deprives the child of unified directives and of the opportunity of assimilating the benefits of marital and family mutuality: if she conveys her dissatisfactions with her husband, she undermines his worth as an object for a son's identification, or his value to a daughter as a model of a love object; if, because of her inadequacies as a wife, or even because she cannot meet a husband's unreasonable expectations, she becomes an object for her husband's contumely, her worth as an object of identification and love to the children is diminished. A mother who breaches the generation boundaries by seeking her major source of emotional support and a sense of completion from a son rather than from her husband not only impedes the formation of boundaries between herself and the son, but also confuses the child's passage through the oedipal phase. The woman who assumes the male role in the family, or who cannot fill the feminine expressive-affectional role disturbs a child's apprehension of masculinity and femininity and his achievement of a secure sexual identity. In general, we may say that the provision of a relatively conflict-free area within the family in which the child can feel secure, and the opening of the proper channels for him to move into and gain rewards for doing so, depend upon the creation of a suitable family structure by the parental interaction. The mother's role as a wife exerts a pervasive influence upon her children throughout their formative years.

The Mother as a Transmitter of Instrumental Techniques

A child's development into an individual capable of directing his own life depends upon the acquisition of countless adaptive techniques and the conscious and unconscious assimilation of the institutions of his culture. The fundamentals are gained within the family with the mother as a basic teacher. The fundamentals extend beyond the skills of primary socialization and include complex patterns of relating appropriately to different categories of persons and the assimilation of a variety of social institutions. Basic to all but the simplest tasks is the acquisition of the language and meaning systems essential for learning, communicating, and self-direction. The learning of language is particularly pertinent in a consideration of schizophrenia, an illness distinguished by distortions of the symbolic processes. Mothers who fail to respond to the child's early efforts, who respond inconsistently, whose nonverbal and verbal communications are contradictory, who place the child in insoluble "binds," who respond to their own feelings or needs projected onto a child, whose promises or bribes are forgotten after they have achieved their purposes, who blur and fragment meanings, who obliterate meaningfulness, etc., confuse the child's development of meanings. As the ability to categorize experience depends upon possessing the words that indicate the categories, and because the meanings of words provide predictability, confusions of linguistic meanings impair ego functioning (Lidz, 1963c). Inculcation of distrust in the usefulness of verbal communication as well as teaching to use words to avoid the implications of events can prepare a child to attempt to solve conflicts by breaking through the confines imposed by the culture's meanings and logic.

We believe it useful to note how these women carried out the three sets of maternal functions that we have just designated: (1) to provide maternal nurturance and relate to the child in a manner that fosters a sound foundation for the development of ego autonomy; (2) to contribute to the formation and maintenance of a family system that provides integrating directives to the child's developing personality; (3) to transmit the basic adaptive techniques of the culture to the child, particularly the inculcation of the shared system of meanings of the culture. None of these mothers filled any of these functions competently, and all were gravely deficient in at least one of these areas—a deficiency uncompensated by assets in the other areas, and aggravated by the father's characteristics and behavior.[1]

CASE ILLUSTRATIONS

The series of seventeen mothers contains some very discrepant personalities. There is no one set of characteristics common to all, but

[1] Consideration of these three aspects of being a mother is not meant to neglect the importance of the mother as an object for identification and as a love object to the child. Much of the child's personality development depends upon internalization of characteristics of the mother and other objects, and much of the direction and the "leverage" for directing the child's socialization comes from the child's wish and need to gratify the love object. This is not the place to attempt to deal with a highly involved topic that has been further complicated by theoretical confusions. The integrative value of the mother as an object depends upon all three sets of functions discussed as well as other factors. The mother is both the primary object for identification and primary love object for children of both sexes—becoming more of the first for a daughter and more of the second for a son. Initially she is neither when the child is still in symbiosis with her: with differentiation the mother divides or is divided into an identification object that is internalized and a love object with whom the infant seeks an equilibrium and from whom he later seeks love and approbation. In this manner, the problem of identification, internalization, and object relationship relates to ego, superego, and ego-ideal formation, and also to what must be repressed into the unconscious. Adequate consideration of the topic requires an exploration of basic psychoanalytic theory. For present purposes, it suffices to recognize that the mother's security and self-esteem enter into the child, as also does the father's esteem for the mother. In addition, the father's value as an object for identification and as a love object also involves the mother's way of relating to him, as will become apparent in the illustrations. Harmonious and integrated personality organization probably requires harmony between the object for identification and the love object. A son's father who is the object of the boy's identification should also be desired as a love object by the mother.

Khan's (1962a, b) observations about the intrafamilial childhood relationships of patients with a specific type of polymorphous perverse schizoid character are pertinent. The mother expressed devotion to her husband and demanded a similar intense devotion from her child, but confused the child by involving him in premature confidences about her husband and because serious conflicts between the mother and father existed. These parents not only failed to achieve a satisfactory relationship with each other but did not act in coalition as parents. Although these mothers were adequate mothers to the patients as infants, the mothers could not relate well to the toddler, all having difficulty in shifting from "a primary identity to recognition of independence in the child." Winnicott (1960) also emphasized the difficulties mothers can have in making this transition, and how some women have particular problems in this area.

certain patterns recur frequently, with some of the mothers having very similar ways of relating to both their husbands and children, and having become caught up in very similar family situations. A division of the mothers according to the sex of the psychotic child helps clarify some of the discrepancies in the literature in the descriptions of the mothers of schizophrenic offspring. As we have indicated in Chapter XV, the developmental tasks of boys and girls differ, and certain types of parents are more detrimental to children of one sex than to children of the other. However, some notable differences also exist among mothers of schizophrenic children of the same sex, particularly among the mothers of schizophrenic sons.

Rather than continue to deal with abstractions, we shall describe some mothers with differing characteristics. Viewing their ways of relating and communicating as mothers and wives together with their own developmental and marital problems will help avoid placing undue emphasis upon certain isolated characteristics, and may also provide a modicum of understanding of these women as persons.

Mothers of Schizophrenic Sons

We shall first consider a schizophrenic boy's mother who can serve as a paradigm of the "schizophrenogenic mother." The deleterious nature of her behavior and personality seems apparent. It is difficult to imagine how a son she raised would not be seriously disturbed, if not schizophrenic. She provides an example of a woman who can devote virtually all of her energies to rearing her children to their detriment. The gross and apparent disturbances in such mothers guide toward the recognition of similar difficulties in less disturbed mothers.

Two excellent private hospitals had refused to retain Jack Newcomb as a patient because their personnel could not tolerate his mother's constant and insistent intrusions into her son's therapy. She would dogmatically insist that he suffered from an endocrine deficiency and hound the staff to use a preparation that allegedly had cured a boy she knew. The separation from Jack caused her intolerable anxiety, but her frequent visits clearly aggravated his condition. No one other than she could understand her son and care for him properly. Her capacity to deny the obvious was remarkable. When, upon her insistence, a hospital had permitted Jack to spend a week at home, he had made unwelcomed advances to a girl whom he knew slightly. Despite the girl's complaints, Mrs. Newcomb insisted that she was leading her son on. When stopped from trailing the girl, Jack became refractory. An ambulance was called to return him to the hospital and when he became combative, the police were required to help subdue him. Thereafter, Mrs. Newcomb steadfastly maintained that Jack had done very well at home until the police appeared and mistreated him. On another occasion, a nurse saw Jack strike his mother on the back, almost knocking her down. Mrs. Newcomb expressed surprise at the nurse's concern, and insisted that her son had only tapped her playfully. Interviews with the Newcombs were extremely frustrating. They were dominated by Mrs. Newcomb, and even when questions were specifically directed toward her husband, Mrs. Newcomb answered, and like a cracked record repeated assertions and questions that had been discussed hundreds of times before. If an interviewer did not agree with her, Mrs. Newcomb seemed to believe that she could not have been understood properly, and rephrased her remark. When Mr. Newcomb was seen without his wife, he still served primarily as a spokesman for her. Mrs. Newcomb's bland expression gave little indication of feelings, but she readily became anxious and depressed. Her entire life and sense of well-being were wrapped up in her son. She refused to relinquish hope that he would eventually return home, and all of her energies and the family resources were devoted to this end—to the neglect of her daughter's needs and interests. Mrs. Newcomb thought of her son throughout the day and eventually confided that she feared that she would forget him if she did not think of him constantly. In actuality, her persistence over many years despite the discouragement of many psychiatrists finally won out.

Mrs. Newcomb had been successfuly pursuing a career in commercial art when her husband, several years her junior, proposed marriage. She was taken by surprise, not having realized that he was at all interested in her. Mr. Newcomb, orphaned in early childhood, had been raised by friends of his parents. He behaved like an orphan with his wife, grateful for her attention and deferring to her leadership and judgment. The Newcombs considered their marriage to be almost ideal: disagreements were rare for Mr. Newcomb rarely dissented, partly because he had learned that his wife's ideas could not be changed by reasoning. Mrs. Newcomb was delighted when she gave birth to a son about a year after they were married. However, she was extremely insecure in handling the baby, and her husband had to bathe the child because of her fears that she might accidentally drown her son. A daughter born two years later was also welcomed. Mrs. Newcomb was overly concerned and protective of both children. During her frequent and prolonged incapacitations by a variety of ailments, a maid took care of the children. Although most of her complaints seem to have been neurasthenic and hypochondriacal, she also suffered from severe menorrhagia, but she deferred having her uterus removed for many years, unable to tolerate the idea of losing her womb even though no more children were desired.

The children were virtually isolated from other children during their preschool years. They played in a fenced-in yard where they would be safe and where they could run about in the nude for their health. The family lived in a rather isolated area and had only superficial contacts with neighbors. Later, Mrs. Newcomb became the despair of the teachers (one of whom we interviewed) because of her frequent intrusions into the classroom and her unreasonable demands to secure a proper education for her children and adequate recognition of their abilities. She considered both children to be unusually gifted. They certainly possessed talent—Jack's mechanized and repetitious playing of the piano gave evidence of much practice and some former brilliance. Although Mr. Newcomb was a successful man to whom Mrs. Newcomb was devoted in her fashion, she clearly conveyed to Jack that she had little esteem for her husband as a man and that she had much higher aspirations for her son. Despite her anxieties about her children's well-being, but perhaps partly because of them, she sent them to preparatory schools. Jack managed to get along, although he socialized very poorly and concentrated on his music until he became flagrantly psychotic during his first year in college shortly after being in an auto accident in which a classmate was killed. His sister, who had long been accident prone, then became severely upset, secured psychotherapeutic help, and broke completely with her mother.

When we turn to Mrs. Newcomb's developmental history, the

shades roll up to reveal the psychopathology of an earlier generation. Despite the gaps and the potential unreliability in Mr. and Mrs. Newcomb's reconstructions, the evidence seems clear that the trend toward eccentricity and irrationality goes back at least to Mrs. Newcomb's parents. Her father was a man of great erudition who made brilliant starts on several careers but became a dilettante who achieved little. He displayed a rigidity and imperviousness that was characteristic of both Mrs. Newcomb and her son. He antagonized all of his children by seeking to direct and dominate their lives and by his penurious treatment of them. Mrs. Newcomb expressed open hatred of her mother whom she described as a woman who considered herself a great beauty, spending many hours each day admiring and beautifying herself. Her mother had come from a very wealthy family and let her children know that her wealth and beauty had been wasted in an unsatisfactory marriage. She neglected the household, hated housework, never prepared more than one meal a day, and paid little attention to her children. Mrs. Newcomb had grown up feeling unwanted because she was a girl. She became particularly embittered because her father refused to spend his wife's money to provide her with a college education, despite his emphasis upon the overriding importance of education. He saw no reason for a girl to attend college. He forbade any of his three daughters' boy friends to enter the home, and actually chased several out of it. Mr. Newcomb was the only suitor whom he had permitted to visit.

Dr. Margaret Singer interpreted Mrs. Newcomb's projective tests completely blindly. She confirmed the clinical appraisal, emphasizing the hypochondriacal, neurasthenic, obsessive, and highly intrusive trends, and the relative absence of ego boundaries. Quoting the personality description obtained from the tests would be redundant, but Dr. Singer's analysis of Mrs. Newcomb's thought processes is particularly significant.

She is an extreme blurrer of meanings, blurring in many ways and at many different levels. She gives a response and then soon comments that the blot no longer looks the way it did. She comments, "I don't see anything that looks like anything," and, at various times, says that there is little or no meaning to be found. Her content is very vague and when questioned about a vague response, she shifts, becomes more indefinite, and is impotent to account for her impression. When asked which Rorschach card she liked best, she "didn't see anything to like about any of them—this is the least questionable but I don't say I like it." When asked which she liked least, she commented, "This one is kind of humorous." The response forced the examiner to ask whether that meant she liked it or did not like it, to which Mrs. Newcomb replied, "I don't have any feelings one way or another about it." She takes a negativistic viewpoint and kills off meanings by saying that she feels nothing. She keeps conveying that meaning is hardly worth seeking because one cannot find anything likable or clear; and, furthermore, she will not try. She will not talk directly about anything. One might predict that this is a pervasive style of interacting with others, characteristic of her behavior in general. At the same time that she blurs meaningfulness, she creates an aura of being a nice, sweet person. Her references to people concern children, nice things, pretty little things; yet she also takes a carping outlook that makes others feel low, guilty, dejected, and hopelessly morassed by her. She is a person with low energy, with a limp indecisiveness, an unhappy neurotic life of a psychasthenic sort. She repeatedly creates the impression that the tester is to blame for her lack of clarity and her feelings of pointlessness. On her TAT responses, she is agonizingly contradictory, and when the tester inquires about an inconsistency, Mrs. Newcomb simply slaps down the examiner and further blurs meaning by stating that the picture does not make any sense. For example, she says that this is a young boy or a young woman and then talks about the boy. When the tester asks about the young woman, Mrs. Newcomb says, "The pose doesn't make sense in that case, it just looks like a child in distress and as if they haven't drawn it right." She repeatedly "recognizes" in others her own carping, unhappy, dissatisfied, displeased, and negativistic ways. In telling a story about a mother and her son, she says, "Things can be a mess if you don't have your own way." She can make any interaction seem nonsensical by claiming that it is illogical, but she never says what is logical. She destroys reality, but offers no reality to which she can adhere. She became extremely angry, diffuse, and attacking when a sexually toned picture was shown, but then talked about what an unhappy scene it was and how very upsetting; she ended by saying that her son would not tell a story to that card because she knew it would not make any sense to him either. References to her son indicated that she feels that she has him convinced that there is no reality where she says there is not to be any. Nothing about reality seems to please her or seems right, logical, or consistent. Sexuality is among her worst topics. People are both male and female at the same time.

The résumé of Mrs. Newcomb's behavioral patterns and the material from her projective tests convey the severity of her psychopathology, but it is difficult to classify her according to the usual terminology. Alanen (1958) has used the term "schizoid pattern of interpersonal relationship" and Delay et al. (1962) "psychotic character" to designate such mothers. She does not become disorganized because of her strange reality testing, the sterility of her relationships, and her fluid ego boundaries, but imposes her view of the world upon those few persons with whom she lives and whom she turns into extensions of herself. She maintains her own life and the family life within the narrow confines that she can tolerate and control in order to retain her equilibrium. Her own needs and those of her son are not clearly distinguished, and she expects him to feel and perceive as she does; she is intrusive into his life, but impervious to him as a discrete individual.

Turning to the three parameters by which we are assessing capacities for motherhood, serious difficulties are apparent in each sphere. Mrs. Newcomb, despite her desire for children, was too fearful lest she harm her first-born to provide proper nurturant care during his infancy, nor could she restrain her needs to control him as he grew older. Unable to set boundaries between herself and her son, he continued to respond to maternal needs and tensions as if they were his own. Yet, there are clear indications that she could never properly cathect her son, and instead consciously and constantly had to maintain an awareness of him. The family as a system did not achieve an organization requisite for directing the ego integration of its offspring, but the flaws were created by both parents. Although the Newcombs as spouses achieved reciprocal role relationships that were adequately satisfactory to both, the relationship was skewed. The family transactions followed the dictates, the peculiar and even bizarre dictates, of Mrs. Newcomb which were rarely, if ever, countered by her husband. Generation boundaries were broken because Mr. Newcomb filled the role of a child rather than of a husband within the confines of the home; and because Mrs. Newcomb displaced her husband by her son, gaining her major emotional gratifications from the children and making her husband subsidiary to them. Although Mrs. Newcomb expressed some ideas that she would have liked a husband to provide more guidance, there was ample evidence that she could not relinquish the direction of the family. The sex-linked roles of the parents obviously went askew because of the subsidiary role filled by the husband. In addition, Mrs. Newcomb's own confusions concerning sexual identity and her deep-seated lack of self-esteem as a woman created further complications for her children. Little need be said about Mrs. Newcomb's capacities to transmit instrumentally useful meanings to her children. She blurred meanings, denied the obvious, insisted upon her own deviant perceptions, and conveyed hopelessness of finding a meaningful view of life.

Mrs. Newcomb is an example of the type of mother of schizophrenic patients that has made the most profound impression upon psychiatrists. Two or three other mothers in the series showed a similar and equally deleterious configuration of traits. Mrs. Nebb, who has been depicted in detail in Chapter XII, was even more eccentric and even more intrusive into the lives of her twin sons. She was flagrantly seductive in sleeping with them, bathing them, and administering enemas to them well into their adolescence; and she was overtly contemptuous of her husband. A severely phobic and hypochondriacal woman, her communications were seriously disturbed and her ideas bizarre. She had been raised in an isolated community, and seriously rejected by her eccentric mother. Mrs. Narab, an overtly schizophrenic woman lived for her sons, in her sons, and through her sons —but the sons of her fantasy rather than the actual children. She conveyed a blurred perception of the frightening and hostile world of her delusions and hallucinations. In a sense, the study should be concerned with her mother. And, indeed, her mother was also an anxious, overly protective, intrusive, confused woman who grew up believing herself the younger sister of her mother—still another woman who had led a strangely confused life. Here evidence of serious pathology extends across four generations. Mrs. Schwartz might also be placed in this group of mothers because of her intrusive control of her sons and her marriage to a weak and chronically depressed man. She was a paranoid woman who believed that the family was persecuted, the telephone tapped, etc., but she ran the family business successfully and pushed her sons upward. However, she was not preoccupied with her schizophrenic youngest son because her thoughts, concerns, and indulgences focused upon her favorite eldest son who had become an embezzler. Although neglectful of the patient, she was also tactlessly overcontrolling and intrusive with him. She had emerged from a devastating childhood in Russia, orphaned at a very early age and raised without affection by her impoverished older siblings.

Mrs. Dolfuss was a very different type of woman who does not resemble the mothers under discussion, but the nursemaid to whom she abdicated the maternal duties for the first eight years of her son's life was a highly intrusive, controlling person whose life seems to have been bound up in her charge. She permitted the boy little initiative, held grandiose ambitions for him, and was sexually seductive with him. The nurse, as did the mother, shared the delusion that Mr. Dolfuss was a reincarnation of an Asiatic divinity. Both parents took a formal, distant interest in their children but had little idea of just how they were being raised by the servants. The deviant milieu has been presented in Chapter IX.

Although one overtly schizophrenic mother of a schizophrenic daughter, Mrs. Thomas (who will be discussed later) was much like Mrs. Newcomb in some ways, no mother of a female patient in this series related as she did to both her husband and child. However, we have encountered such mothers of schizophrenic daughters outside of the series. For example, a woman who was a good musician of local renown dominated the interviews held with both parents, scarcely permitting her husband to finish a sentence. She had very set ideas and impressed them upon her family. She insisted that her daughter was a genius who would emulate and surpass a world-famous musician. Her own frustrated career would reach attainment through her daughter, not through her sons. She had little interest in her daughter as she was, or wished to be, and was oblivious to the girl's own aspirations. When a psychiatrist pointed out that the woman artist whom the daughter was to emulate had committed suicide, the mother stated without hesitation that such creativity would be worth the price of a life of unhappiness and ultimate suicide.

The extreme form of mother who engulfed and intruded, unable to set boundaries between herself and the child, while treating her husband as a secondary figure, and who communicated in bizarre, blurred, and virtually psychotic ways accounted for about half of the mothers of schizophrenic sons.

Only one of the mothers of the male patients had been overtly rejecting of her unwanted son and cold and aloof toward him. Mrs. Forel created a very different impression from Mrs. Newcomb. Mrs. Forel was an attractive woman with a very distant manner. As one psychiatrist stated, "The room seemed to chill when she entered." With great reluctance she came for a few interviews, but she remained extremely guarded. She was the only mother of a patient admitted to our hospital during the past twelve years who refused to visit her child. Mrs. Forel insisted, "It would upset him too much to have his mother see him in a mental institution." Most of the information about her was obtained from her three children whose accounts agreed and interdigitated. She assumed little responsibility for her adolescent son, expecting him to take care of himself.

Mrs. Forel had never paid much attention to her youngest son who was an unwelcome product of an attempted reconciliation with her husband. Her marriage had been a hostile encounter from its inception. Inordinately bound to her mother and two older sisters who directed much of her life, she stubbornly resisted her husband's attempts to draw her away from them. She treated her husband with contempt; paid little attention to his opinions and wishes; ridiculed his outbursts. She was a tease who enjoyed attracting men and making her husband jealous; but she was frigid, permitting occasional sexual relations until her daughter was born, after which she refused her husband for the twelve years prior to the patient's conception. Mrs. Forel capitulated when her husband finally threatened divorce unless she moved to a city where he was offered a good business opportunity, and unless she resumed the sexual relationship. When she soon became pregnant, Mrs. Forel became enraged and the marriage became even more conflictful. Several attempts to induce an abortion failed. She paid scant attention to her infant son, but his father and older siblings tried to compensate for her obvious rejection of him. Feeling lost separated from her sisters, Mrs. Forel began to drink heavily and to carry on numerous flirtations. Mrs. Forel treated her husband as an outsider and constantly derided him to the children. Mr. Forel, unable to gain direction of his family, gave vent to his frustrations in frequent childlike tantrums.

When the patient was six years old, Mrs. Forel was disfigured in an automobile accident for which Mr. Forel was responsible. She became depressed and remained secluded in her room for more than a year until her appearance was surgically restored. Guilt ridden, Mr. Forel catered to her wishes but only met with rebuffs. When he developed a malignancy several years later, Mrs. Forel avoided being near him lest she contract cancer from him. After her husband died, Mrs. Forel lived for a time with her married daughter, and then she moved in with her oldest sister, even though the sister refused to let the patient, then a young adolescent, into the house. He boarded in the neighborhood and his mother occasionally ate with him. Finally, faced with her sister's extreme hostility to her youngest son, she made a home for him by taking in female boarders with whom she formed intense friendships. Although usually distant and cold, Mrs. Forel, when intoxicated, became highly seductive with both of her sons, acting as if they were boy friends, embracing and kissing them so sensuously that they were afraid to remain in her proximity.

Although relatively little is known about Mrs. Forel's early development, her difficulties in relating to men fit her family background. Her mother, a teacher, was a "strong" woman who dominated the family, and there is evidence that the pattern of female dominance went back to the patient's maternal great-grandmother. Mrs. Forel's sisters had even more pronounced difficulties in regard to men. The oldest constantly proclaimed her antipathy for men, derogated them, and sought to dominate them. She asserted that she might marry when she became old in order to have a man around who would be subservient to her. The second sister had never gone out with a man, though she was a pretty woman. Mrs. Forel's attitudes toward men antedated her marriage: she liked to tell her children how she had made dates in adolescence simply to stand up the boy. Even without direct evidence, it seems apparent that there must have been something strange about a family that raised three daughters with such attitudes toward men.

Projective tests could not be given to Mrs. Forel, and we can say little about her style of communication as she was seen on but a few occasions very early in the study before we paid specific attention to the problem. She was a difficult woman, aloof from her husband and children, impervious to the feelings of others, highly narcissistic, frigid, and at least latently homosexual. Her poor integration and profound immaturity are evident from her lasting anaclitic involvement with her sisters and the extent of her alcoholism when separated from them. She appears to have defended her weaknesses by attacking others and by her imperviousness to their feelings. She was an extremely poor wife and scarcely anything of a mother to her younger son.

Although Mrs. Forel was very different from Mrs. Newcomb, some parallels are noteworthy. Their range of roles was extremely limited and, for the most part, they adhered to one characteristic pattern to which they forced family members to adjust. They could not set proper distance between themselves and others, or alter the distance in accord with the situation and the child's developmental needs: Mrs. Newcomb was overwhelmingly intrusive, and Mrs. Forel was coldly distant except when she was intoxicated at which time she became threateningly seductive to her sons. Neither could really share tasks with a husband, and both, in different ways, destroyed their husbands' worth as useful father figures.

It seems unnecessary to elaborate upon Mrs. Forel's deficiencies in being nurturant to her son and in guiding his development. Her shortcomings in filling the role of a parent, in forming a coalition with her husband, and in filling a feminine role created serious distortions of the family system. Confusions were created in the patient because his father filled the maternal role; because women came to be feared as hostile, nonsupportive, and castrating to men; because masculinity was derided and a cause for rejection by women. Mrs. Forel's breaching of generation boundaries by her physical seductiveness fostered incest panic in the patient during his adolescence. Although we could not examine her use of language and her ways of thinking, she conveyed a strange and culturally deviant view of the world and also a pervasive meaninglessness concerning many cardinal relationships.

Not all of the mothers of schizophrenic sons were as strange, disturbed, unempathic as the six who have been discussed. The remaining three showed capacities to relate to their children in more reasonable ways despite significant personality difficulties. They were all caught up in marriages to seriously disturbed men that preoccupied them, created a pervasive sense of despair, and contributed to the rigidity of their defenses. Their husbands were major factors in creating disturbed and confusing family environments.

Mrs. Newberg was an attractive and friendly woman who spoke clearly, and willingly discussed her problems in raising her children and her serious marital difficulties. She was not rigid, recognized her inadequacies, and sought help to modify her way of relating to her children. Her inordinate attachment to her older sisters, her anxious oversolicitude for her sons mixed with an aloofness, her need to find compensation for her marriage in her sons, her antagonisms toward her husband—all adversely influenced the development of her two sons who became psychotic. However, Mr. Newberg was a confused and confusing man who talked incessantly in a driven manner. In many ways Mr. Newberg resembled the poorly organized "psychotic characters" with poor ego boundaries and distorted meaning systems more commonly noted among mothers of schizophrenic patients. He was intensely rivalrous with his sons. It seems likely that the pathogenic trends in Mrs. Newberg's personality and ways of relating to her children reached serious proportions because of her husband's serious psychopathology, her efforts to counter his influences on the children, and because of the circular feedback of apprehension, mistrust, and defensive maneuvers between the couple.

If, however, we look beyond these hypothetical reasons for Mrs. Newberg's behavior, it is clear that her ways of relating to her husband and children were highly detrimental to her offspring. She was a very anxious mother who was afraid to absent herself from her children, even though her mother and two sisters with whom the children were very familiar lived in the same building. She left the children so rarely that when it became necessary for her to visit an obstetrician during her third pregnancy, the two children, then three and four years old, both suffered from severe anxiety. All her children suffered from serious anxiety upon entering school and verged upon having school phobia. Her indulgence of her younger son—her catering to his whims about food and his need to have her with him until he fell asleep at night—aroused jealousies in her older children. All three children had feeding and bowel-training problems, and suffered from enuresis. Despite her concern and indulgence, she was rather aloof in relating to them—an absence of spontaneous warmth rather than a coldness. She had very limited contacts other than with her sisters and their families and discouraged her sons from playing with children other than their cousins lest they become involved with bad companions. She held high hopes but not unrealistic aspirations for her sons. She came to depend very heavily upon her older son for emotional support and for compensation for her marital unhappiness. Quarrels between the parents were frequent, with Mrs. Newberg expressing her lack of confidence in her husband, her despair over his many eccentricities, and his lack of help in raising the children—concerns and complaints that were realistic. Her sisters, omnipresent figures, were even more open with their hostile and vituperative remarks about Mr. Newberg, freely expressing their feelings in the presence of his children. Mrs. Newberg believed that she remained with her husband only for the sake of the children; the marriage, however, was almost unique in the series in that both partners had, at times, gained very real satisfaction from their sexual relationship.

Mrs. Newberg had grown up in the unhappy and impoverished home of immigrant parents. As the youngest of four daughters, Mrs. Newberg had felt unwanted and a burden to her parents in their poverty. Her mother was an uneducated woman who considered herself a great beauty and felt cheated because her parents had broken up a romance with a man who later became very wealthy, a self-centered woman who paid relatively little attention to her children and constantly belittled her husband, who was a warmer and more considerate but passive and ineffectual person. Mrs. Newberg remained intensely attached to her oldest sister who had filled the role of mother to her, and she always became frightened at the threat of separation from her—a concern that created conflict with her husband and contributed to her oversensitivity to her children's separation fears. The sister, also unhappily married, shrewishly continued to dominate Mrs. Newberg's family life, belittling and antagonizing both Mrs. Newberg's husband and her own.

Mrs. Newberg despite her good looks had always considered herself an ugly duckling and was surprised by Mr. Newberg's ardent courtship. She had found Mr. Newberg, as a suitor, physically and sexually attractive, and considered him a self-assured "go-getter." Whatever her conscious and unconscious reasons for marrying him, she soon found that she had married a highly erratic, childishly dependent man who required constant bolstering of his self-esteem, and who was closely tied to his near-psychotic mother. Mrs. Newberg had good reasons to fear that he would give up his job to pursue some crack-pot scheme or, like his father, desert the family. Later, Mrs. Newberg feared that her sons would come to resemble their disturbed and unpredictable father, and clearly conveyed her dissatisfaction with her husband to them.

We have already noted that Mrs. Newberg was one of the few mothers who could think and talk clearly and rationally. Dr. Singer's blind analysis of the projective tests confirms both the clarity of the thought processes and Mrs. Newberg's relative detachment; but it also points up how her styles of thinking, perceiving, and of relating have a seriously detrimental impact upon her children.

The tests present a picture of a distant, detached woman who maintains a rigid barrier against any spontaneity or warmth and steadfastly conveys the feeling that she regards everything in life as a task, an unpleasant task. Her Rorschach indicates that she will appear a rational, sterile, nonintrospective person who sees the conventional meanings in a colorless, impersonal way. Her percepts are deadly accurate and will not give any clues about what she is like inside. She shows little if any warmth, and there will be almost no nuances in her feelings. She will have relatively little capacity for empathy and will not recognize the "inner person" in others at all.[2] To Mrs. Newberg, life is a task assigned and the world is an unpleasant place. She does not say that it is anything in particular but more of what it is not. She does not project but simply sees life as a task with an inevitable unhappy outcome. She expects unpleasantness, sarcasms, "thrusts" as she calls them, and is looking forward to only such unpleasantnesses. Thus while some parents of young schizophrenic patients have been termed unreal characters because they have a fixed pleasant version of life, this woman in her negative way fills a similar role because she expects an undeviatingly negative outcome. Power struggles are part of her

[2] The investigators who knew Mrs. Newberg consider this an overstatement of a relatively accurate impression—perhaps created because Mrs. Newberg was requiring inordinately strong defenses at the time she was tested because of the psychoses of both of her sons.

world. However, these may be very covered over, because she has resigned herself to a fortified role in relation to an impersonal overpowering force against which struggle is useless. She seems to have severed relations with her affects. Again, it should be noted that in this family it is the father who was the blurrer of meanings—a person who beclouds everything with his nebulous, shifting thought processes. He is the epitome of vague ego boundaries in a man who reasons negatively.

In this brief portrayal of Mrs. Newberg we can again note serious impediments to a wholesome mother-child relationship: her overly anxious care of her children during early childhood, her difficulties in permitting them to gain a sense of autonomy and become separate from her, her need to gain a sense of fulfillment through her sons, her detachment, etc. In her role as a wife she could not shift the center of family authority from her sisters to her husband and she undermined the worth of her husband to the children, albeit because her husband's personality and behavior made it difficult to do otherwise. Although more aggressive and active, Mr. Newberg, like Mr. Newcomb and other fathers of schizophrenic sons, breached generation boundaries by behaving in many respects as a member of the childhood generation, but by being rivalrous with his sons rather than by being an adjunct to his wife. Neither parent had become independent of his family of origin.

Mrs. Lamb came from a very different background and was married to a highly successful business executive, but her make-up and problems were essentially similar to Mrs. Newberg's. She, too, could perceive and communicate clearly but related in an aloof way that covered her disillusion and hopelessness. However, she tended to believe in spiritualism, and she had a sister with very eccentric ideas. Mr. Lamb was a seriously disturbed alcoholic who philandered openly to cover homosexual tendencies that he may have concealed from himself but not from his wife or son. He was extremely jealous of his son, and his outbursts constantly interfered with Mrs. Lamb's attempts to devote herself to her son as an infant and small child. She, too, was insecure as a mother, could not set limits, and her son had many serious childhood neurotic problems. Her efforts to support a positive image of Mr. Lamb who was a poor husband and a worse father confused her son, particularly as she clearly conveyed that she expected him to be an intellectual or an artist and not a crude man like his father. Mrs. Lamb had little esteem for herself as a woman and had shown a proclivity for sociopathic men other than her husband before her marriage. Her mother had been a militant feminist and her father a man who lived on his inherited wealth. In contrast to most other mothers in our series, Mrs. Lamb had been favored over her brother by their mother, but in a strange way. Her mother had sought to use her to demonstrate the superiority of women by pushing her to surpass her brilliant brother academically. Mrs. Lamb, however, displayed no feminist competition with men, but rather seemed to seek a masochistic subservience. The projective tests indicated aloofness, disillusion, and hopelessness about finding positive aspects in life—similar to Mrs. Newberg.

Mrs. Benjamin displayed characteristics that have already been noted, but in a different configuration. She was a seriously scattered woman who could be a profound blurrer of meanings. When anxious she would talk incessantly and ask countless questions without waiting for her respondent to answer any of them. However, when supported, she could converse meaningfully and with insight. Much of the time she seemed somewhat removed, caught up in her preoccupations and fantasies. She felt defeated and hopeless in her marriage to a very difficult man who sought to dominate the home and to blame her for his impotence—which left her feeling frustrated and disillusioned. Mrs. Benjamin was clearly very fond of her son, and she did not restrict his separation from her or his development of autonomy, nor did she instill grandiose hopes for his future. She had left his care for the first years of life largely to a nursemaid. Her relations to her son were marked by swings between preoccupied aloofness and an attentiveness that threatened by its seductive quality. Her interaction in the marriage filled with hostile recriminations was more akin to what transpired in many families with schizophrenic daughters in that she was the defeated member of the marital partnership. However, she also demolished her husband's worth as a model for their son. Here again it is important to note that Mr. Benjamin could, in a different way, confuse and obfuscate meaning as effectively as his wife. The complexities of this disturbed marriage and the confusing milieu created cannot be described here. Mrs. Benjamin also had a narcissistic, mixed-up, and near-psychotic mother who bemoaned how her career as an actress had been blighted by her marriage to an ineffectual man.

Certain characteristics appeared in all of the mothers of schizophrenic sons, including Mrs. Forel who differed most markedly from the others. They all had difficulty in achieving proper distance in relating to the child—in investing the child properly. They varied between extremely intrusive oversolicitude and overt disinterest—but even the oversolicitude reflected a difficulty in relating to the child as a separate individual. Each of these women related to her husband in a way that conveyed that he was incompetent as a husband, diminishing or demolishing his worth as an object for a son's identification, and thus formed a model of a woman who is nonsupportive and even dangerous to males. All of the mothers—abetted by their husbands—conveyed a confused system of meanings and distorted ways of perceiving and thinking. The two mothers who could think clearly contributed a sense of hopelessness about finding anything meaningful.

The four or five mothers who were either psychotic or near-psychotic clearly could not establish boundaries between themselves and the child. They treated the sons as extensions of themselves who would realize the mothers' frustrated ambitions and bring meaning to their lives. These mothers, in many respects, related to an imaginary child and implicitly threatened to reject the child who did not objectify the fiction. They needed and used a son to compensate for their own sense of emptiness and worthlessness as a woman, having married passive men who could not complete their lives and who would not intrude into their symbiotic relationship with a son. Indeed, for them males are but adjuncts to a woman's life, useful in giving them the penis they do not have as women or the child they cannot have without a man.

Mothers of Schizophrenic Daughters

When we examine the mothers of schizophrenic daughters, some very marked differences from the mothers of schizophrenic sons as well as some profound similarities become apparent. Although most of these mothers were protective and frequently extremely intrusive, there was, as Alanen (1958) has pointed out, an inimical quality to the protectiveness. Further, with one notable exception, they were not the controlling figure who set the pattern for the family but the devalued and defeated member in a schismatic marriage, considered to be inadequate wives and mothers by their difficult and often paranoid husbands. Although the mothers of schizophrenic daughters are more alike than are the mothers of schizophrenic sons, they are more difficult to describe because of their rather indefinite personality organization and their nebulous and confusing ways of communicating.

Some of the critical similarities to and differences from the mothers of schizophrenic sons can be noted in Mrs. Grau, a woman whom we have described in some detail in Chapter VIII. She was an unusually vague, rambling, and scattered person who could talk a great deal and leave the listener puzzled as to whether she had said anything. Her remarks were filled with platitudes, clichés and "pseudo-mutual" statements that attempted to give a thin sugar-coating to the bitter leaven of her marriage. She created the erroneous impression of being feeble-minded. We could understand why her husband could become enraged when he tried to settle an issue with her. Her psychotic daughter said that her own thinking and speech had become vague after she decided to copy her mother's style of talking to avoid her mother's unbearable intrusiveness into just what she did when out of the home.

Mrs. Grau had very much wanted a child despite her husband's opposition to having children, but she was extremely insecure as a mother. In her uncertainty she had rigidly adhered to rules prescribed in books at a time when rigid, early habit training was advocated. She had been controlling and restricting, and often punitive when her older daughter who, very docile when small, became alienated from her mother and fractious by the time she entered adolescence. Unable to gain direction by sensitivity to the child's needs, Mrs. Grau became anxious and sought control by keeping her within close range in an effort to know everything the child did. She sought to be a devoted mother, but gained little pleasure or sense of fulfillment from the anxiety-provoking task. Throughout the patient's formative years, Mrs. Grau was disheartened to despair by her conflict with her husband that focused upon the child's religious upbringing but extended into every cranny of their lives. She was a woman who depended upon authority for direction, but she could not accept the authority of her husband when he forbade raising the children in the Catholic faith and constantly derided all Catholics.

Mrs. Grau never gave up her struggle for her daughter's religious salvation, and to make the girl an ally in the unending struggle with her rigid and determined husband. She used circumventions which further increased her paranoid husband's distrust and defamation of her. She virtually eliminated herself as an object for the girl's identifications by her intrusive but uncomprehending ways, while her worth as a wife and mother was demolished by her husband's constant attacks upon her.

As with everything else about Mrs. Grau, the picture of her own family background remained rather vague. We do not know much about her mother except that she was a devout Irish-American Catholic, and that Mrs. Grau felt that she received little attention from her. The father was a harsh and domineering German, but because she was her father's favorite, Mrs. Grau did not have as difficult a time with him as did her mother and brothers. Mrs. Grau married a man who resembled her father in many ways, but gained little support or affection from a man who was even more set and dominating than her father. The intense and enduring conflict between them in which the patient was caught has been discussed in Chapter VIII.

In studying Mrs. Grau's projective tests, Dr. Singer noted:

Her responses and remarks create a picture of a nebulous, vague, and evasive woman who scarcely ever gives a direct reply to what she is asked. She diverts from the testing situation and brings in extraneous material. At first one gains an impression that she did not really give any responses to the test at all. Only after one searches through her evasions does one note that she has given a few partial, fragmented responses in ways that create the impression that she had really said nothing. She is circular, putting virtually everything in the form of a question, thus failing to convey that she had found any meaning at all. The way in which she manages her world is by darting her attention about and giving partial responses in question form. Absolutely meaningless circularity is treated as a reasonable communication. To cite an example: she saw a sad girl on one TAT card. Eventually the tester asked what the girl might have done, to which Mrs. Grau replied, "It looks like she is probably broken up over what she was crying about." Such double talk actually conveys no sensible meaning even though it sounds as if it might. The general mood tone is one of aversion. She does not expect to like things very well. In effect, she says that people are not going to be interested in what is going on; they are not going to be able to stand one another; and it would be best for them not to be together. Yet, at the same time, she appends pseudomutual themes here and there, just enough to create a *non sequitur* effect to her responses and interactions. She conveys two messages: the stronger and more frequent message is that she has many aversions to interacting with people and that she expects most interactions to turn out unpleasantly; but she also inserts some platitudes about how nicely things will turn out someday.

Mrs. Grau had little confidence in her ability to care for the child and followed a rigid unempathic pattern and had even less confidence that the child could care for herself as she grew older. Her concerns for the girl's moral welfare in adolescence led to intrusiveness that conveyed an impression of complete distrust. The marital schism together with the mother's behavior virtually destroyed the mother's worth as a model for the girl to follow into adulthood, and turned the child into an object for the parents' competition as well as the scapegoat for their unhappiness. Both parents inculcated a distrust of people including the other parent. The mother's constant blurring of meanings had a direct effect upon the patient's style of communicating and thinking, but the father contributed by his paranoid distortions.

The situation in the Reading family was strikingly similar to that of the Grau family. The birth of the patient, the older daughter, precipitated an enduring conflict in which she served as a pawn and scapegoat. Mrs. Reading, somewhat stronger and more direct than Mrs. Grau, was constantly attacked and derogated by her paranoid husband in a home that became increasingly chaotic. She was a seriously obsessive woman who sought to supervise and control her daughters in an extreme manner. Whatever capacities Mrs. Reading may have had as a mother were dissipated in her struggles to maintain herself in the marriage. Mrs. Reading is distinctive in one respect. She is the only mother among the seventeen in the series who spoke warmly of her parental home. She felt that her parents had been strict but kindly, and she had been very close to her four sisters.

Mrs. Thomas resembled the most disturbed mothers of schizophrenic sons in being unable to tolerate separation from her sick daughter and in her conviction that no one other than herself could or would take care of her daughter. She, too, could not clearly differentiate her needs and feelings from those of the patient. Mrs. Thomas was schizophrenic, a wealthy woman who appeared dilapidated and who spoke in an almost incomprehensible manner. Her remarks were peripheral to what she sought to convey. After considerable experience in talking with Mrs. Thomas, the interviewer recognized that she only hinted at her intent, lest she antagonize someone upon whom her daughter's care depended. She had reason for such concern as her intrusiveness had alienated doctors and nurses; and her husband had long disregarded her desires and opinions and openly showed his contempt and repugnance for her. She correctly recognized that her paranoid husband was just as disturbed as she, but that few outside of the immediate family recognized his paranoid tendencies because of his great prestige in the academic world. Her authority and worth as a model to her four daughters had been destroyed not only because of her dilapidation, but also by her husband's calculated conniving to use her wealth and social prestige. When Mrs. Thomas felt that someone sought to understand her and was willing to listen to her, she demonstrated considerable good sense and judgment. As her daughter had already been ill for many years when taken into the study, it was difficult to re-create the child-rearing patterns, particularly as they had been carried out primarily by a constantly changing array of governesses. Although a devoted mother, Mrs. Thomas was inept and extremely anxious, seeking to improve her daughters' care by changing governesses and later by shifting the schools they attended. Despite her obvious psychotic incapacitation, Mr. Thomas left her in charge while he found a position that kept him away from home for long periods. Mrs. Thomas, as Mrs. Newcomb, devoted her efforts and much of her thoughts to her sick child and had difficulty in tolerating separation from her.

Mrs. Thomas, an only child whose mother had died at her birth, was raised by governesses and by a father who moved her to various parts of the world while paying little attention to her. She married a self-made man who found her wealth and social position highly useful and who had previously been engaged to another psychotic woman.

At least four of the five remaining mothers were markedly aloof and virtually disinterested in the daughter who became schizophrenic. Mrs. Ubanque was almost consistently rejecting, having little use for her second daughter whom she obviously disliked, calling her a "nasty little stinker" and insisting that her hebephrenic daughter was not ill but simply acting up through spite. In referring back to different periods in the girl's life, she had no hesitancy in making such comments as, "She was exasperating to live with; . . . everyone [her husband] spoiled her—she wanted to be queen." Her husband claimed that his wife had been envious of the patient's delicate physique and dainty appearance, resenting the attention he gave her.

The negative attitude seems to have pervaded Mrs. Ubanque's relationship to the patient since she had been conceived. Although Mrs. Ubanque had been delighted at giving birth to an older daughter after several miscarriages, she had become very upset and cried for days when she found herself pregnant again only five months later. She was further disappointed in having another girl and remained depressed for some months after the delivery. An obsessive housekeeper, Mrs. Ubanque, too, raised her children according to the books, following a rigid, clock-watching routine with them. A drooling baby on a clean rug was repugnant to her. When the patient was small, Mrs. Ubanque spent little time with her, encouraging the child to play by herself with her dolls and not annoy her mother. The patient remained a bed wetter and head roller to the age of seven, behavior that provoked angry punitive reactions from her mother. According to the patient, her mother had particular concerns about masturbation and would frequently smell her hands to find out if she had been "touching herself." During a remission, the patient complained bitterly about the mother's absence of interest and understanding, and her refusal to ever listen and respond to her pleas for help with her problems.

Mrs. Ubanque's talk was as scattered, inconsistent, and almost as nebulous as Mrs. Grau's. Mrs. Ubanque was even less empathic and seemed uninterested in trying to understand her daughter. She impressed us as being the most impervious mother in the study. She had little difficulty in changing reality to fit her needs, unable or unwilling to hear what she was told. At a time when any untrained observer could see that the patient was out of contact and in a desperate condition, Mrs. Ubanque insisted that her daughter was well enough to be taken home; the real reason was that the family had run out of funds. Soon after the patient emerged from her seriously disorganized state, an attendant who accompanied the patient on a drive with her parents reported that Mrs. Ubanque spent most of the time admonishing her daughter for past trivial misbehavior. She attributed her daughter's difficulties to misbehavior, to the mistakes of teachers, to the influence of college roommates who had talked to her about sex, and blocked discussion of her relationship with the patient.

Although Mrs. Ubanque spoke of her childhood as having been "normal" and of her parents' happiness before her father died, she had a rather tragic background. Her father had been an obsessive man, a slave to rigid routine, "who kept everything to himself." She thought that she had been his favorite and recalled how he would read to her each night precisely from 7:00 to 7:45. He committed suicide when she was six. Mr. Ubanque described his mother-in-law as a difficult, domineering, and highly emotional woman. Mrs. Ubanque said that she had been brought up fairly liberally, but also told how her mother had watched over her like a hawk during her adolescence. She admits that her mother was closer to her older brother who helped support the family after the father's death. The brother developed epilepsy in his adolescence and drowned when he was twenty-one.

Mrs. Ubanque had married the first man who had shown an interest in her, and she looked forward to marriage in childishly romantic terms. She had little interest in sex, "Mr. Ubanque felt cheated early in marriage because when I was bighearted it was twice a week, otherwise once." When the couple were interviewed together, Mrs. Ubanque clearly dominated the situation, ignoring or interrupting her husband whenever he entered the conversation. He seemed to accept this as part of his lot, taking a passive position in these sessions. Although both parents stated that they had been happy together, the patient spoke of many quarrels and of her father's infidelities. Her older sister intimated that many difficulties existed within the family, but would not elaborate and soon removed herself to a distant city, refusing to visit the patient or come for further interviews.

Mrs. Nussbaum could be severely rejecting of her daughter but, in contrast to Mrs. Ubanque, was extremely guilty and disturbed about her own attitude. When her daughter became disturbed, Mrs. Nussbaum tried to devote herself to making amends. Mrs. Nussbaum was upset by the birth as she and her husband had become embroiled in a serious and enduring conflict a few months earlier. Mrs. Nussbaum, incapacitated by an injury during the first year of the child's life and probably depressed, left the care of the child to a nursemaid. She never gained any pleasure or satisfaction from her daughter who soon developed behavioral problems which increased her impatience and irritability with the child. Mrs. Nussbaum suffered from periods of depression with marked irritability and may have verged upon psychosis, but at the time of the study had benefited from several years of intensive psychotherapy. Although she was still a difficult woman, she was, according to her husband, much less so than formerly. Mr. Nussbaum lavished seductive attention upon the girl, seeking the admiration and affection he could not gain from his wife, and the affection between father and daughter increased Mrs. Nussbaum's resentment of her. Her husband purposefully fostered his wife's jealousy not only by his seductive attention to their daughter but also by pretending that he was having affairs. The patient became a focal point in their dissension and a scapegoat for much of their conflict, but the schism had antedated her birth. When the girl first went to boarding school in adolescence, Mrs. Nussbaum sent her off with the remark, "I hope you come home in a coffin." Later, she suggested dual suicide. Still, when the patient became overtly disturbed, Mrs. Nussbaum devoted herself completely to her daughter's care, rarely leaving her. She had been a much more satisfactory mother to her son who had been born before the marital conflict had started and in whom she invested a great deal. Mrs. Nussbaum had felt unwanted as a girl having been raised in a large family by a mother who openly and frequently expressed her preference for her sons and who had a low opinion of women in general.

Mrs. Robb knew that she had been a poor mother to her two daughters, both of whom became schizophrenic. She had not been hostile or overtly rejecting but tended to be apathetic toward them. She had left them in the charge of nursemaids, although she took care of the son who was born between them. She knew that she had gained more pleasure from the boy. She became increasingly preoc-

cupied with her husband's infidelities and her own vengeful involvements with other men. Her own insecurities as a wife and mother
were heightened by her husband's disparagement of her efforts, and
by his insistence that she follow the advice of a young woman teacher whom he had brought to live in the home and to whom he paid
more attention than to his wife. The complexities of the Robbs' marital situation will not be reviewed here, but the discrepancies between
the public image of the successful and understanding man and his
behavior at home, and between the sedate mother and her extramarital involvements, created a confusing environment for the children.
Mrs. Robb also had difficulties because of her own family background.
Her family had moved a great deal because of her father's diplomatic
career. Her mother had been an ardent feminist who left Mrs. Robb
to the care of governesses. The father, of whom she had been so
proud during her childhood, suffered a deteriorating organic psychosis when she was adolescent and had behaved in a way that had
made her deeply ashamed of him—a circumstance that had affected
her life profoundly.

Mrs. Frei was an inadequate mother to both her daughters in a basically schismatic marriage, but both spouses masked the schism from
each other and themselves. The older daughter suffered from ulcerative colitis and the younger became schizophrenic. The younger
daughter's upbringing, her bizarre eating habits in particular, became
a focus of contention between the parents.

Mrs. Frei was the neglected youngest of nine children, and while
intelligent enough to learn four languages in childhood, had only
very sketchy formal education, which stopped altogether after her
father's accidental death when she was fourteen. She then lived with
married siblings, apparently moving from one to the other without
having a definitive home where she belonged. Like other mothers in
our series, she tried to overcome her uncertainty about mothering her
first-born by rigid adherence to schedules and books, and turned over
the care of both daughters to servants as soon as financially feasible.
While she was more flexible in tending to her second child, she was
handicapped during the child's infancy by a breast abscess and probably was depressed. She often became angry enough to hit the baby
with a towel. Mrs. Frei showed other characteristics already de-

scribed with regard to the other mothers of schizophrenic girls, so that they can be mentioned but briefly. She was distant and aloof and concerned herself with the mechanical aspects of her daughter's problems rather than dealing with her needs. She tended to blame her husband for the patient's illness, and yet maintained that they got along well together, and she blamed the patient for "doing this to her," her mother. At the same time she overidentified and refused herself pleasure and gratification as long as her daughter did such "bad" things as starving herself. (The patient weighed seventy pounds on admission.) Mrs. Frei was indeed impervious to her own feelings as well as to those of others. On the Object Sorting Test, she as well as her husband showed thought disorder, reflected in abnormal scores. Both parents were pervasively concrete and fragmented, tending to ramble on and on about the separate objects, unable to conceptualize the group as a whole. While both have some tendency to change the function of the objects in an arbitrary manner and to confabulate, building up unrealistic stories around them, Mr. Frei showed more arbitrary and confabulated responses than did his wife. However, she demonstrated looseness of concept boundaries and tremendous stress on orality, giving the impression of being engaged in a desperate struggle to survive.

The seven mothers of schizophrenic daughters who have been discussed were all rather vague and poorly organized women, deficient in self-esteem as women and caught up in unhappy schismatic marriages in which they were the defeated and devalued partner. They gained little satisfaction from their daughters, and though some were intrusive and overcontrolling, there was an aloof, hostile or an overtly rejecting quality to the relationship. However, the remaining mother, Mrs. Lerner, though also unable to cathect her daughter properly, was a very different type of woman, and her presence in the series prevents the formulation of a consistent picture of all of these mothers of schizophrenic daughters and of their life situations.

A satisfactory understanding of Mrs. Lerner and her family presented inordinate difficulties because of thorough falsification of the history. However, the misrepresentations were fundamental to her personality, and a manifestation of her profound need to maintain an image of herself as a successful, self-sacrificing mother who had made an eminently satisfactory marriage. The need to mask reality had permeated her life and the lives of the other family members requiring them to lead a life of pretense, and had forced the patient to deny her perceptions of the obvious, including what her parents were like and how she felt toward them.

The picture, as originally presented, was of an exceptionally well-knit and harmonious family life blighted by the illness of the highly gifted but extremely sensitive daughter. Their financial resources had become limited because Mr. Lerner, an eminent attorney, had suffered a stroke a year before the daughter's hospitalization. Mrs. Lerner now supported the family by pursuing her profession instead of working part time as she had previously. The patient had presented some special problems in child rearing, because she had very early displayed an unusual artistic gift—a talent that had been associated with insanity in several relatives. Mrs. Lerner had been caught between wishing to redirect the child into more usual feminine pursuits and the feelings of obligation to help her develop her endowment.

In reality, Mr. Lerner's success had ended twelve years earlier with the suicide of his partner when the patient was eight years old. His practice had declined rapidly, but the Lerners maintained the image of the eminently successful legal scholar to the world and to their children—his office expenses being paid out of her inheritance and earnings. The stroke had actually lightened the burden by providing face-saving grounds for his retirement. The marital roles had been reversed many years earlier, with Mr. Lerner doing most of the shopping and cooking while his wife pursued a career that had become essential to her self-esteem as well as the support of the family. In a similar vein, the daughter's illness had to be carefully concealed lest it injure the mother's professional reputation and diminish her earnings. It gradually became apparent that Mrs. Lerner could not acknowledge having married a man who was a failure or having raised a daughter who had become mentally ill. As the patient improved and sought to discuss the family circumstances or to indicate faults in her parents, her mother regularly cut off such "misperceptions" and, with her husband's support, turned the discussion to the difficulties the patient had displayed since her birth.

We do not like to fall back on *post hoc* reasoning in evaluating a mother's maternal capacities, but the patient had presented severe feeding problems and suffered from extreme separation anxiety that mounted to a school phobia on entering kindergarten. Mrs. Lerner had been preoccupied with her older son's rheumatic fever during the patient's first two years of life and had left her largely to the care of nursemaids. When the girl had been sent to camp at the age of twelve to help her overcome her separation anxiety, she wrote letters home that were filled with delusions of persecution which would have led much less educated mothers to take the child home and place her in treatment, but Mrs. Lerner steeled herself and kept herself from even visiting her daughter.

Mrs. Lerner had grown up feeling unwanted and superfluous as the youngest of a series of daughters with a younger brother upon whom the family hopes rested. Although she admired her father and identified with him in many ways. She considered him a rigid and dominating man, and she had a marked antipathy for her mother for reasons that never became very clear. She had shown little interest in men until she fell in love with her husband who appeared to be a mature and competent man who loved and needed her. She felt that for the first time in her life she was accepted and wanted as a woman. Actually, he was a rather rigid but kindly man who had little interest in children and needed to be admired as an important figure by a woman. In contrast to her liberalism, he was a rigidly conservative reactionary. He readily ceded the control of the family affairs to his wife, and eventually the support of the family as well.

The clarity of Mrs. Lerner's conversation covered distortions created by her need to maintain her self-esteem and to combat despair by seeing things as she required them to be. But her projective tests resemble those of Mrs. Newberg and Mrs. Lamb.

She seemed to take the TAT pictures as a grim reality and the persons she described were overcontrolled. The world she perceived was a cheerless place in which one makes one's own bed and stays in it. Everything seemed matter of fact, detached, overcontrolled, dispassionate. People are sad and heartbroken but stolid and defiant, manage to cope somehow. Children are sad but detached, running from fears into a fantasy world. On her Rorschach, in striking contrast to the TAT, there are many fantasy responses in which she seeks to empathize with various childlike situations

and has fun in her fantasying. There was a blatant, "pseudomutual" Polly-
anna quality to her ideas. While an extremely bright woman, she has a
very dreary outlook about all social interactions as they are but a Polly-
annalike fantasy life about how things might be.

These few comments from Dr. Singer's interpretations of Mrs.
Lerner's tests appear to reflect the dichotomy in her life in which she
sacrifices herself, struggles, and carries on; basically she finds the situation hopeless, but she must maintain a front to convince herself and
others that things have really turned out well.

Something had gone very much amiss in the relationship between
Mrs. Lerner and her daughter from the earliest days. Perhaps specific
difficulties engendered by the daughter's endowment created an unfavorable feedback, but very tangible difficulties in the mother's management soon arose. The disturbances in the family organization seriously affected the girl's development, notably because of the marked
reversal of gender-linked roles in the parents in which the father carried out many of the wifely tasks. In the process, the patient had
somehow never been taught many rudimentary skills about dressing,
shopping, housekeeping, etc., but had learned that things were not
the way they seemed to be, that facts could and must be altered to
suit needs, and that openness would lead to rejection. Such difficulties
also affected her career, for she had to maintain a shell of excellence
that prevented learning certain rudiments of her craft, believing that
as a genius she was supposed to know without study many things that
require arduous effort and specific education.

These mothers of schizophrenic daughters all led difficult and unenviable lives, caught up in extremely unsatisfactory marriages. In
contrast to many of the mothers of schizophrenic sons, they were,
with one exception, the defeated and derogated partner in highly conflictful marriages. All had felt neglected or unwanted as girls in their
parental homes, and they had sought paternal figures as husbands but
managed to marry men who further undermined their self-esteem as
women and increased their insecurities as mothers. They had difficulty in forming warm and close relationships and seem to have had particular difficulty in cathecting a daughter properly—not gaining any
sense of fulfillment and gratification from a female child. They could
be oversolicitous and even intrusive, but sought to control without

warmth and closeness and often with an inimical quality to the relationship. All of these mothers conveyed a sense of defeat in life and hopelessness about being a woman. As has been amply illustrated, they were, with one exception, rather amorphous, nebulous persons and concomitantly profound blurrers or fragmenters of meanings and of meaningfulness. One aspect of the problem requires mention, though it cannot be documented from this study. In a series of female schizophrenic patients treated analytically, it became apparent that the homosexual tendencies of their mothers had confused the mother-child relationship: the mothers needed to maintain distance from their daughters, but sometimes showed a highly eroticized interest in the girls' bodies.

DISCUSSION

Although a large proportion of these mothers of schizophrenic patients are much alike in certain essentials, no personality description will encompass all of them. However, certain highly characteristic patterns recur frequently, and an appreciation of these differing configurations can further our understanding of the etiology of schizophrenia and remove some of the confusions created by an expectation of finding a single specific type of mother. Dividing the series according to the sex of the patient enables more pertinent description and categorization, for there are significant differences between the mothers of male and female patients and also more clear-cut similarities within such groupings. We have carefully considered the possibility that such grouping reflects different ways with which women with essentially similar personalities respond to male and female children, rather than differences between these mothers. However, some of these mothers clearly formed more satisfactory relationships with children of the opposite sex from the patient, and as the mothers of male patients relate differently to their husbands than do the mothers of female patients, we believe that the personalities of the parents and the family configurations of male and female patients tend to be different, creating more serious developmental problems for the children of the sex of the schizophrenic child.

The most striking type of mother is the strange, near-psychotic or even overtly schizophrenic woman who has been termed "schizophrenogenic." Although a description of them sounds extreme, it pales before the reality. However, such mothers are in a minority. About half of the mothers of the male patients in the series, but only an occasional mother of a female patient fits the description that follows. However, some very important traits of these women are also found in other mothers of schizophrenic patients.

This type of mother seeks compensation for her dissatisfactions with life and the burdens of being a woman by finding completion through a son. She expects little from men whom she considers as weak figures dependent upon their wives or mothers. She may have married primarily to have a son and consciously or unconsciously selected a weak man who will remain an adjunct to her. She has a narrow range of ways of relating and effectively delimits the family pattern to conform with her needs, and she distorts her perceptions and masks what is untenable to maintain her emotional equilibrium. She manages to be impervious to the needs and wishes of other family members if they do not fit her preconceptions of how things should be. As her psychotic or very strange concepts remain unchallenged by the husband, they create reality within the family. Her communications are vague, fragmented, stereotyped, but they are spoken as if meaningful, creating perplexity in the listener. The husband's worth as a father figure to a son is demolished by her control of him, or because of his gross inadequacies.

She may have very much wanted the baby and fantasied how her child would fulfill her dreams by his greatness. The tangible reality of a child who needs her care is another matter; and she is uncertain and insecure despite her controlling attitudes. Obsessive oversolicitude commonly masks the mother's anxiety or meagre responsivity to the actual child. She continues to relate to the child of her fantasies and lacks empathy and awareness of the child's needs. She envisions and seeks to establish a very special relatedness between herself and her son through which her dormant and frustrated potentialities will flow into her offspring. Lacking adequate ego boundaries, she fails particularly in setting boundaries between herself and the child and has difficulty in differentiating her own needs from those of the child. She commonly projects her own insecurities onto the child and becomes overprotective of him. Her feelings of unity with the

child, her need for him, and her protectiveness, as well as her controlling attitudes toward males, hinder the child in differentiating and
from gradually achieving a sense of autonomy. Parental figures and
directives cannot be properly internalized as a superego and remain
predominantly derived from the mother. The mother's use of a son
in place of her husband as the major source of emotional gratification,
which frequently includes highly eroticized and seductive behavior,
confuses the oedipal transition. When the engulfing behavior provokes antagonisms in her son or her eroticized care makes him seek to
withdraw from her, she may take refuge behind such platitudes as
"a child always shows some anger to the person he loves most."
Nevertheless, she suffers from periods of incapacitating anxiety or
depression during which the burden of filling her emptiness or allay-
ing her concerns falls heavily upon the son.

Four of the mothers of male patients were different types of persons. Two were somewhat aloof women who were not engulfing and
intrusive and could communicate and think clearly and rationally,
but they were uncertain, anxious, and overprotective with sons whom
they needed as sources of emotional gratification, particularly because their husbands were very disturbed and difficult. Their disappointments with their marriages and their basic hopelessness about
finding anything meaningful in life may have placed this insoluble
burden upon their sons of bringing satisfaction to them. Another
mother was more like the defeated and rather amorphous mothers of
schizophrenic daughters, but she was fond of her son. She does not
seem to have been intrusive and overcontrolling, but she was quite
seductive at times, and her repetitive talk could blur meaning and provoke despair. The one mother who was clearly overtly rejecting of a
son had none of the overcontrolling qualities or confusions between
her needs and feelings and those of her son. But, she, too, had little
regard for men, sought to control her husband and demolished his
worth, and upon occasion was frighteningly sexually seductive with
her sons.

We might note that all of these mothers because of their own personalities and needs, or because of their unfortunate marriages, became dangerous figures to males. They were engulfing, castrating, or
chronically dissatisfied with their husbands. The husbands, in turn,

were either destroyed or destroyed themselves as effective models for the son to emulate, nor were they a source of the son's ego ideal or superego directives.

The mothers of schizophrenic daughters form a more homogeneous grouping. Characteristically, the mother is caught up in a very unhappy and conflictful marriage in which her low self-esteem as a woman is debased further by her husband's deprecation of her. She married a man who needs to defend his own image as a man, and requires the admiration or adulation of a woman but can give little of the paternal support that his wife needs, unconsciously envying the woman's role. The mother is disillusioned about her marriage, filled with hostility toward her husband, and preoccupied with her dilemma. Many are more amorphous than the mothers of the schizophrenic sons, tending to be colorless. A nebulous quality makes her difficult to know and to describe. She is deficient in feminine warmth and affectionate qualities. Her communications reflect her personality, having an illusive, scattered content, and conveying distance in interpersonal relationships. She had felt unwanted as a girl, has a low estimate of women and womanhood, and has grave difficulties in cathecting a daughter. While she may be oversolicitous and overprotective of her daughter, she is aloof from her and an inimical quality shows through the overprotection. The disappointment in having a daughter may be apparent. The mother of the female patient may also have difficulty in differentiating the daughter from herself, but the consequences are different than in the case of a schizophrenic son; her low self-esteem as a woman is transferred to the daughter, and feelings of emptiness in being a female impedes the relatedness to the daughter. We might say that her alienation from her feminine role contributes to an alienation from the daughter. She provides a poor identification model of a woman, wife, and mother for the girl to follow into womanhood, and her husband makes it clear to the daughter that anyone like the mother cannot gain his affection and esteem. Unlike some mothers of schizophrenic sons, she does not have set ideas of what the girl should become. She is more likely to seek to make the daughter an ally in the conflict with her husband, or to find in the dependency of the child a reason to continue her marriage or even a reason to continue living. She conveys a sense of defeat and hopelessness about the lot of being a woman, and perhaps about life in general. In the conflict with her husband, and in her efforts to survive in the struggle, she seeks to alienate her daughter from her father. The girl is apt to be caught in the schism and spends her energies in trying to bridge the gap, or to maintain the mother she needs, or forms divergent ways of relating to two irreconcilable parents—and her own development and integration suffers.

The portrait of the mother of a schizophrenic daughter is an unhappy one of a life of frustration and despair. Only two of the seven mothers in the study differed from it, and only one markedly. One was so impervious to the feelings of others that she suffered less, but her marriage was poor and her life sterile, though she may have managed to avoid recognizing reasons for dissatisfaction. The other was an extremely capable woman who could gain satisfaction from a career, and was the dominant figure in the marriage, willing to shield her husband from the impact of his failure. However, she, too, had difficulties in relating to a daughter, and her masking of reality required the entire family to share the pretense and helped distort the family structure.

Whereas personality traits and patterns common to all of the mothers could not be found, and even such categorizations that have been made are abstractions and are more or less arbitrary, the survey indicates that all of the mothers failed seriously in carrying out their cardinal maternal functions. We have directed attention to three interrelated sets of maternal functions necessary for providing the proper milieu, security, directives, and adaptive techniques to the child if he is to develop into a reasonably well-integrated and self-sufficient individual: the ability to provide nurturance and relate appropriately in accord with the child's changing needs and capacities; the mother's functions as a wife in forming and maintaining a family system with the structural requisites for properly channeling and directing the child's personality structure; the capacities to convey the basic adaptive techniques of the culture, particularly its meaning systems. The marked incapacities of the mothers in all of these areas have been noted and illustrated.

Marked deficiencies and aberrations in the mother-child relationship existed during the child's infancy in all cases—though in some adequate nurturance may have been provided by substitutes. Either apprehensive oversolicitude or impoverished investment of the child affected the child's security and started a feedback that affected the mother. Difficulties may have been even more serious when the child began to show initiative and to differentiate from the mother. Although some mothers may have related to the child reasonably well during one developmental phase, few could shift to relate appropriately as the child matured. Such problems were not confined to infancy or early childhood but continued into and throughout the child's adolescence.

The hypothesis has often been raised that the mothers could not relate properly to the child who becomes schizophrenic because of some inherent deficiencies in the child—a situation that appears to occur with certain autistic children. The evidence does not support the hypothesis, though it may apply in a few cases. Notable difficulties in early infancy were reported in only a few patients; nursemaids took care of a number of these children; serious difficulties in the mother's capacities as a mother in other areas and as a wife were evident. It is more in accord with the evidence to postulate a feedback of disharmony in the mother-child relationship created by a combination of the mother's own difficulties, those of her husband, and the serious problems of the marriage.

The dynamic organization of all of these families was seriously disturbed by the marital schism or skew, the failure to maintain generation boundaries, and by failures of the parents to maintain their sex-linked roles, as we have discussed in previous chapters.

The father is involved as well as the mother, and it is difficult to assign responsibility for such failures. The controlling and dominating wife must have a husband who can be dominated, and some such fathers might be considered to force their wives to assume instrumental leadership of the family. However, as we have indicated, some mothers of schizophrenic sons needed to have husbands fill only adjunctive roles, and also breached generation boundaries by displacing the husband with the son. Most of the remaining mothers could not be supportive of their husbands as husbands or fathers; at the most two, or possibly three, of these seventeen women were adequate sexual partners; and all, in one way or another, undermined the worth of their husbands—though many of these husbands made it difficult for their wives to be supportive.

The deficiencies of all but a few of these women in transmitting and inculcating valid meaning systems were noted in Chapter X. The communications of some are distorted psychotically, and in others by a need to adhere to preconceptions of the way things must be to maintain their own precarious equilibrium, disregarding reality testing when necessary. The re-examination of the protocols of their projective tests by Dr. Singer revealed even more profound and pervasive difficulties. They blur meanings or fragment them, deny their own perceptions, confuse by inserting extraneous material, perseverate a few ideas or perceptions even when clearly inappropriate, etc. There is often an inconsistency between verbal and nonverbal communications. The few mothers who can communicate clearly also conveyed a hopelessness and even a despair about finding anything meaningful in life. The "double-bind" of Bateson et al. (1956) is but one aspect of a more pervasive communication disturbance which requires considerable study.

Here again, it is necessary to emphasize that many of the fathers also contributed to the problem—and in some instances their thinking was far more disturbed than the mothers'. It is clear that the failure to inculcate properly the linguistic meanings of the culture and useful ways of categorizing experiences can prevent the acquisition of other essential techniques and also create serious impediments to adequate ego functioning.

The study serves to emphasize the inadequacies of these women as mothers. Too commonly the psychiatrist who encounters them as mothers of his patients views them and treats them as willfully malevolent or rejecting. Our attention has been forcefully directed to the deficiencies in the mother's own development. Hill (1955) had noted the frequency with which mothers of schizophrenic patients had themselves lacked adequate maternal care, and Alanen (1958) documented the embittered feelings such mothers had about their childhoods and their frequent hostility toward their own mothers. Even though the study was not designed to examine the developmental histories of the mothers and fathers, sufficient information is available for most mothers to indicate clearly that the trend toward social and emotional aberration had originated at least one generation earlier. Only one of the seventeen mothers spoke in positive terms about her family of origin, and animosities toward their own mothers were striking, particularly among the mothers of schizophrenic daughters. The frequency with which the mother's mother was a self-centered, narcissistic woman who felt that her beauty or talent was wasted in her marriage is noteworthy. The mothering that these mothers had received in childhood had been very faulty, suggesting that a woman who has not received adequate mothering herself will have difficulties in being an empathic mother. Their deficiencies in a sense of their worth as women, and even of the worth of femininity, appear to reflect the attitudes of the parents of these mothers toward daughters. Such deficiencies in self-esteem influenced the choice of husbands and left many particularly vulnerable to their husbands' disparagements.

In some instances, the mother's instability may have been due to the traumatic circumstances of her childhood as in the case of Mrs. Schwartz who was orphaned at an early age and raised by older siblings and dependent upon the meagre charity of poor neighbors and relations, and of Mrs. Thomas whose mother died at her birth. In others, as Mrs. Nebb and Mrs. Narab, the disturbances can be traced back for two or more generations. As the fathers of the patients had equally difficult backgrounds, the data suggest that the schizophrenic patient is the offspring of families that have become increasingly deviant in their child-rearing techniques and communication until societal norms and directives were no longer transmitted adequately. We would suggest, however, that because women become schizophrenic at a somewhat later age than men, and because they can remain sheltered longer, more women than men who are disorganized will marry, and that mothers may play a greater part in the production of schizophrenic children for such reasons as well as because of their greater influence upon the child.

The survey of these mothers of schizophrenic patients reveals their serious inadequacies in functioning as mothers. Although they may seem to be particularly strange and difficult women as a group, the study of Delay et al. (1957, 1960, 1962) of French families containing a schizophrenic child which includes many lower-class families describes mothers who are at least as disturbed and some who are extremely bizarre. The evidence does not bear out the suggestion that the mother has difficulty in mothering the child who becomes schizophrenic because of some inherent unresponsivity or hypersensitivity in the infant. The mothers' problems transcend the relationship to the child and usually clearly antedated his birth. These mothers are not only difficult persons but unhappy and unstable, and we have sought to convey some impression of the continuity and increment of such personality problems across generations.

Mothers of persons with problems other than schizophrenia may show similar characteristics, but perhaps not in the same severity or in all three areas. However, as is evident from the other chapters in this book, influences other than the mother contribute to family environments that are conducive to the genesis of schizophrenic conditions.

XVIII

The Limitations of Extrafamilial Socialization

(1964)

Although the family is the major influence upon the emerging personality of its offspring, other individuals, groups and institutions not only implement the family by carrying out various socializing functions, and exert a corrective influence by modifying the family idiosyncrasies, but the child's attainment of an identity and a firm integration depends upon gradually increasing extrafamilial involvements. As Wynne et al. (1958) commented, "Certain of the needs and expectations of family members cannot normally be fulfilled within the nuclear family, necessitating a meaningful participation in the larger society, and parents normally anticipate and facilitate such expression of the growing child's experiences beyond the nuclear family." The child must be so raised within the family that he becomes capable of emerging from it, and his movement beyond the confines of the family should be progressively fostered and encouraged as he matures. We wish to focus attention upon the incapacities of the families with schizophrenic offspring to promote such essential expansion of the child's horizons.

The influences of the extrafamilial world upon the child's developing personality are, of course, legion. We wish, however, to draw attention to a few that interrelate closely with the family processes. As G. H. Mead (1934) pointed out, the "self" forms in response to the attitudes of others, but these "others" must include more than the family members. After the child has found his place, role, and identi-

Theodore Lidz, Alice R. Cornelison, and Stephen Fleck. This paper has not been previously published.

Ezra Vogel's aid in surveying and analyzing the material is greatly appreciated.

ty within the family, he begins to be a representative of his family. He has two names, a first name that places him within the family and a surname that defines him as a family member in relation to the remainder of society, and both contribute to his identity. Most children learn a great deal by spending time with the families of their friends and their parents' friends: their own parents and their own families take on definition by the comparisons thus afforded; and the idiosyncrasies concerning roles, meanings, and expressions of affect that exist in all familes are modified by such associations. The nature of the transition through the oedipal phase which sets its indelible stamp upon the personality involves extrafamilial attachments. Whereas frustration of the eroticized attachment to the mother permits the turning of energies and attention to peer groups and learning, the converse also applies: the withdrawal of cathexis from the mother is aided by involvement with peer groups and the channeling of energies outside the family. Childhood groups play a major role in transmitting age-appropriate roles, skills, mores, and knowledge. The child remains within one family throughout the years of his immaturity, but he repeatedly shifts from one childhood subculture of his society to another, becoming apprentice, member, and then teacher in each, before moving on to repeat the cycle in a more advanced group. The peer group affords a background of shared experiences and value systems, common expectations, and ease of communication with others. Within such groups a child learns to fit into a society of peers, and finds himself evaluated and learns to evaluate himself on the basis of different attributes than those that gain approval or censure within the family. "Chum" relationships, as H. S. Sullivan (1946-1947) emphasized, are critical during latency and early adolescence. Having a "chum" contributes to the child's gaining a firm identity as a member of his sex; decreases his feelings of isolation when separating from his family; supplies an "alter ego" that helps withstand and modify both superego and id pressures; lessens feelings of unworthiness that sexual and aggressive impulses can foster; permits the sharing of problems that arise in relating to adults, etc.

The adolescent revolt against parental authority which is often essential in overcoming dependency strivings may be possible only when conformity to peer group standards supplies a stabilizing influence; and often the first moves toward intimacy with the opposite sex occur with the support and protective restraint afforded by the presence of other couples. The achievement of independence and identity as a mature adult depends not only upon the proper internalization of parental directives, but also upon the modification and alteration of the superego and ego ideals through the internalization of attributes of other objects and their ways of living.

Now, the extrafamilial socialization of schizophrenic patients has received some scrutiny in studies of the importance of social isolation in the etiology of schizophrenia, a consideration raised by Faris in 1934. Faris later attributed the isolation of the child who becomes schizophrenic to parental oversolicitude which promoted isolation from all but the intimates within the family and then led to "persecution, discrimination, or exclusion by children outside the family," and eventually to the child's withdrawal from a hopeless goal and the development of a "seclusive personality that is characteristic of schizophrenia" (Faris, 1944). Kohn and Clausen (1955) found that about one third of the forty-five schizophrenic patients they studied in contrast to only 4 per cent of the controls had been isolates at the ages of thirteen or fourteen. As two thirds of the patients seemed to have socialized reasonably well in early adolescence, isolation could not be considered to be a necessary precursor of schizophrenia. Further, they found "no evidence that the patients classified as isolates had different experiences in respect to availability of playmates, childhood illness, residential mobility, or parental restriction upon their activities or choice of friends. They were not kept from social participation." These investigators wonder why Faris seized upon isolation as a crucial factor, since the questions of why the child was rebuffed in the first place, and why he reacted so extremely, seem more pertinent. An interpretation which they consider more in harmony with their findings is "that as a result of inadequacies in their social relationships both within and outside the family, certain individuals come to feel that they do not belong . . . that is, they become alienated from their peers. Under severe enough conditions, alienation may lead . . . to isolation. But it need not. . . ." Isolation indicates that the "individual's interpersonal difficulties [are] so great [that he is] no longer capable of functioning in interpersonal relations . . . how he got that way is not a question of social isolation per se" (Kohn and Clausen, 1955).

We would agree that social isolation is a resultant of the individual's interpersonal difficulties, but, as we have noted, the isolation or alienation will, in turn, augment developmental problems. We must note, however, that Kohn and Clausen's way of judging social isolation was rather inadequate, because the problem is far more complicated than the presence or absence of friends in early adolescence; moreover, their judgments were based upon relatively meagre retrospective information.

The adequacy of a child's socialization within the family cannot readily be separated from his extrafamilial socialization. The child's ease of movement beyond the family depends upon having a secure base from which he can venture forth, the parents' abilities to foster autonomy, how well the enculturation within the family prepares for living in the society in which it exists, and the nature of the linkages of the family to the outside world. The serious deficiencies of the intrafamilial environments in which schizophrenic patients grow up have now been amply documented by ourselves and others. Children whose interpersonal relationships and socialization processes within the family are deviant will have difficulties in relating to peers, teachers, and other adults. Playmates, for example, are apt to be ill at ease with a child whose behavior and ways of communicating are unpredictable and even exclude him from group participation. Many of the mothers foster separation anxiety either because of their difficulties in cathecting the children or because they project their own insecurities about caring for the child onto the child: serious school phobias are relatively common in children who later become schizophrenic. We wish, however, to turn from the handicaps imposed by faulty and eccentric intrafamilial nurturance and socialization to examine the many problems that arise from the family's alienation—the deficiencies of these families in relating as a group and as individuals to the extrafamilial environment and of fitting into the societal milieu.

Wynne and his coworkers (1958) noted that in some such families, "when there is a continual effort . . . to maintain pseudomutuality, the family members try to act as if the family could be a truly self-sufficient social system with a completely encircling boundary." This is one of many types of situations found within these families that created a barrier to the child's extrafamilial socialization. The divergent personalities, interests, and backgrounds of some of the spouses as well as intense conflicts between them made it difficult for some couples to have friends who were congenial to both. In some, the paranoid distrust of one or both spouses led to open discouragement of friendships. Some families were more or less isolated by cultural or social class incompatibilities with other families in the environs. Eccentricities and emotional disturbances of parents interfered with making or maintaining friends. As we did not study the community reactions to these families, we cannot examine the problem of how the community may have excluded these families from its social life. However, it seems very likely that other families and community groups may well have tended to withdraw from them because of these parents' eccentricities, deviant beliefs and mores, tendencies to be intrusive and enveloping, and because of a general difficulty in feeling at ease when associating with them. Attachments of some of these parents to their own families of origin were intense, and although such connections provided the children with associations beyond the nuclear family, they were of limited value because of the shared value systems of the extended family, and the intensely dependent attachment of one parent or the other to their relatives.

The various reasons for the relative social isolation of these families are, in a sense, outward extensions of the same factors that create the intrafamilial problems. We shall consider the impediments to forming relationships to other individuals, families, and groups created by (1) the psychopathology and idiosyncrasies of one or both parents; (2) the incompatibilities of the parents; (3) cultural and social factors. We shall then illustrate how the convergence of several factors in a family can create serious blocks to a child's opportunities for socializing.

THE PSYCHOPATHOLOGY OF PARENTS

The personality problems of one or both parents created difficulties for all of these families in several ways. People tended to withdraw from these parents because of their more or less unacceptable behavior, or simply because they found it difficult or unpleasant to maintain a relationship. Some parents sought to remain aloof and keep the family aloof because of paranoid feelings. Other family members avoided close relationships with outsiders because of shame over the peculiarities or inadequacies of the disturbed parent.

To establish and maintain a comfortable relationship, if not a friendship, most persons expect the other to be able to communicate meaningfully, to find a "distance" appropriate to the relationship, to behave sufficiently in accord with established mores to permit comprehension of their actions, and to be consistent enough to permit expectations to be realized. As over half of the patients had at least one parent who was schizophrenic or clearly paranoid, and still other parents were "near-schizophrenic" or "psychotic" characters who do not decompensate but confuse and perplex those with whom they live, it seems evident that such parents would have difficulty in forming firm relationships. Even psychiatrists and social workers found it difficult to remain with Mr. Newberg for an hour, listening to his incessant and driven talk and trying to follow his scattered concepts and descriptions of his "harebrained" inventions. He mistook friendly and polite interest in one of his schemes for serious commitment, and avoidance seemed the simplest way to escape involvement. Mrs. Benjamin, though pleasant enough much of the time, would speak in scattered fashion when under stress and provoke feelings of profound frustration by asking questions and then interrupting the start of any response with another question. Mrs. Newcomb seemed to believe that if someone disagreed with any of her unacceptable ideas, she could not have been understood and would rephrase and repeat the same idea.

The inability of a number of these parents to relate at a "proper distance" was very apparent. An overfamiliarity, particularly on the part of some fathers, caused people to be guarded with them. Mr. Thomas, a professor of education, told even the gas station attendants in the rural town in which the family lived about his wife's body odors and failures to maintain proper feminine hygiene. Mr. Benjamin would discuss his son's mental illness and hospitalization with strangers. Mr. Nussbaum repeatedly became involved in the personal affairs of his female clients, much beyond what was appropriate for his business, and in a similar vein repeatedly sought to involve the social worker in discussions of her life, and offered advice about situations that derived largely from his fantasies about her. When, for example, the social worker took the patient for a day's visit to the Nussbaum's home, Mr. Nussbaum made a number of "off-color" jests disregarding his wife's signals and displeasure and his daughter's embarrassment. When the Nussbaums learned that the worker could not see them for one week, they both erroneously assumed that she would be on vacation. They argued as to where she should spend the vacation and ultimately agreed that she should visit in their city and that she could stay in their daughter's room—neglecting their daughter's feelings about being displaced as well as remaining oblivious to the untoward familiarity they were displaying. When Mrs. Nebb's twin sons had difficulties soon after entering kindergarten, she visited to ferret out the cause, and soon took over the class from the astonished teacher in order to demonstrate how her sons should be drawn into the activities. We gained the impression that similar imperviousness to reactions to her intrusion into social groups led to her exclusion from them.

A number of parents, on the other hand, were "distant" setting a barrier of detachment between themselves and others. Even the two mothers whom we considered the most normal and clear thinking, Mrs. Lamb and Mrs. Newberg, conveyed an aloofness that was difficult to define, but which was apparent to acquaintances as well as to our staff. Further, undue intrusiveness is not incompatible with "detachment" because such intrusive parents are characteristically impervious to the individuality of others.

Paranoid distrust of outsiders not only fostered the isolation of some families, but also was taught directly to the children. Mrs. Schwartz who dominated the lives of her four sons and her passive and chronically depressed husband believed that her family was subjected to persecution similar to that which she had experienced in Poland during her childhood when relatives had been killed in pogroms. Mr. Grau explicitly warned his daughters against trusting any outsiders. He was particularly suspicious of Catholics, and forbade his daughters to go with their mother to church and later to date Catholic boys. Mr. Reading similarly distrusted outsiders, fearing that what people learned about the family would be used against them, and he specifically ordered his wife not to join the church sewing circle or any other social organization. Both Mr. and Mrs. Dolfuss shared and conveyed to their children the belief that neighbors would not wish to associate with them because they were Austrian and enemy aliens during World War I. While there may have been some truth in this belief many years ago, it seems unlikely that the community retained such attitudes. Mrs. Narab, an overtly schizophrenic mother, believed that her sons were in danger because of hatred for the ethnic group to which they belonged.

Covert distrust was pronounced in the Lerner family where family matters were concealed assiduously. The efforts to hide the true state of the family finances and Mr. Lerner's career failure required stringent limitations of social contacts. Later, the disgrace of the daughter's mental illness had to be hidden even more thoroughly because of the blow to Mrs. Lerner's self-esteem. These attitudes not only served to isolate the family but also implied to the patient that failure or weakness left a person extremely vulnerable. Such implicit attitudes dominated many family transactions even though the Lerners would deny having them.

Embarrassment and shame over the peculiarities of a parent or the family's way of life interfered with the formation of friendships. Children are apt to feel ashamed of their parents at some periods in their lives even under favorable circumstances. In some of these families there were understandable reasons for a child to feel embarrassed. The Thomas girls could not be but reluctant to have friends meet their unkempt and confused schizophrenic mother whose good qualities were not superficially apparent. Once, after Mrs. Thomas visited her daughters at a fashionable boarding school, a friend asked whether she was the family cook. The situation was aggravated because Mr. Thomas expressed his disgust with his wife but left his daughters in her care while he found reasons to remain far from home much of the time. The Grau girls would be embarrassed whenever they brought a new acquaintance home because the parents, locked in a struggle over the girls' religion, would cross-examine the person about religion: if Protestant, Mrs. Grau showed her disapproval; if Catholic, Mr. Grau might make disparaging remarks. A number of other parents or parental couples could cause their children considerable embarrassment by their intrusiveness as well as because of their eccentricities or untoward behavior. Although the Lambs were almost unique in this series in having a very active social life, their son had ample reason to become embarrassed by his father's behavior: Mr. Lamb regularly disrupted social gatherings by his boisterous drunkenness, and was probably tolerated because of his wife and his business position; at the time his son became adolescent an affair with a neighbor created a scandal. When the Lambs entertained, he habitually insisted in a latently hostile manner that his shy and embarrassed son display his vocal talents to the guests.

Parental Incompatibilities

In order to form and keep friends and community relationships a couple must have some shared interests and tastes. In many cases the lack of any such common elements was striking. When, as in many of these families, their interests were in conflict, it became difficult to form friendships as a unit. We can somewhat arbitrarily group these problems under three headings: (1) incompatible interests and tastes; (2) inabilities of the spouses to relinquish attachments to their families of origin; (3) ethnic, religious, and social class discrepancies. However, the problem often could not be clearly separated out into these categories, for in many families serious emotional difficulties and conflicts between the spouses prevented bridging the gaps between them.

The Lerners each formed friendships or acquaintances in their careers which they did not or could not share because of their divergent interests and ideals. Mr. Lerner was a corporation attorney impressed by big industry and industrialists with whom he maintained business contacts and superficial friendships, whereas Mrs. Lerner was a social worker interested in social issues. Mr. Lerner was a conservative reactionary, whereas Mrs. Lerner tended to associate with and admire liberals. Their close relationships based on personal needs could be threatened by a mingling of their respective friends and associates. Further, after Mr. Lerner's professional failure, Mrs. Lerner could maintain the myth of having an eminently successful husband more easily if her socializing did not include her husband and entertaining at home.

The Robbs were even more clearly split by different political and social interests. Mrs. Robb came from a conservative Philadelphia "Main line" family and felt at ease only among an exclusive social set, and she wished to raise her children as members of her group. Her husband had markedly liberal political tendencies which he tended to flaunt among her Republican friends. Although superficially the discrepancy might seem to involve differences in social status, in actuality, Mr. Robb also stemmed from an upper-class family against which he was in permanent revolt. Although Mrs. Robb sought to fit in with her husband's friends, she had difficulty in concealing her antipathy for them and her uneasiness with them. She knew that she continued to have marked anti-Semitic feelings despite her efforts to overcome them, and she resented her husband's insistence on spending several summer vacations together with the family of a Jewish colleague. Although her children belonged to the segment of society included in the social register, they were partly alienated from it because of their father's refusal to comply with its customs, and his contemptuous attitude toward many of its members.

Mr. and Mrs. Nussbaum had very different tastes and interests, and when their respective families became antagonistic, as will be discussed below, they had little in common and perhaps sought to hurt each other by attacking the other's family. Mrs. Nussbaum objected strenuously to his "gangster" friends and refused to go out with such shady characters. There seems to have been good reason for her complaints, and it is not at all clear why Mr. Nussbaum wished to go with these people since he was not engaged in activities that were legally questionable.

The Readings were divided because Mr. Reading liked to associate with groups of men in convivial fashion, but opposed his wife's desires to become a member of the proper social set in the town in which they lived. He not only refused to participate in entertaining and being entertained but kept his wife from belonging to any groups.

The inabilities of one or both spouses to separate from their natal families and transfer their central attachment and interest to their marital homes interfered with the attainment of a shared way of life in seven of the seventeen families and created very serious difficulties in four. Of course, to a greater or lesser extent the inability of the spouses to form a stable marital coalition contributed to the continuing dependence on relatives for emotional support and companionship.

Mrs. Nussbaum came from a very close-knit and large family. Mr. Nussbaum was dependent upon and loyal to his oldest brother who had supported him and paid his way through college. The Nussbaum marriage involved the close friendship between the two extended families. A few years after the marriage, Mrs. Nussbaum's family accused Mr. Nussbaum's oldest brother of business dealings that led to the suicide of Mrs. Nussbaum's father. A lasting feud ensued, and both spouses remained loyal to their kin, resenting the other's loyalty. Mrs. Nussbaum continued to spend much of her time with her relatives who tended to exclude her husband from any of their family activities. For a time, some common socialization continued because Mr. Nussbaum was in business and friendly with the husband of Mrs. Nussbaum's favorite sister. Then, the brothers-in-law quarreled, broke up the partnership, and refused to visit one another. Mrs. Nussbaum who gained little satisfaction from her marriage needed her sister and continued to socialize with her.

The Newbergs both retained strong ties to their parental homes, and the absence of any relationships between the two families greatly limited shared social activities for the spouses. Because Mrs. Newberg refused to leave the block on which her three sisters lived, her husband had to spend four hours each day traveling to and from work. Mr. Newberg spent one or two evenings each week with his mother and stopped off to see her en route home on still other evenings, but his wife did not feel welcome at her mother-in-law's. Mrs. Newberg was continuing, in a sense, to live within her parental family—in the same apartment house with her mother and two of her married sisters, and her extended family remained the center of her life. She discouraged her sons from playing with children other than their cousins. The Forel family was caught in a similar situation created by the spouses' attachments to their respective families. Mrs. Forel had also refused to leave the proximity of her parents and sisters for many years, and when eventually she did, she became alcoholic and extremely hostile to her husband. Yet in both the Nussbaum and Forel situations, attachments to the extended families modified the nuclear family eccentricities for the older children, whereas the youngest children who became schizophrenic were deprived of close relationships with grandparents, aunts and uncles.

In this series, ethnic, religious, and social class discrepancies between spouses were not prominent; notable differences existed in only four of the seventeen families and they were a major source of difficulty in the case of only two couples. The serious blocks to forming social relationships caused by the religious differences between the Graus have been amply discussed. In addition, Mr. Grau came from a well-to-do Midwestern German farm family, whereas Mrs. Grau came from a lower-middle-class urban family that probably was just emerging from lower-class immigrant status. In any event, the Graus' concepts of marital roles, family life, and child rearing were divergent, and Mr. Grau's paranoid suspiciousness and jealousies accentuated the difficulties. Although Mr. and Mrs. Narab were nominally of the same ethnic and religious backgrounds, in actuality they came from totally different backgrounds. Mrs. Narab came from a wealthy Americanized family in which the father had pointedly turned away from the background of his ancestors. Mrs. Narab in seeking an identity married a scholar from abroad and sought to fit into his culture, but their interests were only superficially similar and their backgrounds were totally different. Mr. Thomas was a self-made man who acquired status through his education, whereas his wife was a schizophrenic heiress. Perhaps his drive for status made his wife intolerable to him, but in general the social discrepancy did not seem an important factor. Mrs. Nebb came from a poor family in a remote mountain community and married an orphan from an upper- or upper-middle-class background. Here, too, the significance of the class difference was difficult to evaluate because of Mrs. Nebb's serious emotional instability. However, Mrs. Nebb's social ambitions kept her associating in circles in which her ineptness made her an outsider.

SOCIAL AND CULTURAL FACTORS

A variety of social and cultural factors that served to separate or alienate the family as a whole from the community requires discussion. Neither geographic isolation of the family nor frequent changes of residence were prominent factors in this series of families. The Newcomb children were effectively isolated but more because of their mother's psychopathology than because of the relatively isolated area in which they lived. To cope with her anxieties about their safety, she had kept them in a fenced-in yard when they were young, and as she was too anxious to learn to drive a car, she could not take them to play with other children. The Thomas family moved several times, and the last move was to a remote country home, perhaps because Mr. Thomas wished to remove his schizophrenic wife from circulation. The influences with which we are concerned here are not so readily classified.

The Schwartz children were not only taught to be suspicious of neighbors by their paranoid mother, but the family continued to live behind its store in a slum neighborhood even after becoming reasonably prosperous. Mrs. Schwartz had high aspirations for her four sons and struggled to gain sufficient wealth to educate them to become professional men and scholars. The boys increasingly felt like outsiders in associating with neighborhood boys and later went to Ivy League colleges very poorly prepared to make friendships or to participate in any social life. The Thomas family, before moving to a remote estate, had lived in a slum area because of the father's settlement house activities. The children were urged to associate with neighborhood playmates; at the same time they were taught to feel superior to them. When they were sent away to school, Mrs. Thomas kept shifting them from one school to another because of her concerns about the adequacies of the schools. The Dolfuss family lived as expatriate nobility in a Boston suburb feeling both superior to their neighbors and unaccepted because they were "Austrian." Their way of life differed markedly from that of the community to an extent that must have made them objects of curiosity as well as creating difficulties for the children in learning to associate with peers. A uniformed chauffeur transported the children to and from school. The home life was extremely formal, the children spending scheduled hours with their parents. Mrs. Dolfuss, in dinner dress, together with her carefully groomed children, greeted Mr. Dolfuss at the door each evening. The two children's closest relationships were with the nursemaid and the butler in a manner somewhat reminiscent of *The Turn of the Screw* until the nurse was discharged upon the advice of the boy's schoolteachers, because he had not been taught many rudiments of self-care. In addition, the family's aberrant belief system set them apart from others: they belonged to a minute esoteric religious sect, and the family members considered Mr. Dolfuss to be a reincarnation of an Asiatic divinity.

The Narab family had problems other than those created by the mother's paranoid fears, but they are difficult to describe briefly. Mrs. Narab who had married a foreign member of her ethnic group had gone to live in his native land. She felt herself an outsider unaccepted by her husband's family and friends. When the country was threatened by the Nazi invasion, the family returned to the United States. Her family had lost its wealth, and the sons were sent to public school in New York, although they were unable to speak English; there they thought themselves unwanted and in danger because of their religion and foreign origins.

As has been noted, the social life of the Readings was limited by Mr. Reading's suspiciousness as well as the absence of interests shared by the spouses. The situation was further aggravated just as the daughters entered adolescence. Because Mrs. Reading had informed her husband's mother of his marital infidelity, Mr. Reading took revenge by selling their home in the best neighborhood in town and moving the family into a two-family house in a much less desirable neighborhood. He was striking a blow at his wife's social ambitions and her concern that her daughters associate only with "proper" companions. The move not only heightened the marital schism but seriously impeded the maintenance of friendships. The Benjamins, when the children were small, moved to a suburb in which Mrs. Benjamin had grown up and had a number of friends. However, they may not have been accepted readily because of Mr. Benjamin's rather crude behavior and his difficulties in knowing how to find and maintain proper distance. Still, a critical factor in their failure to make or maintain friends arose because Mr. Benjamin, in his usual impulsive way, had bought a very large house which they could not afford and then could not furnish for about ten years. As they could not invite people into a sparsely furnished home, they could not entertain and therefore could not accept invitations.

Although the impediments to extrafamilial socialization of the children in these families have been grouped under various headings for clarity in presentation, it is evident from these brief illustrations that the problems within each family created several such difficulties in relating to the community and to other families. Thus, as has been noted, the Thomas family lived for a time in a slum area where the children were differentiated from peer groups by their wealth and social position; then the family moved to a relatively isolated area; the mother being schizophrenic was incapable of forming friendships for the family, and the father estranged people by inappropriate confidences and intrusions; the children were shifted from school to school because of the mother's insecurities; the father remained away from home for extended periods; the parents had few if any interests in common; the children had realistic reasons to feel ashamed of their mother's appearance and peculiarities; whereas the family belonged to the social elite because of the mother's background, the mother was too disorganized to participate in social activities; the father was occupied with establishing his own position among people of wealth and prestige, which meant using his wife's wealth but excluding his wife from contacts with his acquaintances.

The children who grow up in these families are not only poorly prepared within the family to become integrated individuals capable of adjusting within society—as we have described in previous chapters—but are also further handicapped because the family provides limited access to the extrafamilial world. We are not suggesting that "social isolation" is the cause of schizophrenia, but that it is important to recognize that these patients as children and adolescents were more or less isolated—not always in the sense of physical isolation as much as in having been relatively alienated or estranged. Such limitation of extrafamilial socialization in turn creates serious impediments to integrated development.

XIX

The Relevance of Family Studies to Psychoanalytic Theory

(1961)

Family studies in psychiatry received much of their impetus from psychoanalysis, and investigators have depended upon psychoanalytic concepts for guidance in analyzing and understanding their findings. It has, however, become increasingly apparent that although current analytic concepts have provided essential landmarks, guideposts, and even taught ways of proceeding, they are insufficient for coping with the complex observations of family transactions, and that family studies have posed new questions about some old problems as well as uncovering new problems that require scrutiny. When new techniques lead to new observations that touch upon fundamentals, prior conceptualizations must be questioned and re-evaluated. The history of science indicates that nothing can blind an investigator's path into the future as much as the axiomatic acceptance of a theory that has proven its value. We must ask if the new data derived from family studies can be properly organized and understood through current analytic theories: Do they confirm and supplement the theory, or do they remain confused or fragmented unless the theory is altered?

Let us first glance at a handful of family studies to note their impact upon psychiatry and something of their theoretical implications. The first organized study of patients' families was reported by Bruch and Touraine in 1940; this investigation of the families of obese children that opened a new era by studying the feeders as well as the

Theodore Lidz: The Relevance of Family Studies to Psychoanalytic Theory. Journal of Nervous and Mental Disease, Vol. 135, 1962, pp. 105-111. Copyright © 1962, The Williams & Wilkins Co., Baltimore, Md. 21202, U.S.A.

fed. It revealed how the mother's own childhood insecurities, the type of marriage she made, and her culturally and emotionally determined attitudes about food, affection, and security influenced the child's food intake and expenditures of energy. Bruch's (1961b) amplification of these findings to elucidate how the child fails to learn the physiological signals of hunger and satiety in such families blends with Bateson's et al. (1956) double-bind hypothesis of schizophrenia that concerns the paralyzing and distorting influence of the confused and contradictory communications in families with schizophrenic offspring. Johnson and Szurek's (1952) studies of families of sociopaths also concerned faulty directives, and their recognition of the lacunae in the parents' superegos has profoundly altered our concepts of psychopathy; other studies have shown that delinquents stem from disturbed homes as much as from disturbed neighborhoods. The work of Spiegel and Kluckhohn (1954) demonstrates the ways cultural differences between parents, or the rapid acculturation of a family, can create role confusions in the children that lead to behavior disorders. It is difficult to realize that prior to the studies by Lidz and Lidz (Chapter I) and by Reichard and Tillman (1950) little, if any, attention was paid to the fact that schizophrenic patients virtually always grow up in seriously disturbed families—as is now apparent to any careful observer. What schizophrenic patients said, or tried to say, about their strange families was usually discounted as irrelevant or as further evidence of their disordered minds. The subsequent intensive family-oriented investigations of schizophrenia by teams at the National Institute of Mental Health, Yale, Palo Alto and elsewhere all have broader connotations concerning the relationship between family integration and ego integration. They have raised a variety of challenges to analytic theories—even when no overt challenge has been intended. I shall not attempt to encompass them in this paper. As I believe that many of the theoretical difficulties emerge like spokes from a common focal point, I shall seek primarily to designate the nature of this core problem.

The efforts to analyze and to understand properly the data derived from family studies have emphasized that while it is essential to recognize that the family is composed of individuals who relate and interact with each other, it is insufficient. Even though most family studies have been conducted by psychoanalysts, new strange terminology enters their writings—"reciprocal role relationships," "pseudomutuality," "family schism and skew," "generation boundaries," "parental coalition"—and they cite such strange names as Bentley and Dewey, Parsons and Bales, and G. H. Mead, rather than Freud, in their search for orienting hypotheses. The family is not simply a collection of individuals: it constitutes a true small group, a dynamic entity with a life, structure, and institutions of its own. Within the family, the action of any member affects all, producing reactions and counteractions, and shifts in the family's equilibrium. Reciprocally interrelating roles must be found, or the personality of one or more members will become distorted. The emerging child assimilates its mores, its ways of thinking and communicating, and its patterns of interrelating as well as internalizing parental characteristics. His self-esteem is affected by the family's position in its society and the ways others regard him as a representative of his family. In short, the family is a social system. It is the nuclear social system that exists everywhere in the world, an essential building block of society, and the sheltered training ground in which the child takes into himself the culture's instrumental ways and institutions suited to each phase of his development, to learn how to live as a social being. It is equally clear that the family is a subsystem that must be suited for existence in a larger social system and be capable of transmitting the mores and techniques of the society into which the child must emerge. The society, which has an existence of its own, even though it exists only through individuals, has evolved a culture over countless generations—its own particular pattern of ways of coping with its environment and of relating to others—which includes a family suited to its way of life. As soon as we become involved with the child's development within the family unit, we cannot continue to avoid studying how much man's development into a person depends upon his growth into and his internalization of the institutions and instrumentalities of a structured social system, as well as the internalization of attributes of persons who themselves have assimilated the culture in one way or another.

We are not back in the old conflict concerning the biological and cultural determinants of personality that had formerly created schisms in the psychoanalytic movement. We are paying due attention to that unique characteristic of the human biological endowment—the structure of the brain that permits the utilization of abstract symbols for communication and thought, that enables man to develop and hand on the adaptive techniques by means of which he alters nature to his ends and which permits him to build upon the acquisitions of his predecessors. Man cannot even survive unless he assimilates in childhood an organized filtrate of the cumulative experiences of his forbears. Controversies about biological versus cultural determinants of personality become anachronistic. The emphasis upon the need to study the family as a social system derives from a biological rather than a cultural orientation. The family is an omnipresent human phenomenon *in part* because the human biological make-up is such that the infant requires prolonged nurturant care and primary socialization within a small social system, composed of persons to whom the infant's welfare is as important as their own. In the study of the family, the psychiatrist concerned with the individual and the sociologist who studies social systems must inevitably meet and influence each other. The individual incorporates the fundamentals of the social system through his experiences in the family, while the personalities of the individuals who constitute the family markedly influence the structure and nature of the family, and its ability to meet the needs of the broader society.

Now such conceptualizations are not alien to the mainstream of psychoanalytic theory, but there have been difficulties in assimilating them properly, and their potential for leading toward the objective of a general theory of human development and behavior remains to be realized. Their proper integration has awaited upon developments in the behavioral sciences as well as in psychoanalysis, for, as Opler (1959), in discussing the field, noted, "While we have known that culture includes traditional systems transmitted as methods for relating behavior, ethics, and attitudes, this transmission through families and social units has only recently become a subject for research." In circular fashion, the behavioral sciences have depended greatly upon advances in psychoanalytic theory to fit dynamic personality development into the studies of the family and of larger social systems.

From its earliest days psychoanalysis has, of course, been interested in the family, and particularly in parental influences upon the patient. The central position of the oedipal situation in shaping the personality; the significance of actual or fantasied traumata experienced from parents; the formation of the superego through the incorporation of aspects of the parental superego; problems of identification and other such findings and concepts; all seemed to point to the extreme importance of the intrafamilial environment. Nevertheless, Freud kept family relationships peripheral in his theories, probably because the approach did not fit into his more dominant interest in the vicissitudes of the instinctual drives. Further, when he recognized that patients were presenting reconstructions of childhood or adolescent fantasies rather than actual memories, a critical turning point in the development of psychoanalysis, his interest in the precise family transactions diminished. While the discovery opened the way for the development of psychoanalysis through proper appreciation of the import of the oedipal strivings, the force of the unconscious upon memory, and the like, family studies now indicate that the insight was only partly correct, for when memories of childhood seductions do not mirror actual events, they often reflect fantasy-provoking situations; and it is found that family circumstances are commonly more disturbed and traumatizing than patients recognize, because of their wish to preserve the parental objects who have in a sense become part of them.

Although Freud (1913, 1921) recognized the importance of social factors in personality development, and made significant contributions in relating psychiatry to anthropology and sociology, the path for psychoanalytic investigations of the transmission of cultural acquisitions through social systems, including the family, seemed to open when Freud (1933) stated, "We have come to realise that the difficulty of childhood consists in the fact that the child has, in a short span of time, to make its own the acquisition of a cultural development which has extended over tens of thousands of years; it has, that is, to attain instinctual control and social adaptation, or, at any rate, their first elements. It can only achieve a part of this alteration through its own development; a great deal must be forced upon it by education." However, he immediately went on to say, "The child has to learn to control its instincts. . . . The function of education, therefore, is to inhibit, forbid and suppress, and it has at all times carried out this function to admiration." The focus was still upon the limiting, suppressing aspects of education rather than upon the process of enculturation. Although Freud's emphasis upon the functions of the superego in shaping social behavior (through conveying the traditions of the race and the people) clarified the process of transmission, the concept continued to emphasize the restrictive and did not include the enculturating activities of institutional social systems. A suitable and useful concept of the family can be fitted into Freud's own theories only through reinterpretations such as Parsons' (1958), using the potentialities opened by Freud but later neglected or even negated by him.

Flugel explored the contributions of early psychoanalytic theories to the understanding of the family as an institution, and while his work influenced therapy, it provoked little feedback into psychoanalytic theory. No papers specifically related to the family appeared between the publication of Flugel's book in 1921 and the report on the symposium on "Family Neuroses and the Neurotic Family" in 1936 (Spitz, 1937). The family as a unit, as an enculturating agency, as a social system that the child assimilated, received little attention, but increasing study of parent-child relationships, sibling rivalries, processes of identification and object love constantly added to understanding of certain aspects of family functioning. A somewhat unfortunate trend entered as well, when the search for the origins of pathological behavior moved backward, toward and into the infancy of patients. Attention was frequently focused upon dyadic relationships, particularly the mother-child dyad, and the father became reduced in importance. At times, the metaphor seemed forgotten in focusing upon the "mouth" and the "breast" or upon other fragments of the persons.

The theoretical reorganization introduced by Hartmann in 1939 made room for the consideration of the family and other social systems in psychoanalytic developmental theories; indeed made their introduction and study imperative. Hartmann utilized an ecological orientation, "Human action adapts the environment to human functions, and then the human being adapts to the environment which he has helped create." He recognized the enculturating purposes and tasks of social structures as part of the human technique of maintaining his biological equilibrium. "Man not only adapts to the community but also actively participates in creating the conditions to which he must adapt. . . . Thus the crucial adaptation man has to make is to the social structure, and his collaboration in building it." Although these and similar statements appear crucial to his understanding of human adaptation, after the publication of his astute paper on "Psychoanalysis and Sociology" (1944), he did not develop this phase of his theory. Indeed, his later studies seem to indicate a less comprehensive view of the importance of social systems and cultural institutions (Hartmann, 1950; Hartmann, Kris, Loewenstein, 1951). Nevertheless, the reorientation has had an increasingly profound influence.

Erikson, however, clearly and specifically opened the way for the integration of the study of social systems, including the family as a social organization, into psychoanalytic theory when he wrote in 1946:

The phenomenon and the concept of *social organization* [italics added], and its bearing on the individual ego was, thus, for the longest time, shunted off by patronizing tributes to the existence of 'social factors' . . . The focus of psychoanalytic research . . . has . . . turned to the problem of the infantile ego origin in organized social life. Instead of emphasizing what social organization denies the child, we wish to clarify what it may first grant to the infant, as it keeps him alive and as, in administering to his needs in a specific way, it seduces him to its particular life style. Instead of accepting the Oedipus trinity as an irreducible scheme for man's irrational conduct, we are striving for greater specificity by exploring the way in which social organization co-determines the structure of the family.

Although this statement has precursors in psychoanalysis, it is a distinctive and unencumbered preface to studies that have done much to integrate psychoanalysis into the body of both biological and sociologic theory (Erikson, 1950a, 1956).

Family studies and insights derived from them can find a place in psychoanalytic theory, as both Hartmann's and Erikson's basic concepts appear to require further study of the family as the critical enculturating social system. However, such conceptualizations cannot remain peripheral, but require considerable reorganization of psychoanalytic theory that necessitates discarding of incompatible hypotheses.

Let us turn to look briefly at a few of the potentialities that derive from regarding the family as a social system.

Because the family mediates between the biological and cultural endowments of the child, and between the individual's needs and the society's needs, the study of the family affords critical opportunities to examine what is genetically inherent in man and how this genetic endowment must be supplemented by the internalization of instrumental techniques and institutions, some of which are found in all societies, some of which are specific to a given group, and some of which are unique to individual families.

We may, for example, hypothesize from family studies that within any society the child requires a suitable family framework to guide the development of the ego into a unified and consistent structure. In all societies the nuclear family is divided for biological reasons into two generations and two sexes, each with prerogatives, limitations, and role assignments of its own. For the family to form a proper milieu for child rearing, the parents must form a coalition as members of the parental generation, and adhere to their appropriate sex-linked roles and be capable of transmitting the basic instrumental ways of their culture to offspring. There is not space to discuss this simple formulation, but its utility can be illustrated. In all families with schizophrenic offspring serious difficulties have been found in almost every sphere of interaction; I believe the fundamental problems can be understood in the failure of the system to maintain any of the basic requisites designated immediately above. Parents have failed to form a coalition, either because of serious schisms between them (which includes rivalry for children), or through one parent abdicating his parental role to the other. They have breached the generation boundaries by behaving as a child of the spouse, by being a rival of the child, or through using the child as replacement for the spouse. They have failed to maintain their gender-linked roles, either grossly because of homosexual proclivities or more subtly by role reversals, as when the mother cannot fill an expressive-affectional nurturant role, or the father does not provide masculine instrumental leadership. Failure in transmitting the basic instrumental ways of their culture has occurred because of the paralogical ideation of one or both parents, the distorted or masked communications or the confusion resulting from conflicts between the two parents' directives.

A sketchy illustration may serve to indicate the altered perspective that derives from viewing the family as a unit. We shall consider a few of the consequences to a boy's development in a hypothetical family in which the father fills the role of a passive child of his wife who, in turn, conveys her contempt for the husband she dominates, while obtaining her major emotional gratification from her son. He is tied to completing his mother's life and prematurely burdened with satisfying her needs; the mother fails to carry out a cardinal function of frustrating his preoedipal eroticized attachment to her to free his energies for cathexis outside the home; the son does not seek to identify with his father in order to gain or retain his mother's affection, but instead seeks to differentiate himself from his father, thereby lacking a masculine model to introject and to follow into manhood; his mother, who has denigrated the father and engulfed the son, is seen as a castrating or devouring person; the son's images of male and female roles are distorted and he fears marriage as a threat to a man's integrity.

In contrast, if the parental coalition, the generation boundaries, and the gender-linked roles are generally maintained, then despite some aberrations in the child-rearing procedures, or the unavoidable exigencies that arise in any family, the son—or the daughter—will be guided into the position of a child relating to two parents who mutually support each other, particularly in their attitudes toward the child and his rearing. Thus the child cannot continue a primary eroticized attachment to either parent, and gains security in the role of boy or girl, with unconscious rewards for moving into an identification with the parent of the same sex and gaining his or her strength. I am, of course, saying in different terms that the oedipal situation will be resolved because the structure and role relations of the family are suited to promote its resolution rather than because the libido had fortunately not become fixated at an earlier developmental phase.

Leaving the specific issue of the potential insights that derive from considering the way the child develops in the family social system, recognition of the need for the child to assimilate social institutions has drawn attention to several gaps in the psychoanalytic concepts of psychosexual or psychosocial development. The acquisition of language and meaningful ways of communicating and thinking that play a central role in ego development require careful scrutiny, for it becomes apparent that the innate potentiality for symbolic usage is directed by parental patterns of verbal and nonverbal communication. We might consider not only how the child obtains his conceptual tools for self-direction but also how he attains a basic trust in the utility and validity of symbolic communication without which his integration rests on very shaky footings.

Another gap concerns how the child achieves identity as a member of his or her sex. The older analytic assumptions that biological sex determines gender role identity and that confusions of gender, such as homosexuality, are indications of biological bisexuality or inversion, are untenable (Hampson et al., 1955). Scrutinizing the gender role assignments and assumptions within the family and the sexual identity of the parental models that are introjected sheds new light upon the requisites for attainment of a secure sexual identity upon which rests the nature of the oedipal resolution—and, indeed, much of the stability of the ego structure.

A variety of analytic concepts appears to require reworking. Even the basic dynamic unconscious broadens to include material that had never been repressed, does not derive from the id and yet wields strong power in determining behavior. Many patterns of family interaction and many cultural institutions never enter consciousness but are assimilated as the accepted and natural way of behaving and feeling. Of course, as has now been stated repeatedly, the institutions of a society cannot be regarded primarily as repressive limitations but rather as the means through which man's amorphous potential gains direction and realization. I cannot here discuss other consequences of studying man's development in relation to social systems. Fortunately Talcott Parsons, one of the most constructive critics of psychoanalytic theories, has provided a good start. In his paper on the incest taboo (1954), he has re-evaluated the oedipal situation in terms of the necessity of frustrating the preoedipal child's eroticized attachments to his parents both for the sake of the child's ego development and for the maintenance of proper role relationships within the family. In his studies of the superego (1953), Parsons has clarified the confusions between the concepts of the ego and superego that have arisen from the failure to appreciate how much of ego development is based upon internalization of institutions, family transactions, and parental characteristics.

The consequences to theory and practice that derive from studying personality development and structure in relation to the actual family setting are far-reaching, but I have sought primarily to express my belief that the major relevance of family studies for psychoanalytic theories lies in forcing recognition that man's biological make-up requires that he grow into social systems and assimilate their instrumental techniques. Much rethinking and reorganizing lie ahead of us. The extent of the impact of such studies upon psychoanalytic theory cannot be estimated as yet. A great deal will depend upon future development of constructs suited to the dynamic study of the family. However, we must recognize that the formulation of a consistent general psychoanalytic theory also remains a task for the future. We have only an array of more or less related psychoanalytic theories, many of which are incompatible. It is possible that many of these inconsistencies remain because data essential to a theory of personality development and functioning have been excluded. I believe that the trends that I have touched upon do not run counter to the fundamentals of psychoanalysis, but can lead to a more dynamic and complete understanding of human behavior.

XX

Family Studies and a Theory of Schizophrenia

(1964)

The phrase "of unknown etiology" has almost become an integral part of the definition of schizophrenia. However, we question the extent of the "unknown." A great deal concerning the etiology of schizophrenia seems reasonably well established. In this chapter we wish to assay an outline of a theory of the etiology of schizophrenia that encompasses the findings of our intensive studies of the family environments in which schizophrenic patients grew up and the findings of others who have been engaged in similar studies. The formulation of the theory awaited considerable reconceptualization of psychoanalytic and psychodynamic theories to permit appreciation of the pervasive and decisive role of the family in personality development and human adaptation (Lidz, 1963a).

We had, originally, set out to explore the family environments of patients hoping to find something within the radius of the family circle specific to the etiology of schizophrenia. Difficulties arose not from the paucity but the plethora of findings that seemed to have potential significance. Whatever facets of the family transactions we examined, we found something markedly amiss as we have reported in previous chapters. As every area of interaction in these families was found to be faulty in some respect, the question arose whether something was not fundamentally wrong with the capacities of these

Theodore Lidz and Stephen Fleck: Family Studies and a Theory of Schizophrenia. Presented at the 1964 annual meeting of the American Psychiatric Association. The American Family in Crisis. *Copyright* © *1965. Forest Hospital Publications, Forest Hospital, Des Plaines, Ill.*

parents to establish families capable of providing the essentials for the integrative development of their offspring. The emphasis of the hypothesis directing the analysis of the data shifted from asking not only what had gone wrong early in the lives of these patients, but also what had been lacking. We began to consider the possibility that schizophrenia might be a deficiency disease rather than only the resultant of distorting or traumatic influences—a deficiency of the nurturance, guidance, and transmission of the basic adaptive techniques that must be provided a child within the family if he is to become capable of directing his own life as a reasonably independent adult.

Although the deficiencies and distorting influences of the parents and the families they created were many and differed from family to family, when a child's developmental needs are taken as the focus of attention, they could be grouped into three categories. (1) Deficiencies of parental nurturance—which we shall relate to the patient's difficulties in achieving adequate autonomy; that is, to attain sufficient independence, boundaries, and responsibility for the self. (2) The failures of the family as a social institution that directs the integrated development of the child by channeling drives and by providing conflict-free areas and roles appropriate to the offspring's age and sex into which he can grow, and motivating him to do so. The deficiencies in the family structure will be related to the faulty structuring of the patient's personality—to achievement or maintenance of an integrated ego structure (Lidz, 1963b). (3) The defects in transmitting the communicative and other basic instrumental techniques of the culture to the child. The large topic of the family's essential task of enculturating its offspring will be considered primarily through focusing upon the transmission of linguistic meanings. Recognition of the relationship of words and their meanings to ego functioning—the capacity to direct the self into the future—clarifies the connection between the aberrant conceptual thinking and the ego disorganization of schizophrenic patients (Lidz, 1963c). Until recently only the first of these three sets of factors, parental nurturance, has received any appreciable attention in psychoanalytic theories of personality development, or been considered of potential moment in the genesis of schizophrenia.

FAILURES OF PARENTAL NURTURANCE

Faulty or impoverished nurturance has been related to the etiology of schizophrenia in the many studies and theoretical essays concerned with maternal rejection, maternal oversolicitude, and maternal failures to establish boundaries as the child emerges from the need for a symbiotic tie to the mother. We wish to connote something broader by the term "parental nurturance"—the parents' abilities to relate appropriately and meet the needs of the child during each phase of psychosexual or psychosocial development. Disturbances occur in virtually all developmental stages of the child who later becomes schizophrenic, and such panphasic disturbances could not be attributed only to frustrations or fixations in the oral phase that prevented proper passage through subsequent developmental periods, for continuous serious impairments of the parent-child transactions were apparent. Inculcation of trust in others, in the self, in the reliability and worth of verbal communication, instilling a firm identity and self-esteem as a boy or girl, acceptance and proper frustration of the child's erotic ties to the parents, fostering peer group relationships, etc., were all deficient. The father's ways of relating cannot be neglected. Even in the first year he is important as the first intruder into the mother-child relationship, and later his attitudes and interaction with the child are important in many ways. White (1963), through utilizing Erikson's developmental phases, has noted how Schreber's parents failed to meet his basic needs throughout his developing years, emphasizing, as had Niederland (1951, 1959, 1960), the father's aberrant ways of relating to his son. Because of the need for brevity, we shall consider only the mothers' nurturant capacities during the first years of their children's lives.

The mothers in our series all had grave difficulties in relating to the infant and young child. The paucity of investment (cathexis) or the marked overcontrol cannot be taken to mean—in clichélike judgment —basic rejection of the child. Some mothers desired a son intensely, and devoted all of their energies and attention to rearing him very much to the son's detriment. Difficulties often arose because of deficiencies in the mother's own development: her own early experiences in being mothered had been faulty, and her insecurity in being able to care for a child profound. In others, depression or despair and preoccupation over an unbearable marital situation prevented proper investment of the child, and led to resentment at being bound to the marriage by the child. Her difficulties became more acute when the child began to ambulate, when her anxieties about being able to care for the child were projected onto the child's capacities to care for himself. To lessen her anxiety and to undo the negative aspects of ambivalences, the mother restricted and limited the child and, unable to empathize, she would constantly intrude in order to know what the child was doing and to be able to control. To permit brief discussion, the mothers of schizophrenic offspring will be divided somewhat arbitrarily into two groups. One type of mother cannot set boundaries, treating the child as an extension of herself. These mothers have felt inadequate as women, and some are ambulatory schizophrenics, insecure about themselves and even more anxious about the child, particularly when they can no longer fully control his behavior. She seeks to realize the fantasy of a child who will give completion and meaning to her life. This type of relationship is more common with schizophrenic sons. It can impair a boy's development more than a girl's, because a son must differentiate from the mother more completely. His primary identification with the mother must shift to an object love as part of the achievement of his sexual identity as a male, and to permit intimacy with a woman without fear of engulfment or loss of identity. The mother limits his exploration and makes decisions. The child does not learn to differentiate his drives and needs from those of the mother. He does not become a person in his own right but is held in a syncytial tie to the mother. The mother continues as an omniscient figure who directs her son's perception and comprehension, and who seems to the child to know the way and the why of living which remain unfathomable to him. The child has little opportunity to gain confidence in his ability to become autonomous. Later, the mother's inability to rescind her ties to the child, when he should be passing through the oedipal phase, blocks the internalization of parental directives and the formation of a superego adequate to provide the inner guidance essential to ego autonomy.

The second type of mother is unable to invest the mother-child relationship, tending to be apathetic toward the infant, and remaining emotionally withdrawn from the older child. Even when she controls and intrudes, there is an aloof and even an inimical quality to her overconcern. Unable to give of herself to the child, she provides little basic security. A child properly extends the range of his life space and increasingly assumes initiative through feeling that security can always be found at the center of his widening circle until he has sufficient internalized controls to feel secure when independent. The children of these mothers continue to seek the security they are not provided. Such maternal attitudes are common in mothers of schizophrenic daughters: these mothers, profoundly deficient in self-esteem as women and usually derogated by their husbands, cannot gain gratification from a female child. The daughter, in turn, does not gain a sense of worth in being a woman through identifying with such a mother, nor can she internalize the maternal, feminine feelings she needs to grow into womanhood. Children of both sexes are deprived of the foundation for capacities for intimacy. We might say that children with such aloof and inimical mothers do not gain a sense of trust in others and capacities for closeness, whereas children with symbiotic mothers gain little trust in themselves. Both are poorly prepared to assume initiative and move toward autonomy.

The deficiency in a sense of autonomy forms a critical aspect of schizophrenia. The patient does not feel capable of guiding his own life but seeks direction and decision from others. Parental directives and ideals are not internalized properly. Indeed, boundaries between the endopsychic and the external, between his feelings and those of others, are diffuse. Impulses and motivations are projected or externalized, and—something that has been largely overlooked—controls of forbidden motives are also externalized in hallucinated or delusional form, i.e., an extrojection of poorly internalized introjects. Unable to assume responsibility for the self, direction is often found through reading it into the expressions of others or even through magical interpretations of casual, essentially meaningless events.

Although such defects in early maternal nurturance have been considered as the cause of schizophrenia, it is apparent that persons suffering from other types of psychopathology can suffer similar deprivations. Such circumstances may be essential to the later development of schizophrenia without in themselves being sufficient cause. Indeed, some, but not all, mothers who are so impaired in relating to the infant and toddler will be frustrated by and frustrating to the older child. The father becomes increasingly important, but fathers who are still seeking mothering or who require constant feeding of their narcissism provide little parental nurturance. They fail to stimulate a son's masculine efforts or to provide an adequate identification model. A daughter's femininity is too dangerous either during the oedipal transition or later with the onset of her puberty to permit any intimacy that is not seduction. A variety of deprivations continue to impede the child's development. A few common deficiencies of parental behavior can be cited as examples. Problem solving through verbal communication is poorly rewarded; play with peer groups is impeded or considered dangerous; transfer of the child's care to a teacher is obstructed by the mother's anxiety; the mother experiences movement of the child toward others, even toward the father, as abandonment. Some of these situations and other related difficulties can be discussed and evaluated more easily by turning to the consideration of the other parameters by which we are assessing the family's influence upon the developmental process.

Failures of the Family as a Social Institution

Structure affects and even determines functioning. In all of the families studied, serious disturbances in the organization of the family as a social system existed, and we wish to comment briefly on how such failures of the family structure can misdirect the structuring of the personality and prevent the achievement of adequate ego integration. This aspect of personality theory—the influence of the family as a social system in directing and organizing the developing personality—has been virtually overlooked in psychiatry but has been emphasized and clarified by Parsons and Bales (1955), and its importance has become apparent in our investigations.

The form and functions of the family evolve with the culture, subserving the needs of the society of which it is a subsystem, and it must be suited to the production of new members of the society: but the family everywhere fills certain common functions and has some common structural features. In a society with relatively isolated nuclear families, such as ours, the way in which the spouses interrelate and find, or fail to find, reciprocal roles, markedly influences the dynamic organization of the family. The spouses may interrelate in a wide variety of ways and have a harmonious marriage provided that the pattern is suitable to both partners. However, in order to form a milieu suited to the integrated development of offspring, the marriage must fill certain minimal requirements. It is in the family that the child obtains his foundations in group living, in the meanings and values of social roles and social institutions (Chapter XIX). He is involved in a multiplicity of social phenomena that leaves a permanent imprint upon him; such as the sense of security derived from belonging to a mutually protective unit; the rewards that can be obtained from renouncing some of one's own wishes in favor of the welfare of the collectivity. He learns about hierarchies of authority and the relationship between authority and responsibility. He experiences not only the changing roles and statuses of a child and the expectations held for a child at each developmental phase, but also the roles of father and mother, husband and wife, man and woman, boy and girl and how they relate and conflict. The family value systems, role definitions, patterns of interrelationship, meaning systems, etc., enter into the developing child through the family behavior even more than through what is taught or even consciously appreciated by the family members. The child's ego becomes structured through such acquisitions and by the way the family's organization directs him into certain patterns and closes off other potentials, channels drives, attachments, identifications, and permits dependency or requires independence according to age, sex, and position in the family.

Biological givens that are built into the family determine the basic structure of the family as a social system. The family has two leaders, a father and a mother, each with different but interrelated functions. The mother, no matter how subjugated, is the expressive-affectional leader for the children and the prime carrier of the child-rearing traditions and techniques, and the father is the provider and instrumental leader. Unity of direction and organization requires a parental coalition. The biological division of the nuclear family into two generations and two genders provides a basic structure: each generation and sex has different obligations and prerogatives which serve to lessen role conflict and to direct the development of offspring. We posit that for spouses to form a family conducive to the integrated development of their offspring, they must form a coalition as parents, maintain the boundaries between generations, and adhere to their respective gender-linked roles. The requirements sound very simple, all too simple, until their ramifications are explored. None of the families with schizophrenic offspring met any of these several conditions. In a sense, it seems unnecessary to consider other structural deficiencies of these families if such foundations cannot be achieved or maintained.

The parents not only failed to form a coalition, but in the majority of these families a pervasive antagonism in which each parent undercut the worth of the other and competed for the loyalty of the child split the family; and, in the remainder, one spouse, usually the father, abdicated his role to the other who had eccentric ideas of family life and child rearing. The tendency of all groups to divide into dyads— a tendency that creates rivalries and jealousies—is diminished if the parents can maintain a unity in relating to their children. The coalition helps direct the child's oedipal transition by frustrating his fantasies of dividing the parents, and redirecting him to the reality that requires repression of such wishes. The child properly requires two parents; a parent of the same sex with whom he will identify and who provides a model to follow into adulthood, and a parent of the opposite sex who becomes a basic love object; but a parent can fill neither function effectively for the child if depreciated by the spouse, and is of still less value if castrated, despised, or treated as an enemy.

With serious failures of coalition between parents, the growing child may invest his energies in seeking to bridge the gap between the parents, or fall into the role of scapegoat whose difficulties mask the parental discord. He may feel responsible for satisfying the needs of both parents; or more commonly, he focuses on supporting and completing the life of a parent he needs rather than investing energies into his own development. The child may be caught in a "bind" because satisfying the wishes of one parent elicits rebuff and rejection from the other. The child who is reared in a schismatic family can develop a split ego structure. The parents who are irreconcilable in reality become irreconcilable introjects, and to satisfy both the child develops alternative ego and superego formations.

Failures to maintain the division into two generations occurred in every family because of childlike dependency of one parent upon the other, because of the intense rivalry of a parent with the child, or, frequently, because a parent used a child as a replacement to fill needs unsatisfied by the spouse—at times, to the extent of incestuous proclivities on the part of the parent.

When a parent uses a child to fill the needs unsatisfied by the spouse, the child finds an essential place in completing the life of a parent that should be closed to him and need not—and perhaps cannot —turn to the extrafamilial world for self-completion. The oedipal situation can continue unresolved into adolescence, causing incestuous problems and fears. Further, the excluded parent becomes jealous and hostile, and the child's fears of retribution and retaliation are then not simply projections but can be based on reality. A mother who cannot establish boundaries between herself and the child is also violating generation boundaries. The son is expected to live out the life closed to the mother because she is a woman, and her husband fills a subsidiary role. The son learns that he is not to grow up to be like his father who is simply the mother's means of obtaining children and providing for them. When the father is more of a child than a spouse, and offers his wife little except satisfying her needs to mother, he offers a weak figure for a son to emulate. He is someone who can be displaced rather than a figure whose prerogatives with the mother must be recognized.

The problems presented by fathers who are passive adjuncts of their wives, or by mothers who assume the prerogatives of fathers, lead to the topic of the importance of the parents' maintenance of gender-linked roles. The parental adherence to appropriate sex-linked roles not only serves as a guide for the achievement of reciprocal role relationships by parents but also plays a major part in guiding the child's development as a male or female. Of all factors entering into formation of personality characteristics, the sex of the child is the most decisive; and security of sexual identity is a cardinal factor in the achievement of a stable ego identity. Probably all schizophrenic patients are seriously confused in their sexual identity. Clear-cut role reversals in parents can obviously distort the child's development as when a parent is overtly homosexual or when they concern the division of major tasks between the parents. However, the inability of a mother to fill an affectional-expressive role, or of a father to provide instrumental leadership for the family also creates difficulties. Either a cold and unyielding mother or a weak and ineffectual father is apt to distort the family structure and a child's development. Failures to maintain gender-linked roles by parents as well as failures of one parent to support the spouse's gender role were very striking in these families—failures ranging from strong homosexual tendencies through assumptions of male roles by mothers and female roles by fathers to absence of effective paternal leadership and maternal coldness and aloofness.

Although the various complications that arise from such deficiencies in parents' adherence to sex-linked roles deserve more discussion, we should note that if a mother is consciously or unconsciously rivalrous with men and denigrating of her husband, a son can readily learn that masculinity will evoke rebuff from her, and fear of engulfment or castration by the mother can outweigh fears of retaliatory castration by the father. The schizophrenic patient's faulty sexual identity, including homosexual tendencies and concerns, are related to the parents' confused gender roles and the resultant imbalances in the family's dynamic structure.

The relationship between family structure and the structuring and integrating of the offspring's ego development is an extremely involved topic. We have only indicated a new and important parameter in the study of personality development. Still, a little contemplation leads to the realization that such matters as minimizing intrafamilial rivalries, the provision of identification models and motivating toward proper identifications, security of sexual identity, the transition through the oedipal phase, the proper repression of incestuous tendencies, etc., are affected profoundly by the family structure. Although other factors enter into the child's achievement of a firm identity, the foundations for a reasonable outcome are established if the parents form a firm parental coalition, maintain boundaries between the generations, and adhere to their respective gender-linked roles. Whereas few families maintain all of these requisites all of the time, in the families of schizophrenic patients none is maintained—the parents are deficient as individual models, and in their relationships with each other, and interfere with the child's internalization of unifiable personality traits.

DEFECTIVE TRANSMISSION OF INSTRUMENTAL TECHNIQUES

In turning to the family's cardinal task of transmitting the basic adaptive techniques and institutions of the society to its offspring, we are again concerned with a topic that has remained peripheral in psychoanalytic theory. The topic cannot be encompassed here, and we shall limit ourselves to a few considerations concerning the importance of linguistic meanings, the family's role in their acquisition, and the relationship between language and ego functioning.

The task of enculturating the young cannot, of course, properly be considered separately from the nurturant capacities of the family, the emotional atmosphere, and the patterns of family interaction. As we have noted, it is within the family that the child gains his fundamental knowledge of social roles and social institutions. We shall focus only upon the family's function in transmitting linguistic meanings, and then in only a most cursory manner. We do so partly as an illustration, but primarily because after the first year of life the acquisition of most other instrumental techniques depends upon language; and because cooperative interaction with others, so critical to human adaptation, depends upon the use of a shared system of meanings; and because the capacity to direct the self—one might say, to have any ego functioning at all—depends upon having verbal symbols with which one constructs an internalized symbolic version of the world which one can manipulate in imaginative trial and error before committing oneself to irrevocable actions (Lidz, 1963c).

Critical to the understanding of the importance of language to ego functioning is the appreciation that for anyone to understand, communicate, and think about the ceaseless flow of his experience, he must be able to divide his experiences into categories. The world and the events that transpire in it can be categorized in an almost endless variety of ways. Indeed, each culture is distinctive in the ways its members categorize their experiences—and members of very divergent cultures have great difficulties in communicating with one another and in understanding the other because their ways of categorizing are so different. The basic problem is not in translating the words but in gaining insight into the different conceptualization of experience. Each child must learn his culture's system of categorizing not only to be able to communicate but also to be able to think coherently. No one can start from the beginning and build up his own system. Each language is the resultant of the cumulative experiences of all prior generations of that ethnic branch of mankind. The vocabulary of the language is, in essence, a catalogue of the categories into which the culture divides its world and its experiences (Whorf, 1956).

One other essential attribute of words requires consideration because of its importance to ego functioning. Words, even though we may not be aware of it, have a predictive capacity upon which we base much of our action and without which our world would be much less predictable (Brown, 1958). A "chair" can be sat upon; "pneumococcal pneumonia" but not "viral pneumonia" can be treated with penicillin. The accuracy of the predictive capacities of a word depends upon how precisely the word is defined or the proper recognition of the critical attributes designated by the word. A person who defines a "mother" as "a woman with nurturant feelings toward her children" will be led into erroneous expectations that would be avoided through a more critical definition such as "a female parent."

The proper learning of the words and of the syntax of the language is essential to human adaptation, but this system is not built into the structure of the brain and there is no assurance that it will be learned correctly. The correctness and stability of the child's learning rest upon his teachers—primarily upon the members of his family.

These shared *communicative meanings* of words narrow and gain precision as the child gains experience under proper tutelage, but the *personal meaning* of words broadens to include his many experiences with the word and what it designates. Whereas the personal meanings should fit under the communicative meanings, the two sets can conflict. As we cannot consider the many ramifications of such concepts, we shall only emphasize that the child learns meanings as a way of solving problems, and that meanings are learned rapidly or slowly, accurately or vaguely, correctly or incorrectly, according to the manner and the consistency with which they are used by the child's teachers, and how effectively and consistently the child's use of the words is validated or invalidated by others.

Unless we grasp the importance of words in categorizing experience and in permitting predictability, and of the syntax with which they are used in reasoning, we can neither properly understand the essence of the human techniques of adaptation nor the nature of schizophrenia. Idiosyncratic usage of words, confusions between communicative meanings and idiosyncratic personal meanings, failures to automatize basic meanings that permit primary-process associations to intrude, etc., impede efforts to cope with and solve problems, to learn from others and one's own experience, to collaborate, and to guide the self into the future.

The foundations of language are established within the family. Whether the child gains trust in the utility and validity of verbal communication as a means of understanding and collaborating with others, or learns that words are in the service of fantasy rather than problem solving, or are a means of avoiding recognition of the obvious, or are used to blur and obfuscate, depends upon the nature of the intrafamilial communications. The topic is crucial to the study of schizophrenia and extremely complex. Here, we can only assert that these families in which schizophrenic patients grew up fail to inculcate consistent or instrumentally valid meanings. From retrospective accounts, from direct observation, from tests of family members, we can document that the meaning systems of these families are strikingly vague and idiosyncratic. The way in which the child should perceive is blocked by a parent who insists that things must be perceived as the parent needs them to be—a type of "brainwashing" that starts in infancy. The verbal and nonverbal cues, punishments and rewards of one parent are apt to be inconsistent, and those of the two parents conflicting. Parents, particularly the mothers, show impairments in the ability to categorize significantly more frequently than control parents (Chapter XXI). The styles of communication of both parents are often vague and fragmented to the extent that their responses to various projective tests can be differentiated from those of parents of other types of patients with a high degree of statistical significance as the work of Singer and Wynne (1963) has demonstrated.

The systematic investigations of the thought processes of parents of schizophrenic patients that are being carried out by our group at Yale and by the National Institute of Mental Health investigators are producing clear evidence that the thought disorder that forms a critical characteristic of schizophrenia does not arise *de novo* in the patient but has clear antecedents in one or both parents, and, further, that the deficiencies in the patient's thinking appear to relate specifically to the styles of communicating and ways of thinking of the parents. Studies of the family's communications as a group, even with the patient absent, reveal blurring, idiosyncrasies of usage, difficulties in focusing on a topic, paucity of interchange, and other such problems that convey how difficult it had been for the patient to have gained a sound foundation of his linguistic development in such settings. Such studies are, we believe, laying the foundations for a new and more meaningful understanding of the etiology and nature of schizophrenia.

The faulty transmission of adaptive techniques extends beyond problems of language. When attention is paid to the behavior of schizophrenic patients in remission, striking gaps are often found in their knowledge of how to perform relatively simple tasks or in the fundamentals of relating properly to others. They are, in many ways, simply unprepared and lack the tools and techniques required for relating to others and directing their own lives.

COMMENT

Now, it is clear that in the families with schizophrenic offspring the three parameters that have been considered—the failures of the family to provide adequate nurturance to permit the child to develop autonomy, to achieve the essential structure required to direct the structuring of the personality, and to convey the basic adaptive techniques of the culture—are all manifestations of the same core situation deriving from marked deficiencies in the parents' personalities, their faulty marital interaction, and parental behavior. However, such difficulties need not and do not always go together. A seriously scattered mother who blurs meanings can still relate well to her husband and children; a couple who cannot achieve a workable parental coalition can be properly nurturant and communicate clearly; failures in nurturance may be partially compensated by adequacies in family structure. Such difficulties will affect the offspring deleteriously, but not necessarily to the extent of leading to a schizophrenic development.

The deficiencies in these three basic family functions vary in severity, and the different effects of various combinations of different degrees of deprivation remain to be studied. It seems tenable to consider that extreme deprivations in these areas may lead to early onset and potential chronicity of the type conventionally labeled "process schizophrenia," whereas less severe family impairments lead to more acute breaks or to the onset of schizophrenia later in life. Efforts have not yet been made to relate various configurations and intensities of family problems to different types of schizophrenia, but Wynne and Singer (1963b) have found a relationship between the parental styles of communication and the severity of the patient's illness.

Such considerations obviously extend beyond problems of schizophrenia. They offer new approaches to questions of the determination of various personality characteristics, symptoms, and syndromes that can implement, and in part supplant, concepts focusing upon libidinal fixations, isolated traumata, and innate differences in the ego Anlage. We believe that the concepts that we have been considering in relatively primitive fashion in this chapter are more in accord with observed relationships between parents' personalities, styles of behavior, and family patterns and the personalities of their children.

In the theory which we have presented in but very broad outline, schizophrenia is, in essence, regarded as a deficiency disease, resulting from the family's failure to provide the essentials requisite for reasonably integrated personality development: deficiencies in parental nurturance were related to failures to achieve autonomy; the faulty family structure to improper structuring of the personality; and failures properly to convey the culture's basic instrumental techniques to failures in ego functioning of the patient. The theory is in accord with the view that proper understanding of the nature of human adaptation virtually requires the existence of a condition such as schizophrenia as an end result of gross failures of the process of enculturation. The theory can serve, as it has served, to direct investigators into paths that progressively clarify problems concerning the etiology, nature, and treatment of schizophrenia.

PART III

Studies of Thought and Communication of Parents

XXI

Thought Disorders in the Parents of Schizophrenic Patients: A Study Utilizing the Object Sorting Test

Part I

(1962)

This paper presents a replication of an experiment by McConaghy (1959) in which he found that 60 per cent of the parents of ten schizophrenic patients and at least one parent of each patient showed a disorder in conceptual thinking on the Lovibond (1953) version of the Object Sorting Test in contrast to such findings in only 9 per cent of parents of sixty-five controls. The findings suggest a dominant mode of inheritance of schizophrenia and hold great potential significance to the study of schizophrenia. We had previously drawn attention to the marked distortions in communicating and relating in each of the fifteen families of schizophrenic patients studied intensively (Chapter X); in at least nine of these families one or both parents were either schizophrenic or paranoid, and in the remainder the aberrations in the parents' ways of thinking and relating could have undermined their offsprings' foundations in reality testing and rational thinking. The high incidence of psychotic and borderline disorders in these parents, none of whom had been hospitalized for them, suggested that focusing upon proclivities to symbolic distortions in family members rather than upon the incidence of manifest schizo-

Theodore Lidz, Cynthia Wild, Sarah Schafer, Bernice Rosman, and Stephen Fleck: Thought Disorders in the Parents of Schizophrenic Patients: A Study Utilizing the Object Sorting Test. Journal of Psychiatric Research, *Vol. I, 1963, pp. 193-200. Copyright © 1963, Pergamon Press, Ltd.*

phrenia might further the study of the genetics of schizophrenia. Mc-Conaghy's procedure appeared to offer a simple and useful approach to the study of a critical aspect of the thought processes in relatives of schizophrenic patients.

McConaghy followed a hypothesis promulgated by Kallmann (1946) that "the factor for schizophrenia, even though recessive, may sometimes be expressed in a merely heterozygous condition, but only to the extent of schizoid personality changes. . . . Schizoid types may be either heterozygotes with little resistance to an intermediate expressivity of their single gene, or strongly resistant homozygotes." He sought a means of determining whether one or both parents of schizophrenics might not exhibit schizoid traits more commonly than a control population. Lovibond (1953) had developed a scoring technique for the Object Sorting Test for conceptual thinking that had enabled him to obtain a numerical score showing a high correlation with clinical estimates of the severity of thought disorders in schizophrenic patients. Since Rapaport and his coworkers (1945) had found the Object Sorting Test useful in diagnosing schizoid personalities as well as schizophrenia, McConaghy considered that Lovibond's technique might serve his purpose.

Description of the Test

The test is administered according to Rapaport's instructions. The subject is confronted with thirty-three common objects such as tableware, smoking items, and toy objects. The test is divided into two sections. In the first section, the subject is presented with an object and is asked to place with it all of the other objects that belong with it. After he has completed the sort, he is asked, "Why do all of these belong together?" This procedure is carried out with seven different objects in turn. In the second part the examiner presents the subject with twelve different groupings of the objects in succession, each grouping having some different characteristic in common; that is, they are all tools, all red, all smoking materials, etc. Each time the subject is asked, "Why do all of these belong together?" The subject's verbal responses are recorded verbatim.

Lovibond's Scoring System

The rationale for Lovibond's scoring system is based upon a Pavlovian approach to the nature of schizophrenic thinking. Conceptual thinking requires an inhibition of inappropriate associational linkages. Normally, the context determines what is thought about and what is inhibited; but schizophrenic patients cannot inhibit inessential linkages, and irrelevant material interferes with proper category formation. The scoring directions can be found in his paper and will merely be summarized here.

Lovibond confined his scoring procedure to giving scores to responses that indicated inappropriate or inessential linkages, neglecting other aspects of the test performance. He distinguished eight categories of pathological responses, four of which Rapaport had found useful indicators of thought disorders, and added four new categories which might be considered as variants of Rapaport's categories. He quantified the procedure by giving a score ranging from 1 to 3 for each pathological response according to the extent of its abnormality using criteria provided in his article. The total score is the sum of the scores on the nineteen items; thus the possible range of scores is from 0 to 57.

The abnormal types of categorizations that occur most frequently are: *syncretistic* responses in which the subject groups objects together for a reason that does not explain why other objects are excluded; as "because all are useful," or "all exist"; in *fabulated* responses the subject groups on a concrete, temporal basis by winding a story around them; as explaining the grouping of a ball, eraser, and toy cigar by saying, "The man plays ball, then while smoking a cigar, writes a letter and uses the eraser"; in *chain* responses, the objects are united by a chain of linkages in that the second object shares an attribute with the first, the third with the second but not the first, etc., as when a rubber cigar is placed with the ball because both are rubber, but then matches are added to light the cigar. The remaining five categories occur less frequently. They are: *symbolic* responses where the grouping is formed purely on a symbolic basis, as when a large and small fork are grouped together because "they are father and son"; *arbitrary* responses and *personal* associations that are variants of fabulatory responses; *irrelevant* responses that are a type of syncretistic response; and *impersonal* associations which include clang associations such as, "this is red and this can be read."

Lovibond, on the basis of his study of forty-five controls and thirty-two schizophrenic subjects, considered a total score of 7 or higher to be indicative of a schizophrenic thought disorder, but found that 9 per cent of the controls had scores above 6 and 34 per cent of his schizophrenic subjects had scores below 7.

McConaghy's Experiment

McConaghy selected schizophrenic patients who obtained pathological scores on the procedure, considering that not all schizophrenic patients suffer from a thought disorder. He then tested both parents of ten of them, and compared the results with a control group of sixty-five subjects composed of Lovibond's forty-five controls plus twenty older patients in a general hospital, randomly selected. His results with the parents of the schizophrenic patients are presented in Table I.

TABLE I

MC CONAGHY'S SCORES OF PARENTS OF SCHIZOPHRENICS
WITH "THOUGHT DISORDER" ON SORTING TEST

Patient	Mother	Father
1	7	0
2	7	16
3	10	0
4	14	2
5	3	14
6	0	8
7	4	10
8	11	9
9	0	10
10	6	13

It will be noted that twelve of the twenty parents or 60 per cent had scores of 7 or higher, and that at least one of each set of parents had a pathological score. Six of the sixty-five controls or 9.1 per cent had scores above 6. The results are significant by X^2 test at the 0.001 level.

McConaghy considered that finding a "score indicative of schizoid features in at least one of the two parents of every patient investigated would support Kallmann's concept—that the presence of a gene producing schizophrenia may be indicated in those people who successfully resist the disease by the production of a 'schizoid' personality. The finding that the significant score was present in one parent in all cases, but in both only twice might suggest a dominant rather than a recessive mode of inheritance. If confirmed, the discrepancy with Kallmann's conclusions might be explained by the homogeneous nature of the schizophrenic patients investigated, only those with clinical 'thought disorder' being selected."

Confirmation of McConaghy's results would not be sufficient to demonstrate the value of the procedure as a test for schizophrenia or for a thought disorder in parents that might predispose offspring to schizophrenia. Patients with other psychopathological conditions and their parents as well as populations in various intelligence ranges and socioeconomic levels would have to be tested. However, an experiment of elaborate design did not seem warranted before obtaining a confirmation of McConaghy's results.

Procedure

In the replication experiment McConaghy's procedure was altered in several ways: (1) Hospitalized schizophrenic patients who showed a thought disorder both clinically and on projective tests rather than patients with high Lovibond scores were selected, and they and their parents were tested. (2) Twenty-one pairs of parents formed the control series since parenthood itself might influence the test and because data were needed on the percentage of such couples which contained at least one member with a pathological score. (3) The reliability of the scoring of the psychologist who administered the test was checked by having a second psychologist score blindly; that is, neither knowing whether the subject belonged to the experimental or control series or the marital pairings. (4) The vocabulary subtest of the Wechsler Adult Intelligence Scale was administered to each subject to afford some indication of whether intellectual endowment affected the Object Sorting scores appreciably. Uncorrected scaled scores were utilized. The measure would not be thorough but it appeared essential to limit the testing, and the vocabulary test has a high correlation with the total WAIS score and is affected minimally by psychotic disorders.

Both patient and control groups had relatively high educational backgrounds. The control families, found with difficulty, were provided by three churches of different denominations and were otherwise unselected except to ascertain that neither parents nor any of their children had ever been clinically psychotic. The age range of the control parents was lower than the patients' parents (Table II); but a correlation of only 0.15 between age and the (revised) test scores indicated that age did not influence the scores significantly. Years of education and vocabulary scores of the control and experimental series showed no significant differences (Table II). The mean

TABLE II

AGE, EDUCATION, AND VOCABULARY SCORES
OF EXPERIMENTAL AND CONTROL GROUPS

			Age		Years Education		Vocabulary Scores	
		No.	Mean	SD	Mean	SD	Mean	SD
Experimental Group	Patient	10	24.3	3.13	14.1	2.13	14.3	2.16
	Father	10	58.9	5.74	14.6	3.27	13.1	2.60
	Mother	10	54.0	4.42	13.3	3.02	14.6	2.40
Control Group	Father	21	47.5	4.89	15.1	3.34	13.8	3.06
	Mother	21	45.9	5.62	13.7	3.24	13.4	2.40

of both groups had approximately four years more schooling than McConaghy's and Lovibond's subjects; a difference that may relate to cultural factors, since McConaghy worked in England and Lovibond in Australia.

First Trial

Using test protocols that were not included in the experiment, two psychologists worked out a scoring system according to the instructions in Lovibond's article. Then, scoring the tests independently, they achieved a reliability coefficient of 0.90. As the experiment clearly failed to confirm McConaghy's findings, the data will not be presented in detail. Only five of the twenty parents in the experimental group in comparison with twelve of the twenty in McConaghy's series had scores of 7 or higher. As 11.9 per cent of the control parents had scores above this cutting point as compared to 9.1 per cent of McConaghy's controls, it appeared that the interpretation of the scoring procedure had been reasonably correct.

Despite the failure to obtain significant results, a definite impression was gained from this first trial that clear-cut differences existed between the test protocols of the experimental and control subjects that the scoring procedure had missed. Protocols not used in the experiment were sent to Lovibond for scoring and comment on scoring criteria. Lovibond tended to give higher scores for faulty groupings and, in addition, scored faulty responses that subjects retracted. He also had found in recent work that about 20 per cent of controls rather than 9 per cent scored 7 or higher.

The psychologists modified the scoring technique and rescored the protocols. The new results were in close agreement with McConaghy's except that 19 per cent of the controls in contrast to 9.1 per cent of his controls had pathological scores. The results, however, could not be considered valid as both psychologists were "contaminated" by their previous work with the protocols.

Two new psychologists were trained in the revised scoring technique. Neither of the new scorers knew which were experimental and control subjects. They achieved a reliability of 0.94. The results given in Table III are the averages of their scores.

TABLE III

SCORES OF PATIENTS AND PARENTS
ON OBJECT SORTING TEST
(Revised Scoring)

No.	Patient	Father	Mother
1	9	6	5
2	13	5.5	7
3	6	4	7.5
4	5	35	19
5	9	5.5	5
6	1	6	7
7	12	17	3.5
8	10	9	16.5
9	9	11	1
10	17	1	2

Nine of the twenty parents of patients (45 per cent), four fathers and five mothers, had scores above the cutting point in comparison with eight of forty-two control parents (19 per cent), three fathers and five mothers (Table IV).

TABLE IV

NUMBER OF PARENTS OF PATIENTS AND CONTROLS
WITH SCORES OF 7 OR HIGHER
(Revised Scoring)

	Below 7	7 or Higher	Total
Schizophrenics' parents	11 (55%)	9 (45%)	20 (100%)
Control parents	34 (81%)	8 (19%)	42 (100%)

$$X^2 = 3.37 \quad p < .10$$

Seven of the ten patients had at least one parent with a score of 7 or higher. There were no sets of control parents in which both the parents had a score above 6, so that 38 per cent of the control children had one parent with a score above the cutting point (Table V).

TABLE V

NUMBER OF PATIENTS AND CONTROL CHILDREN
WITH AT LEAST ONE PARENT SCORING 7 OR HIGHER
(Revised Scoring)

	Below 7	7 or Higher	Total
Schizophrenic patients	3 (30%)	7 (70%)	10 (100%)
Controls	13 (62%)	8 (38%)	21 (100%)

$$X^2 = 1.63 \quad \text{not significant}$$

Thus, using the cutting point established by Lovibond, the results neither match McConaghy's findings of 60 per cent of parents of patients giving high scores in contrast to 9.1 per cent of his controls, nor are they statistically significant. However, abandoning the arbitrary cutting point and handling the data in other ways indicates that the series are decidedly different.

First, a median test was applied to the data; that is, the median for the combined experimental and control groups which is between 4.5

and 5 was used as the cutting point. The difference between groups is significant at the 0.02 level (Table VI).

TABLE VI

MEDIAN CUTTING POINT
(Revised Scoring)

	Low	High	Total
Schizophrenics' parents	5 (25%)	15 (75%)	20 (100%)
Control parents	26 (62%)	16 (38%)	42 (100%)

$$X^2 = 5.96 \quad p < .02$$

Second, the experimental and control series, as groups, were compared by the Mann Whitney U Test. The two series were combined into one distribution and given rank scores, 1 for the lowest and 62 for the highest. When the sums of rank scores for the two groups are compared the difference is significant at the 0.01 level.

Thus, although the experiment failed to confirm McConaghy's findings using the Lovibond cutting point, it yielded impressive evidence that the parents of these schizophrenic patients as a group have difficulties with conceptual thinking and category formation to a greater extent than the control parents. The trend is sufficiently firm and clear to warrant further attention to the hypothesis that schizophrenic patients frequently and perhaps always have a parent who suffers from a disorder in conceptual thinking.

There are several possible reasons for the differences between the results of this experiment and McConaghy's.

1. The interpretation of the scoring criteria may still differ. However, considerable experimentation went into seeking to score according to Lovibond's instructions and examples. Such experimentation may diminish the validity of the findings, but in this study we were primarily seeking to learn if McConaghy's results could be validated.

2. All patients whose parents composed McConaghy's experimental series had scores of 7 or higher on the test. McConaghy emphasizes the importance of this criterion for selection. Three patients in this experiment did not meet this criterion. However, all three patients with low scores had at least one parent with a score above the cutting point, and all three pairs of parents with low scores had schizophrenic offspring with high scores (Table III).

3. McConaghy did not indicate whether the same person administered and scored the test or offer data concerning the reliability of the scoring.

COMMENT

Even though the findings of the experiment were not as decisive as McConaghy's, they warrant entertaining the hypothesis that the presence of such thought disorders in a parent may be one essential factor in the appearance of schizophrenia in an offspring; or the alternate hypothesis that if neither parent has this type of thought disorder, it is unlikely that a child will become schizophrenic. It should be specifically noted that some individuals who perform well on this single test will reveal aberrant thinking on other tests. Such hypotheses are worth testing carefully because procedures derived from them could provide a definite and measurable factor associated with the etiology of schizophrenia and could supply a much-needed instrument for epidemiological studies. They are in accord with our clinical studies which have shown that a multiplicity of difficulties exist in families with schizophrenic offspring but suggest that it may be the presence of a thought disorder in one or both parents that differentiates them from other seriously disturbed families. Whether the presence of such thought disorders in the parents indicates a genetic transmission as McConaghy assumes or an extragenetic environmental transmission remains a matter for speculation and study.

Part II

(1963)

The results of the first replication of McConaghy's study warranted further exploration of the usefulness of the technique for differentiating the parents of schizophrenic patients from control parents. A study was designed to collect a larger sample which would provide a better estimate of the incidence of impaired or distorted conceptual thinking in both control and patient-parent populations. Since the first replication sample contained few subjects of low education and social class, it was deemed of primary importance to collect protocols from subjects in these categories. It was anticipated that exploration of the relationship of intelligence, education, occupational level, age and sex of parents to aberrant concept formation as measured by the test would permit evaluation of the usefulness and the limitations of this tool in differentiating parents of schizophrenics from other groups of parents.

METHOD

Subjects

The patient-parent group consisted of sixty-eight parents (thirty-four couples) of hospitalized schizophrenic patients, unselected as to type, or duration of stay in hospital. The presence of a schizophrenic thought disorder, manifested clinically and on projective tests, was used as the basis for patient selection. In this respect, the present method deviates from McConaghy's as he limited his sample to par-

Bernice Rosman, Cynthia Wild, Judith Ricci, Stephen Fleck, and Theodore Lidz: Thought Disorders in the Parents of Schizophrenic Patients: A Further Study Utilizing the Object Sorting Test, Journal of Psychiatric Research, Vol. 2, 1964, pp. 211-221, Copyright © 1964, Pergamon Press, Ltd.

ents of those patients only who received high scores on the Object Sorting Test.[1]

The control group consisted of 115 parents, including forty-nine couples with eleven additional fathers and six additional mothers. These subjects were all paid volunteers, recruited from three religious groups of different denominations, from the volunteer service group of a general hospital, and from the maintenance staff of the same hospital. Subjects from the latter group were chosen on the basis of having less than ten years of schooling. Otherwise, subjects were unselected except to determine as far as possible that neither they nor their children had been psychotic or hospitalized for a mental or emotional disorder.[2]

Test Procedure

The techniques of administering and scoring the Object Sorting Test were the same as reported in Part I.

All protocols were given code numbers so that they could be scored independently by two psychologists without knowing whether the tests were those of patient parents or controls. Since a scoring reliability of $r = .90$ was achieved, the two sets of scores were averaged. It must be noted that neither blind scoring nor reliability measures were reported by Lovibond or McConaghy.

In addition to the Object Sorting Test, the Vocabulary and Information subtests of the Wechsler Adult Intelligence Scale were administered to all subjects except eight of the patient parents. The scaled scores on these two subtests were averaged for each subject.

Data were collected from the subjects concerning age, education, and occupation. The occupation data were rated according to Hol-

[1] The distribution of cases from among six different institutions is as follows: sixteen parent-pairs from the Yale Psychiatric Institute; four from the psychiatric ward of the Yale New Haven Hospital; four from the Veterans Administration Hospital, West Haven, Connecticut; five from the Connecticut Valley Hospital; three from the National Institute of Mental Health; and two from the Institute of Living, Hartford, Connecticut. The authors wish to thank the following individuals for generously cooperating in the collection of data for this study: Thomas Detre, Jacob Levine, Jules Holzberg, David Rosenthal, and Marvin Reznikoff.

[2] The N used in this sample includes the protocols of the twenty patient-parents and forty-two control parents reported in Part I.

lingshead and Redlich's classification (1958) from 1 (high level) to 7 (low level). A reliability on these ratings of 91 per cent agreement between two independent raters was obtained.

RESULTS

The two main hypotheses tested were:

1. The frequency of impaired conceptual thinking as defined by a score of 7 or higher on the Object Sorting Test will be greater in the patient-parent group than in the control group.

2. The frequency of couples in which one or both members obtain a score of 7 or higher will be greater in the patient-parent group than in the control group.

The results pertinent to the first hypothesis are presented in Table VII.

TABLE VII

COMPARISON OF OBJECT SORTING TEST SCORES FOR THE
PATIENT-PARENT AND CONTROL GROUPS

	Number of Scores 0-6	Number of Scores 7 or Higher
Patient Parents median score = 6.9	33 (49%)	35 (51%)
Control Parents median score = 5.3	72 (63%)	43 (37%)

Corrected $X^2 = 2.91$ $p < .05$ 1 tail

As the patient-parent group contains a significantly greater number of high-scoring individuals than the control group, the first hypothesis is upheld. A comparison using an array of scores (with the Mann Whitney U Test) rather than using the arbitrary cutting point of 7 also yielded a significant difference ($p < 0.05$, one tail) in the expected direction. However, the percentages of high scorers in the control group and of low scorers in the patient-parent group differ considerably from McConaghy's findings of 9 per cent and 40 per cent respectively.

Table VIII presents the frequency of parent couples in each group with at least one high-scoring member.

TABLE VIII

NUMBER OF COUPLES IN THE PATIENT-PARENT AND CONTROL GROUPS
WITH AT LEAST ONE HIGH-SCORING MEMBER

	Both Parents Score 0 - 6	One or Both Parents Score 7 or Higher
Patient Parents	8 (24%)	26 (76%)
Control Parents	21 (43%)	28 (57%)

Corrected $X^2 = 2.50$ $p < .10$ 1 tail

Since the two groups are not significantly different, the second hypothesis is not upheld, although there is a strong trend in the predicted direction. It is apparent that McConaghy's finding that *each* schizophrenic patient had at least one high-scoring parent is not confirmed. The different criteria for patient selection do not appear to explain the discrepancy, as will be discussed below.

Sex of Parent and Background Variables

The relationship between sex of parent and incidence of pathological response is shown in Table IX, which presents the comparative findings for mothers and fathers in both groups.

TABLE IX

COMPARISON OF MOTHERS' AND FATHERS'
OBJECT SORTING TEST SCORES

	Number of Scores 0 - 6	Number of Scores 7 or Higher
Control Fathers median score = 5.5	37 (62%)	23 (38%)
Patients' Fathers median score = 5.7	21 (62%)	13 (38%)
Control Mothers median score = 5.2	35 (64%)	20 (36%)
Patients' Mothers median score = 8.7	12 (35%)	22 (65%)

Comparison of Control Mothers with Control Fathers—No Difference
Comparison of Control Fathers with Patients' Fathers—No Difference
Comparison of Patients' Mothers with Patients' Fathers
$X^2 = 3.76$ $p < .10$ 2 tails
Comparison of Control Mothers with Patients' Mothers
$X^2 = 5.69$ $p < .01$ 1 tail

It is clear that the primary source of difference between the control and patient-parent groups is the high frequency of pathological scores among the mothers of patients. The control fathers, control mothers, and patient fathers are not distinguishable groups. The frequency of high scorers among the patient mothers is significantly greater than among the control mothers. A greater frequency of high scorers among the patient mothers than among patient fathers, while not statistically significant, is strongly suggested ($p<0.10$, two tails).

The difference between mothers' and fathers' scores was examined in another way. In order to compare their scores, even when both members of a couple might have high or low scores, the difference between the mother's and father's score for each couple was obtained. A difference of only 0.5 was not counted. An equal number of cases in which a mother's score would surpass a father's and vice versa would be expected by chance. In the control group, twenty-two mothers had higher scores than their husbands, twenty-five fathers had higher scores than their wives, and for two couples there was no difference. By contrast, in the patient-parent group, twenty-one mothers had higher scores than their husbands and only nine fathers had higher scores than their wives; for four couples there was no difference. A comparison by the sign test is significant ($p<0.046$, two tails).

Thus, both methods of analysis demonstrate the greater pathology of the mothers.

The Relation of Age, Intellectual Ability, Educational Level, and Occupational Level to Pathological Score Frequencies

The characteristics of the two groups with respect to the above variables are presented in Table X.

The relationships of age, intellectual ability, and educational level to Object Sorting Test scores were explored by obtaining product-moment correlations. Because of the discontinuous distribution of the occupational ratings, a contingency coefficient (C) was obtained between occupation classes and high-low test score frequencies. Table XI presents these correlations.

The variable of age appears unrelated to the Object Sorting Test measure of thought disorder. The evaluation of this relationship was

TABLE X

AGE, INTELLIGENCE SCORES, EDUCATION, AND OCCUPATIONAL LEVELS
OF PATIENT-PARENT AND CONTROL GROUPS

	Patient-Parent Group		Control Group	
	Range	Mean	Range	Mean
Age	39-70 yrs.	56.7	35-66	48.5
Averaged Vocabulary-Information Scores	4-18.5	12.4	4.5-18	12.7
Years Education	4-21 yrs.	12.5	3-20	12.3
	Number	Per Cent	Number	Per Cent
Occupational Levels				
Low (ratings 5 - 7)	14	21%	35	30%
Middle (3 - 4)	20	29%	24	21%
High (1 - 2)	34	50%	56	49%

TABLE XI

CORRELATIONS OF AGE, INTELLIGENCE, EDUCATION, AND
OCCUPATION LEVELS WITH OBJECT SORTING TEST SCORE

Variable	Patient-Parent Group	Control Group
Age	$r = .03$	$r = .10$
Vocabulary-Information Score	$r = -.08$	$r = -.23$**
Educational Level	$r = -.07$	$r = -.23$**
Occupational Level	$C = .00$	$C = -.20$*

**$p < .02$ 2 tails
*$p < .10$

of particular importance in this study since it is a characteristic on which our patient-parent and control groups are not matched. The original and first replication studies also found no relationship between age and the test scores.

In the control group, the intelligence, education, and occupation measures showed low but reliable relationships to Object Sorting Test scores. The negative direction of the correlations indicates that scores decrease with an increase in intellectual, educational and occupational levels. By contrast, in the patient-parent group these variables are unrelated. These findings required further analysis of the data.

Table XII presents the incidence of high scorers on the Object Sorting Test in the patient-parent and control groups when they are divided into high and low intelligence categories. The over-all median of the Vocabulary-Information scores (12.9) was chosen as the dividing point to form these categories.

TABLE XII

SCORES FOR PATIENT PARENTS AND CONTROLS
OF HIGH AND LOW INTELLIGENCE

		Number of Scores 0 - 6	Number of Scores 7 or Higher
Low Intelligence	Patient-Parent Group median score = 5.7	15 (54%)	13 (46%)
	Control Parent Group median score = 6.2	31 (56%)	24 (44%)
	No Difference		
High Intelligence	Patient-Parent Group median score = 7.2	14 (44%)	18 (56%)
	Control Parent Group median score = 4.7	41 (68%)	19 (32%)

$$X^2 = 4.27 \quad p < .025 \quad 1 \text{ tail}$$

This analysis shows that the first hypothesis of greater incidence of thought disorder in the patient-parent group when compared with a control group is not tenable at the lower levels of intellectual ability. This finding appears to be due to the high incidence of pathological scores among controls of lower intelligence, thus making discrimination between groups impossible. The hypothesis is upheld when the groups compared are of a higher intellectual level.

A similar analysis of the data was performed to permit comparisons between groups of different educational levels. Comparisons were made between groups for subjects who did not complete high school, for subjects who completed high school and for subjects who completed college. As the frequencies of high and low test scores were the same for subjects who completed high school and for those who completed college, these two groups were combined for the statistical test. Table XIII presents the results of this analysis.

TABLE XIII

SCORES FOR PATIENT PARENTS AND CONTROLS
AT TWO EDUCATIONAL LEVELS

		Number of Scores 0 - 6	Number of Scores 7 or Higher
Did not complete high school	Patient Parents median score = 6.5	11 (52%)	10 (48%)
	Control Parents median score = 7.0	14 (45%)	17 (55%)

No Difference

Completed high school and completed college combined	Patient Parents median score = 7.0	22 (47%)	25 (53%)
	Control Parents median score = 4.5	56 (67%)	28 (33%)

$X^2 = 4.14$ p $<.025$ 1 tail

This analysis reveals that the controls and the patient parents with less than a high school education cannot be differentiated. The hypothesis of differences between patient-parent and control groups is supported only when subjects have at least completed high school.

As would be expected, a similar pattern of results emerges for occupational level. At the low level, it is apparent that the control group cannot be distinguished from the patient-parent group, but at the middle and high levels, the groups are significantly different ($p<0.02$). Thus, the hypothesis of a greater frequency of pathological scores in the patient-parent group is supported only with subjects representing higher levels of intelligence, education, and occupation.

DISCUSSION

1. The present study confirms McConaghy's major findings but with important reservations. It seems clear that a greater incidence of illogical and inappropriate conceptual thinking is found among parents of schizophrenic patients than among parents of nonpsychotic

children. However, the frequency of high scorers in our control population is considerably higher than his estimates. McConaghy found only a 9 per cent incidence of high scoring controls while in this study the figure reaches 37 per cent.

It seemed possible that our failure to confirm his original finding of a pathological score for at least one parent of each patient might be related to the different criteria for patient selection. This study was not limited to parents of only patients who obtained a high test score, although all patients showed evidence of thought disorder by other criteria. Object Sorting Test scores were available for twenty-eight patients. The parents of high- and low-scoring patients were compared in order to check on this potential reason for the discrepancy. Thirteen of the fifteen (87 per cent) low-scoring patients in comparison with nine of the thirteen (70 per cent) high-scoring patients have at least one high-scoring parent. Of the six patient-parent couples both of whose members had low scores, four have high-scoring children, and two have low-scoring children. Thus, the difference between McConaghy's method of selection of subjects and that used in the present study does not appear to account for the discrepant results.

The high number of control couples (57 per cent) with one high-scoring member precludes use of this measure as a single, simple screening device. It should be noted that these findings refer to impairments of conceptual thinking only as defined by this particular scoring system for this test. Other tests or a combination of tests may provide a more comprehensive and sensitive index of thought disorder for research and screening purposes. As for theoretical considerations regarding environmental or genetic factors operating in the transmission of schizophrenia, the results cannot be used to support either view.

2. The finding of a greater incidence of disordered conceptual thinking among patients' mothers lends psychometric support to clinical impressions and judgments that mothers of schizophrenic patients frequently show scattering and disorganization of thought (Alanen, 1958; Tietze, 1949; Chapter XVII). This does not imply that fathers of patients are not psychiatrically disturbed. Clinical descriptions of the variety and severity of impaired reality testing and

personality disorders found among schizophrenics' fathers are provided in Chapters V and IX. The particular measure used in this study of formal thought organization may be insensitive to the types of psychiatric disorders more commonly displayed by the male parent, such as paranoid trends which involve less disorganization of thought and looseness of association. Other types of analysis and other tests, including behavioral observations of family interactions, may provide better measures of the thought disorders shown by patients' fathers. The present findings suggest that further studies using this Object Sorting Test measure should focus on patients' mothers, particularly since they are frequently more available as subjects than the fathers.

3. The variables of intelligence, education, and occupational level all affect performance on the Object Sorting Test in a similar manner and are probably interrelated. It is not surprising that a relatively high proportion of control subjects from lower levels of intelligence, education, and occupation give pathological responses on the test, for the capacity to sort into categories varies with intellectual ability; but, since the responses of the patient-parent group were virtually unaffected by these factors, the findings will require further study. They may reflect the higher prevalence of psychiatric disorders among the lower social class population (Hollingshead and Redlich, 1958), with the deficiencies in ability to categorize indicating the presence of psychopathology or possibly contributing to vulnerability to mental disorders.

Removing the subjects of low intelligence, occupation, and education from the sample improved the discrimination of the groups.[8] Further research with this particular scoring method for the Object Sorting Test requires limitation of samples to the middle and upper ranges of intelligence, education, and social class. Many of McConaghy's subjects fell into the low education range as defined in this study. However, as McConaghy worked in England, cultural factors make a direct comparison with our sample difficult.

4. Prior to the present study, considerable experimentation went into attempts to refine, modify, and improve the Lovibond scoring

---

[8] However, the difference found between the control mothers and patient mothers was not improved by comparing only mothers with high education, etc.

procedure. These included altering the weights given to responses, eliminating the scoring of commonly occurring poor responses, and changing from a single score per response to multiple scores; but none of these attempts improved the differentiation between groups.

XXII

*Measuring Disordered Styles of Thinking
in the Parents of Schizophrenic Patients
on the Object Sorting Test*

Part I

(1965)

In Chapter X attention was drawn to the distorted, irrational modes of thinking and communicating that characterize the family environments of schizophrenic patients. Intensive clinical study of the families of fifteen such patients suggested the hypothesis that "these persons are prone to withdraw through altering their internal representations of reality because they have been reared amidst irrationality and intrafamilial systems of communication that distort or deny instrumentally valid interpretations of the environment." Wynne and Singer (1963a, 1963b) and Singer and Wynne (1965a, 1965b) working with projective tests, provided further evidence that family forms and styles of thinking and communicating are related to thought disorder in the offspring. McConaghy (1959) and Lidz et al. (Chapter XXI, Part I and II) reported that the parents of schizophrenic patients show significantly more evidence of thought disorder than control groups on the Object Sorting Test, a test of conceptual thinking. Thus, there is a good deal of clinical and experimental evidence to suggest that patients' parents manifest disturbed styles of thinking and communicating.

The present study was undertaken to see if the criteria developed by Singer (Wynne and Singer, 1963a, 1963b) that seemed to differentiate parents of patients from control subjects on projective tests

Cynthia Wild, Margaret Singer, Bernice Rosman, Judith Ricci, and Theodore Lidz. This paper has not been previously published.

could be applied to the brief, easily administered Object Sorting Test. Another purpose of this study was to determine whether or not her criteria of fragmentation and blurring of attention and meaning could be specified and objectified, so that the protocols could be scored reliably along these dimensions.

Procedure

The method used in administering the Object Sorting Test was described in the preceding chapter. In connection with the study described in Chapter XXI, Part I, protocols had been collected from sixty-two subjects. They included twenty parents (ten couples) of schizophrenic inpatients who showed a thought disorder both clinically and on projective tests. The control group consisted of forty-two parents (twenty-one couples), all paid volunteers, unselected except to determine in so far as possible that neither they nor their children had been clinically psychotic.

To see whether Singer's criteria for differentiating the parents of patients from control subjects on projective tests could be applied to the Object Sorting Test, she was sent protocols of ten patient-parent couples and fifteen control couples (fifty subjects in all). Aware only of the husband-wife pairings, she correctly identified twenty out of twenty-five (80 per cent) of the couples as parents of schizophrenics or of normal offspring. Singer also included comments on each protocol, stating why she had attributed it to a patient parent or control parent. This discrimination seemed successful enough to continue investigating whether Singer's criteria could be objectified into a quantifiable scoring system that others could use with adequate reliability. Accordingly, her comments were used to make up a scoring manual, derived from Sample I. The manual, summarized below, is based on Singer's impression that the parents of schizophrenic patients show disturbances in their handling of attention and meaning, manifested in fragmented and blurred cognitive styles of attending to and interpreting objects in their environment.[1]

[1] During the study, the manual was revised several times. While the specific behavioral manifestations scored remained the same, this present version is somewhat different from the original in terms of organizing and categorizing these manifestations under general headings and represents our latest thinking on which clusters of behavior seem to belong together. Further work will probably lead to more refinement and modifications of the manual.

SCORING MANUAL

A.   INABILITY TO MAINTAIN A CONSISTENT TASK SET

1. Fragmentation of Attention

a. *Intrusions:*   Introduction of extraneous topics, ideas, or behavior that interferes with the testing. Subjects may ask the examiner personal questions, get off on some tangent describing personal experience, or get up and walk around the room.

b. *Shifts of Contexts of Reference:*   Subject has a piecemeal approach to the objects within one sort, seeming to shift fluidly from one frame of reference to another, as from concrete to abstract or from affective to physical aspects of the stimuli, seeming unable to maintain a consistent set. For instance, when confronted with the red objects on Part II, a subject says: "Only in so far as this [red eraser] might relate to eradicating anything that might be written. Or you could light the paper [red paper circle] with the matches [red match book]. The ball [red rubber ball] has no relation to the others—other than that they're both rubber-eraser and ball."

c. *References to Previous Sorts:*   In the middle of responding to one item, subject starts talking about a previous sort.

d. *"Forgetting" of Test Structure:*   For example, after a subject has completed Part I and most of Part II, he asks, "Am I supposed to classify them?"

e. *Overexactness and Quibbling:*   Subject is meticulous in making a sort to a peculiar or bizarre degree. For instance, when presented with the rubber items, a subject says, "I assume the cigar is rubber [toy cigar]. Still have a little metal on the sink-stopper [its handle], paper on the wrapper of the cigar, and abrasives in the eraser."

2. Inability to Maintain the Role of a Subject Being Tested

a. *Controlling Behavior:*   Subject wants to introduce other objects into the test or takes over the tester's role. For example, on Part II, a subject comments, "You haven't done cylinders—I'm waiting for cylinders" or adds another object to the grouping the examiner has placed before him.

b. *Imposition of Structure:*   Subject attempts to impose his own structure on the test and may badger, lecture, or criticize the examiner for not following his own idea of the test structure. Or he seems to project his own idea of the test structure onto the examiner. For instance, when presented with the rubber ball on Part I, a subject says, "I already put that with the rubber. I got to put it with something—you're not satisfied leaving it with the toys?"

3. Negativism

Subject does not accept the basic assumption of the test that there is some reason why the objects belong together, especially on Part II. He actively and emphatically states that the objects do not belong together. For example, when asked why a grouping of round objects belong together, a subject says, "Who says they do!"

B. BLURRING OF MEANING

Subject gives several alternative responses, including the correct one, but the correct answer does not seem to "click," and subject goes on to give another answer or gives the right one with an air of extreme uncertainty or qualification. He does not let any response stand. Nor does he add any evaluative remarks about which of his responses he considers better than the others. Meaning is blurred, and in various ways closure is never achieved. For instance, on Part I, a subject puts the red ball with the red paper circle, saying, "Both reddish and round and otherwise I don't see any real connection with the other things."

C. PECULIARS

1. Peculiar Verbalizations

Subject uses stilted, artificial language that seems to represent extreme distance from the objects, like calling the smoking equipment "long and narrow surfaces in the smoking line." Or personal concerns appear to intrude in a strange manner, as when a subject says that the bell and ball are "not really close—about third cousins." Extreme forms of peculiar verbalizations are clang associations or neologisms.

2. Imprecise Referents

Vague statements about the group of objects that could refer to almost any sort. For example, a subject puts the silverware together because "they're all coordinated," or "you use them together."

A score of 1 is given for each manifestation of the above categories, so that one response can receive multiple scores. A subject's total score consists of the sum of scores assigned throughout the protocol.

The manual makes it clear that verbatim recording is essential for this scoring system. Utilizing the manual, two trained clinical psychologists, one of whom had not been involved in devising the manual, scored the sixty-two protocols with a reliability of .66 (Pearson r). A median test performed with the averaged scores of the two raters showed a significant difference between the control and patient-parent groups ($X^2 = 15.61$, p $< .0005$, one tail). These results seemed promising enough to warrant further investigation. When 121 more protocols had been collected in connection with the study described in Chapter XXI, Part II, these were scored blindly by the same two scorers with a reliability of .91. As a further check on reliability, thirty new protocols obtained from the National Institute of Mental Health were scored by a third trained clinical psychologist, who had had no previous contact with the study, with a reliability of .84 with one of the original scorers.[2] These findings seem to demonstrate that Singer's criteria of fragmentation and blurring of attention and meaning can be objectified and applied to the Object Sorting Test with adequate interscorer reliability.

RESULTS

Findings were first examined with a total sample of 193 subjects including 78 patient parents (thirty-nine couples) and 115 control parents (forty-nine couples, with seventeen additional fathers and mothers).[3] The groups were matched on education, but not on age, the patient parents being approximately seven years older. Although the results showed striking group differences on these measures, significant correlations were found between scores and both education

[2] We are grateful to Dr. Lyman Wynne for his cooperation and to Mrs. Peggy Toohey for her work in making these protocols available to us. We also thank Dr. Dorothy Ciarlo for her help in doing the scoring.

[3] This sample is the same as that described in Chapter XXI, Part II except for the omission of five patient-parent couples whose protocols were not recorded verbatim and for the inclusion of ten patient-parent couples recently obtained from NIH. The patient parents had at least one hospitalized offspring with a clear-cut clinical diagnosis of schizophrenia, and the control parents were all paid volunteers whose children had never been clinically psychotic as far as could be ascertained.

and age. In the patient-parent group, the correlation between score and education was —.38 (p < .01) and in the control group —.11 (ns). The correlation between score and age in the former group was +.15 (ns) and in the latter group +.24 (p < .02). Furthermore, there were significant correlations between education and age in both groups. These correlations, as well as the lack of matching on age, made it impossible to use the total sample to determine the effectiveness of scores in discriminating the patient parent from the control group independent of the effects of age and education.

Therefore, 93 subjects, drawn from the total population of 133, were carefully matched on education and age. Mothers and fathers were separately matched on these variables. Except for the matching criteria, the sample was randomly selected. The final sample consists of 44 patient parents (nineteen couples and six individuals) and 49 control parents (seventeen couples and fifteen individuals). The sample characteristics are presented in Table I. It shows that the patient-parent and control groups are well matched on age and education. While fathers and mothers are well matched on education, fathers are significantly older than mothers (t = 2.34, p < .05, two tails).

TABLE I

CHARACTERISTICS OF MATCHED SAMPLE

Patient Parents vs. Control Parents

	Range	Mean	t	P
Patient Parents (N = 44)				
Age	39-66	50.11	.66	ns
Years Education	4-21	13.16	.25	ns
Control Parents (N = 49)				
Age	41-65	49.45		
Years Education	8-20	13.37		

Combined Fathers vs. Combined Mothers

	Range	Mean	t	P
Total Fathers (N = 42)				
Age	39-66	51.05	2.34	< .05
Years Education	4-21	13.29	.34	ns
Total Mothers (N = 51)				
Age	41-64	48.71		
Years Education	6-20	13.00		

Table II presents the number of *individual* patient parents and control parents with scores above and below the over-all group median of 3.25. It can be seen that more patient parents have scores above the median than control parents ($X^2 = 16.55$, p < .0005, one tail).

TABLE II

COMPARISON OF SINGER SCORES FOR PATIENT-PARENT AND CONTROL GROUPS

	Number of Scores Above the Median	Number of Scores Below the Median
Over-all Median = 3.25		
Patient Parents	33 (75%)	11 (25%)
Median = 6.75		
Control Parents	15 (31%)	34 (69%)
Median = 1.75		

$X^2 = 16.55$, p < .0005   (1 tail)

Two methods were used to analyze the results in terms of *couples* (nineteen patient parent and seventeen control couples).

Table III presents the number of patient-parents and control couples with scores above the over-all median for both spouses, for one spouse, and for neither spouse. It shows that the scores significantly differentiate patient-parent from control couples ($X^2 = 8.43$, p < .02, two tails). Fifty-eight per cent of the patient-parent couples both have high scores in contrast to 12 per cent of the control couples.

TABLE III

NUMBER OF PATIENT-PARENT AND CONTROL COUPLES WHERE BOTH SPOUSES HAVE HIGH OR LOW SINGER SCORES OR ONE SPOUSE HAS A HIGH SINGER SCORE

	Both Parents Above the Median	One Parent Above, One Below the Median	Both Parents Below the Median
Over-all Median = 3.25			
Patient-Parent Couples	11 (58%)	5 (26%)	3 (16%)
Control Couples	2 (12%)	8 (47%)	7 (41%)

$X^2 = 8.43$, p < .02   (2 tails)

Table IV presents the results for couples when the mother's and father's scores are added together. This method of analysis also shows a significant difference between the two groups of parents ($X^2 =$

TABLE IV

NUMBER OF PATIENT-PARENT AND CONTROL COUPLES WHERE MOTHER'S
AND FATHER'S ADDED SCORES ARE HIGH AND LOW

	Number of Scores Above the Median	Number of Scores Below the Median
Over-all Median = 6.75		
Patient Parents	15 (79%)	4 (21%)
Median = 12.25		
Control Parents	3 (18%)	14 (82%)
Median = 4.25		

$$X^2 = 11.15, \; p < .0005, \; (1 \text{ tail})$$

11.15, $p < .0005$, one tail). Comparison of Tables II and IV indicates that the patient-parent and control groups are discriminated better when the parents are treated as couples and their scores summed than when they are treated as individuals. There is no marked difference in the patient-parent group, where 75 per cent of *individuals* and 79 per cent of *couples* have high scores. But in the control group, 69 per cent of *individuals* have low scores in contrast to 82 per cent of *couples*.

Table V presents the comparisons of patient fathers with control fathers and patient mothers with control mothers. Since fathers and mothers were matched separately on age and education, the analyses

TABLE V

COMPARISON OF MOTHERS' AND FATHERS' SINGER SCORES

	Number of Scores Above the Median	Number of Scores Below the Median
Fathers' over-all median = 3.75		
Patients' fathers	15 (71%)	6 (29%)
Median = 6.75		
Control fathers	7 (33%)	14 (67%)
Median = 3.25		

$$X^2 = 4.68, \; p < .025 \quad (1 \text{ tail})$$

Mothers' over-all median = 2.75		
Patients' mothers	20 (87%)	3 (13%)
Median = 6.75		
Control mothers	7 (25%)	21 (75%)
Median = 1.75		

$$X^2 = 17.05, \; p < .0005 \quad (1 \text{ tail})$$

were performed in terms of the fathers' and mothers' group medians (3.75 and 2.75 respectively) rather than the median for the total sample. Table V shows that more patients' fathers have scores above the median than control fathers ($X^2 = 4.68$, p < .025, one tail), and more patients' mothers have scores above the median than control mothers ($X^2 = 17.05$, p < .0005, one tail). While the fathers' over-all median is higher than the mothers' median, further analyses show that fathers do not differ from mothers significantly in either the patient-parent or control group. However, it can be seen that the scores differentiate mothers somewhat better than fathers.

DISCUSSION

These results demonstrate that the criteria of disturbance in the focusing of attention and blurring of meaning that Singer used to distinguish the parents of schizophrenic patients from control parents on projective tests can be objectified, scored reliably, and applied to the Object Sorting Test. They also seem to show that these scores are affected by age and education. The tendency for scores to increase as years of education decrease does not seem surprising, since subjects with less education would be apt to show more evidence of disturbance on a test of concept formation that would challenge their intellectual ability. Similarly, Rosman et al. (Chapter XXI, Part II) in a study including 173 of the subjects from this sample found that education had a strong effect on Lovibond's (1953) measure of thought disorder, so that it differentiated patient from control parents only at higher educational levels. Although an increase of scores with age was not anticipated, since Lovibond's measure of thought disorder showed a negligible relationship to age, this finding does not seem surprising. Such criteria as inability to maintain a consistent task set and giving irrelevant verbalizations appear likely to be associated with age. For example, Singer (1963) found that in a sample of normal, healthy men, aged over sixty-five, one segment classed as showing a "senile quality" in clinically rated behavior exhibited less task-oriented and more rambling verbal behavior on tests than "non-senile quality" subjects. Of course, the results pertaining to education and age could reflect particular sampling characteristics, and more work needs to be done with subjects of different age and educational levels to clarify the relationship of these variables to scores. Clearly, in further studies groups should be matched on education and age.

However, the results from the forty-four patient parents and forty-nine control parents closely matched on education and age appear to demonstrate that the groups differ significantly on the measures independent of the effects of these variables. Furthermore, the two groups of parents are discriminated when they are treated either as individuals or as couples. The first analysis of couples seems to show that the scores discriminate patient-parent from control couples when a criterion of both parents having high or low scores is used. Fifty-eight per cent of patient-parent couples both have high scores in contrast to only 12 per cent of control couples, and 41 per cent of control couples both have low scores in contrast to only 16 per cent of patient-parent couples. However, if one parent has a high score, the groups are not discriminated, for 47 per cent of control couples and 26 per cent of patient-parent couples have one high-scoring spouse. When the scoring unit for couples is the sum of the mother's and father's scores, the summed scores discriminate patient-parent from control *couples* better than patient-parent from control *individuals*. Comparison of Tables II and IV shows that the improvement is more apparent in the control group; and scrutiny of the data indicates that of ten control couples with at least one moderately high-scoring spouse (score of 3.0 - 6.0) nine have a low-scoring partner (score of under 3.0). This observation suggests that a healthier parent may offset the effect of the sicker one, so that the family style of communication is not seriously disturbed. Scrutiny of the data also shows that the summed scores of eight patient-parent couples (42 per cent) are higher than those obtained by *any* control couple. These findings seem particularly meaningful, since Wynne and Singer (1963a) stress that disturbed communication is a function of the interaction between patient-parent couples, rather than the pathology of each individual parent. However, it remains to be seen whether scores of the Object Sorting Test will discriminate between parents of schizophrenics and parents of other psychiatric patients.

The discriminative value of this scoring system seems to be relatively independent of sex of parent, a variable that has been shown to affect other measures of thought disorder on the Object Sorting

Test. For example, Rosman et al. (Chapter XXI, Part II) found that Lovibond's measure of thought disorder distinguished patients' mothers from control mothers, while patients' fathers were not differentiated from control fathers. Thus, the Singer measures, which seem to reflect disturbances in general style of test taking and communication, appear to pick up more pathological indicators in patients' fathers than a scoring system such as that used by Rosman, which is focused on specific manifestations of thought disorder in the conceptual sphere. For instance, a constricted, paranoid person may not reveal much evidence of thought disorder per se, but show striking negativism, controlling behavior, or projection of his own ideas of test structure. Although there is no difference between patient fathers and patient mothers, there is a tendency for control fathers to have higher scores than control mothers ($X^2 = 1.86$, $p < .20$, two tails). However, this finding could be attributed to the fathers' older age, rather than to greater incidence of pathology among fathers.

In sum, these findings suggest that this brief, easily administered test, scored according to Singer's criteria, has potential value as a screening device for selecting a high-risk population of parents who might have schizophrenic offspring or for further investigations of thought disorder.

The results presented in the preceding section indicate that criteria resembling those developed by Wynne and Singer (1963a, 1963b) and Singer and Wynne (1965a, 1965b) for distinguishing the parents of schizophrenics from control parents on projective tests could be objectified, scored reliably, and applied to the briefer Object Sorting Test. These findings pose at least two basic questions: (1) What is the significance of the Object Sorting Test scoring system in terms of the pathology it reflects in the parents of schizophrenic patients? (2) What is the impact of such parental pathology on their children? The purpose of this section is to suggest some implications of the findings in the light of these questions; first, by considering the actual transactions between patient parent and examiner around the test, and then by presenting some speculative, theoretical interpretations.

Singer and Wynne's transactional approach to testing and their major criteria for differentiating patient parents from control parents will be briefly summarized, since they provide a general framework for the following discussion.

SUMMARY OF SINGER AND WYNNE'S APPROACH TO TESTING AND CRITERIA FOR DIFFERENTIATING PARENTS OF SCHIZOPHRENICS FROM CONTROL PARENTS

Singer and Wynne consider that family *styles* of interacting and communicating are closely linked to disturbed thinking in the offspring. They view tests as:

Cynthia Wild: Implications of Disturbed Styles of Thinking Manifested on the Object Sorting Test by the Parents of Schizophrenic Patients. This paper has not been previously published.

. . . a sample transaction between subject and tester, not simply as projections of intrapsychic problems. . . . The transaction between subject and tester provides a relatively standard way of sampling attention, thinking-communication, and relating. . . . Thus, the protocols can be used as a means of studying the same kind of stylistic aspects of thinking as have been observed in the clinical work with the families. . . .

Viewing and responding to the TAT and Rorschach cards corresponds to everyday situations in which two people see a series of different kinds of "reality," but because of their roles, one is the interpreter of the reality to the other. . . .

The parents [bring] to the testing situation the distinctive and enduring styles of behaving also found in their interpretive transactions with their children and with each other.

Further, we have assumed that styles of attending, perceiving, thinking, communicating, and relating used in family transactions are likely to have promoted the cognitive development of the offspring in certain directions, either by serving as models for identification or by eliciting complementary behaviors [Singer and Wynne, 1965a, p. 190].

Thus, since the focus is on the transaction between subject and tester around the test, it does not seem necessary to use specifically "projective" tests; briefer, more easily administered tasks, such as the Object Sorting Test, which involve continuous interaction between subject and tester would seem just as effective in picking up the behaviors Singer and Wynne use to differentiate the parents of schizophrenics from other parents.

Singer and Wynne work not only from the basic hypothesis that family transactional styles are related to cognitive development in the offspring; they assume that disturbed interpersonal relationships are reflected in cognitive disturbances as well. The *style* of the interaction is as important as the style of conceptualization; and even though a parent produces an adequate conceptual response, he may receive a score for the disruptive or blurred style with which it is given. Singer and Wynne focus on four major features of family interaction in differentiating schizophrenic families from others.[4] First, they find basic disturbances in the handling of attention and meaning in the parents of schizophrenics. If a family cannot even

[4] Since the fourth feature—pseudomutuality and pseudohostility—does not seem so relevant to the Object Sorting Test scoring system as the other three features, it will not be discussed here.

begin to focus attention selectively on shared percepts, ideas, or feelings, the possibility of meaningful communication developing is obliterated from the start. These parents seem unable to focus selectively on either external reality or internal states, which would lead to impairment of the child's capacity for selective attention, purposive behavior, or subjectively meaningful experience. In contrast, Singer and Wynne find that in neurotic families, attention is directed toward particular issues over a period of time.

A second major feature of family interaction that they use to differentiate schizophrenic from other families is erratic and inappropriate kinds of distance and closeness in making contact with both human and nonhuman aspects of the environment. These parents cannot maintain a proper cognitive or affective distance from objects or people; nor can they flexibly shift their distance appropriately as transactions develop. This behavior has been described as characteristic of interviews with patients' parents (Chapter IV). Cognitively, on tests, for example, they may show sudden concrete literalness and switch quickly to vague, overgeneralized, syncretistic responses.

A third major criterion Singer and Wynne employ concerns a deep, underlying sense of pervasive meaninglessness, pointlessness, and emptiness to existence, possibly related to a fundamental hopelessness about ever achieving gratification through human contact. Cognitively, this sense of futility seems reflected in an inability to let any response stand, so that closure is never achieved, or to allow a concept to develop clearly and distinctly.

IMPLICATIONS OF THE FINDINGS SUGGESTED BY THE EXAMINERS' REACTIONS TO TRANSACTIONS WITH PATIENT PARENTS IN THE TESTING SITUATION

Since the focus in the testing situation is on the transaction with the examiner around the test, one way of viewing the parental pathology reflected in the Object Sorting Test scoring system and its impact on their children is to consider the examiners' reactions while testing these parents. Therefore, some of the testers' impressions will be presented to illustrate more vividly how Singer and Wynne's three criteria of disturbed patterns of handling attention and meaning, inappropriate switches from distance to closeness, and a sense of pervasive pointlessness to existence were experienced.

Isolated examples do not really convey the total effect of a massing of such behavior. The examiners often felt drained and exhausted after only an hour or so of testing. Sometimes, it seemed as though the parents were spreading themselves in many different directions, so that it was grueling work to try to keep them within the bounds of the task to complete the testing. For instance, long, tangential, rambling speeches had to be cut short; efforts had to be made to get parents to sit down, as with one father who insisted on standing throughout the test; and parents' attempts to take over the testing had to be controlled. In terms of the scoring system developed for the Object Sorting Test, such behavior seems to reflect *Inability to Maintain a Consistent Task Set*, particularly disturbances in the handling of attention.

At the same time, the examiners often had to cope with what felt like a hammering barrage of disruptive questions that seemed to interfere with the task and with communication rather than promoting it. For example, parents would ask questions, interrupting the examiner right in the middle of the initial test instructions, inhibiting development of a meaningful transaction at the outset. Questions were often asked insistently and intrusively, as with a father who, when presented with the bell, asked: "This is what? A bell? Supposed to be, isn't it—what is it—a bicycle bell? What's *this* [red paper circle] supposed to be?" An hour of such questions is wearing, and the examiners received the impression that answering them as well as possible within the requirements of testing or saying, "It's up to you," had little if any effect. Control parents, on the other hand, seemed more able to adapt to the task, ceasing to ask questions after being told "It's up to you" several times. This impression of the patient parents seems related to Singer and Wynne's point about a lack of flexibility in shifting behavior appropriately as transactions develop. It can be imagined how hopeless the children of such parents must feel about ever communicating effectively or making their own needs known to elicit an appropriate parental response.

Pervasive, emphatic negativism also led the examiners to feel that they were beating their heads against a stone wall in trying to call forth any response other than "they *don't* belong together," which must be similar to what the child experiences in trying to get his needs met. Some parents remained as negative as that throughout the nineteen test items, leaving the examiners with feelings of futility and frustration about having made any meaningful communication around the testing situation.

An especially difficult sort of question for the examiners to handle involved the parents' self-engendered assumptions about the test structure, such as, "You mean sort them according to their use?" After being told that they could sort the objects in any way they liked, often they would repeat the same question on the next item, or proceed to sort every item in terms of the objects' use. Sometimes a parent became very angry at the tester for not having told him that his assumptions about the test were not true, even though the parent had not brought them out in the open. For instance, the same father who asked all the questions about the bell said that he saw nothing to go with the ball. When he was asked to try to find something, he said: "Even this stuff we used before?" He had apparently come to his own conclusion that he could not use any objects more than once. When he was told that he *could* use the objects over again, he said angrily, "Oh, you can! You should say so, you should say so if you know about that!" Here, a lack of separation from the tester is suggested in his use of "we" instead of "I" when he refers to "this stuff we used before" and in his assumption that the tester would know what was on his mind without his having to verbalize it.

Such behavior, coming under the scoring category of *Inability to Maintain the Role of a Subject Being Tested—Imposition of Structure* —seems to have more to do with the *transaction* between subject and tester than with cognitive style; and this style of transaction would appear to indicate a lack of clear separation from the examiner on the part of the patient parents. A response given by a patient's mother who was asked to sort objects with the toy pliers seems to provide an even more striking illustration of a blurring of boundaries between subject and tester. She said: "Again, you can go back to toys—or you can again go on. . . . Depends on how far you want to go. . . . If you add the screwdriver, you can add the lock—you could go further— it depends how far you want to go—how much you want to write."

Not only does this mother never come to any resolution or closure; but she almost gives the impression that the examiner is taking the test in her constant use of "you" instead of "I" and in her saying that the sort depends on how much the examiner wants to write. After a time with such parents, testers became aware that they were held responsible for the parents' responses and imbued and suffused with the parents' thoughts and feelings, resulting in a confusion and lack of clarity about who was giving and who was taking the test and about whose thoughts and feelings were whose. It can be imagined how confusing it must be for the children of such parents never to know clearly the difference between "we," "you," and "I," or whether a thought or feeling originates from within parent or child. Constant transactions like these would be apt to lead to serious problems with self-differentiation in the child (Chapter II; Reichard and Tillman, 1950). Such behavior appears to verge on projection and would be apt to foster the development of projective mechanisms in the offspring.

Sudden personal questions were another disruptive behavior that made these parents difficult to test. These questions seem to reflect Singer and Wynne's criterion of sudden switches from tremendous distance and lack of communication to inappropriate, intrusive closeness. Such shifts would be likely to lead to even more serious impairment of the capacity to maintain proper distance in the child, possibly resulting in excessive withdrawal.

Another major difficulty in testing many of these parents was what seemed like the impossibility of ever getting a clear, definite, specific response to any item, leading to a sense of utter frustration and hopelessness in the tester about eliciting a direct, straightforward answer. This pervasive characteristic appears related to Singer and Wynne's criterion of blurring of meaning and lack of closure. Attention may never be clearly focused on the objects, so that any chance of meaning developing is removed from the outset; or if some meaning is achieved, it is not allowed to stand, but blurred or taken away. One basic requirement for meaning to develop would seem to be an initial identification of the objects; and patient parents often seemed unable to identify them, turning over even the basic responsibility of labeling to the tester. One father, given the red paper circle, said:

"I don't know, I don't know what it is—and I don't know of anything to go with it. . . . You must have something to go with it? Depends what this is. You want me to imagine something that goes with it? I see nothing that goes with this little piece of paper—unless this eraser goes with it—or you want to put the matches on it?" Later, when asked if the red objects had any common characteristic, he replied: "Color, shades of red, but this [eraser] is pink. Color—color only." Although this father is capable of identifying the paper circle as "a little piece of paper" and can achieve the concept "red," he produces a feeling of frustration and an impression of slipperiness, for he never seems able to commit himself even to labeling a common, everyday object or to a relatively simple concept, never letting any meaning stand or allowing himself to be pinned down. It can be speculated that the child of such a parent would tend to grow up in a hazy, undifferentiated world—a condition that would lead to difficulty in learning to identify and specify common objects in the environment and to form stable concepts. Furthermore, if a parent is so vague and elusive in labeling everyday objects, like those in the test, he would be expected to have much more trouble with identifying more complex and subtle feelings or affect-laden concepts, such as love and hate.

The majority of patient parents were undoubtedly more anxious than the control parents in the testing situation and some of the scoring categories could be considered as anxiety indicators. However, the behavior rarely occurred in isolation, and there does not seem any reason to expect that this total constellation of pathology reflects anxiety only. For example, while anxiety could account for negativism and tangential speeches, it is difficult to see how it could produce a confusion between "we," "you," and "I," or a tendency to impose structure on the test.

In sum, the examiners' reactions to the patient parents' disturbances in the handling of attention and their negativism suggest the feelings of frustration and hopelessness their offspring must experience about the possibility of ever communicating their own needs effectively or having them met or of ever focusing on and sharing a meaningful experience with their parents. Such behavior would be apt to produce a sense of hopelessness about verbal communication serving as an aid to collaborative interaction and about the value of words as useful tools of problem solving. The parents' *Inability to Maintain the Role of Subjects Being Tested* seems to reflect a lack of clear separation from the examiner, resulting in uncertainty and confusion about whose thoughts and feelings are whose, which would be apt to lead to serious problems with establishing a distinct sense of self in the child. Similarly, sudden shifts from extreme distance to excessive closeness in the patient parents were experienced as disconcerting by the examiners in the relatively neutral testing situation and must seem much more inconsistent and confusing to a child constantly engaged in emotional transactions with such parents. Finally, the blurring of meaning and inability to let concepts or even labels for common objects stand would be apt to lead to a vague, hazy view of external reality and arouse feelings of frustration about ever achieving a subjectively significant experience as well.

SOME TENTATIVE THEORETICAL IMPLICATIONS OF THE FINDINGS

Some more speculative views of the data have already been suggested in the previous section. The theoretical implications presented here are offered only as tentative ways of interpreting the findings, with the realization that they are open to further, alternative interpretations.

As indicated above, Singer and Wynne contribute the idea that disturbed interpersonal relations are reflected in disordered cognitive styles. One often-observed fundamental aspect of parental pathology to which they call attention is a lack of differentiation of self from the environment or a looseness and fluidity of ego boundaries, leading to serious impairments in both ways of relating to people and cognitive functioning. The Object Sorting Test scoring system appears to pick up a number of manifestations of boundary problems in the parents of schizophrenics. In fact, this test, requiring as it does a specification of the similarities and differences between common, everyday external objects, may be particularly sensitive to eliciting reflections of fundamental boundary difficulties both in cognitive styles and in transactions with the testers. Following Schachtel (1959), a case can be made for severe attention disturbances being related to diffuse, indefinite ego boundaries. A capacity for focused attention on external human and nonhuman objects and their particular attributes seems to imply an ability to separate oneself from the environment and to differentiate various aspects of it; and a capacity for focused attention on internal thoughts and feelings would seem to depend on a capacity to maintain mental representations of external objects over time, to separate one's own thoughts and feelings from those of other people, and to distinguish between various kinds of internal states. Otherwise, as in the infant, attention will be global, diffuse, and unselective. It can also be hypothesized that such attention disturbances would lead to an inability to exclude irrelevant aspects of the internal and external environments or to distinguish their separate aspects with any degree of clarity.

The scoring categories of *Controlling Behavior and Imposition of Structure* onto the testing situation, with a greater or lesser apparent loss of distinction between who is giving and who is taking the test, also can be considered as indications of fluid boundaries, leading to confusion between what is inside and what is outside the self. Sudden shifts from excessive closeness to excessive distance could also be seen as reflecting serious boundary problems. The schizophrenic's parent seems almost to become the tester at times, imbuing both tester and test with his own thoughts and feelings, making them over in his own image, so that they no longer have an objective existence as a person and task apart from the parent's internal state.

In addition to differentiation of self from objects, another related requirement for sustained focal attention would seem to be sufficient alleviation of internal need states, so that environmental objects can emerge distinctly and neutrally, independent of personal wishes and desires, and reality can be objectively perceived (Schachtel, 1959). Often, the patient parents' Object Sorting Test performance appears to show an inability to perceive an object apart from their own needs. Some parents seem completely unable to view the objects separate from their *use* in providing immediate gratification. Such parents sometimes give the impression of being in a continual state of "emergency," experiencing a desperate sense of primitive deprivation with respect to issues of basic survival, such as heat and warmth, emptiness and being full, food and shelter. For example, one mother answered almost every test item in terms of how she would *use* the items in an emergency. To a sorting of silverware, she said: "Because if you have a fork, you need a spoon and a knife when you set the table. . . . And if you don't have a knife and fork, you use your hands." Then, to the bell, with which she sorted the tools, she said: "Well, since I'm not a mechanic and if I planned to put this on, I'd have to have one of these [tools]. . . . This [hammer] . . . wouldn't have to use it probably—in an emergency maybe I might need it. If I was going downstairs to my tool chest, I'd take it to save myself a trip to go back." Her lack of neutral detachment from the objects and inability to attend freely to their properties apart from her own needs are evident in these responses. Furthermore, if her own needs color even this relatively neutral area of functioning, it could be surmised that they would have a greater influence on emotional transactions, making it impossible for her to perceive her children's needs apart from her own.

In sum, the attention disturbances that Singer uses as a major criterion for differentiating the parents of schizophrenic patients from other parents could be related to primitive difficulties in separating self from nonself and experiencing the world as separate from internal need states. The often-observed fluidity of boundaries between generations and of sexual identity in schizophrenics' families (Lidz, 1963b) seem like further reflections of problems with self-definition. The *Inability to Maintain the Role of a Subject Being Tested* also could represent problems in keeping a distinct separation between subject and tester and confusion about what is inside the parent and what is outside in reality. This fluidity of boundaries would be likely to lead to vagueness and lack of clarity about how inanimate objects differ from one another, how people differ from one another, how inanimate objects differ from people, and how internal thoughts and feelings differ from one another and from the thoughts and feelings of other people. Singer and Wynne's second major criterion for distinguishing the parents of schizophrenics—inappropriate shifts from extreme closeness to extreme distance—also can be seen as reflecting difficulties in maintaining consistent ego boundaries. At times the boundary is too loose, resulting in intrusive closeness; and at other times, the boundaries are too tight, leading to extreme distance.

If boundary problems are a crucial aspect of the pathology of schizophrenics' parents, what impact might such difficulties have on their children? Generally, these boundary problems would be likely to interfere severely with a child's capacity to establish a separate identity, with resulting impairment of cognitive skills and capacity for developing mutual relationships. At early stages, if a mother has trouble separating herself from her baby and responds to him primarily in terms of her own needs, his own internal states will never be clearly differentiated and labeled if they are not responded to at the time they are experienced, and his needs will not be clearly distinguished from his mother's. Such a mother would be likely to have difficulty empathizing with her baby's experience and with understanding the cues he gives out apart from her own impulses and feelings (Bruch and Palombo, 1961). If the father shows similar boundary problems, the child will have even less chance of learning to separate himself from others as a distinct individual and to label clearly and differentiate objects in the environment. He will also have trouble learning that appropriate instrumental action on his part can effectively alter external reality.

A capacity for sustained, mutual relationships with other people could probably not develop in such a family atmosphere, where the purpose of the child's existence is to meet his parents' needs, so that he cannot experience himself as a person in his own right. The ability to form satisfying human relationships would seem to require a distinct sense of self as a prerequisite, for lack of self-differentiation means that closeness brings the danger of merging, annihilation, and nothingness, as well as the feeling of living in and through another person to serve that person's needs. Such symbiotic relationships also would seem to produce a fear that the parents will die or be destroyed if the patient separates himself from them, a fear that is not without realistic foundation (Chapter II).

Singer and Wynne's third major criterion for identifying the families of schizophrenics—a basic sense of pointlessness and meaninglessness, related to a cognitive inability to ever let any concept fully emerge or stand once it has emerged—would also be apt to have a profound effect on a child. As these authors point out, the sense of futility and hopelessness that these parents show should be differentiated from depression where, despite sadness and despondency, real interactions occur between people. These patient parents seem to show a more schizoid sense of inner emptiness, deadness, and isolation. A child growing up with parents holding such a despondent and pessimistic attitude toward human contact certainly would not feel encouraged to search for relationships outside the family, especially if he could not find meaningful contacts within it.

A final crucial question that should be raised is: How do the patients' parents in the sample, few if any of whom had ever been hospitalized, differ from the patients themselves? As has been pointed out, the parents often seem able to label objects correctly or come up with adequate conceptualizations, which they then proceed to blur. The children in such a family, however, might grow up without learning to label concepts and objects adequately, since the parents never let any meaning stand. This deficiency could interfere markedly with learning to employ words as carriers of concepts, an ability that seems essential for adequate ego functioning and for directing the self into the future. This *transactional* aspect of the scoring system may be what makes it more effective in picking up disturbed parental *styles* of interpreting the environment, which could lead to more serious *thought disorders* and deficient reality testing in their children.

XXIII

Perspectives

In the chapter "Schizophrenia and the Family" we hazarded that "the study of schizophrenic reactions has an importance to the science of man that even transcends the relief of myriads of suffering patients. There are indications that a satisfactory understanding of schizophrenia will be synchronous and synonymous with the opening of vast new insights concerning the integration of man and his emotional homeostasis." The explorations of the family settings in which patients grew up have provided new insights into the nature and the etiology of schizophrenia, but even more significantly have opened approaches that have stimulated rewarding research and fostered new therapeutic approaches. Beyond the topic of schizophrenia, the efforts to comprehend the data required renewed consideration of the functions of the family, and led to some comprehension of the fundamental and inordinately complex role of the family in human adaptation and integration. The grasp of the family's functions, though still understood but incompletely and vaguely, has directed insistently and clearly to the need for some major reconsiderations of current psychoanalytic and psychodynamic concepts of personality development. The closure of the exploratory phase of these studies of the family and schizophrenia is but a clearing of ground for new investigations.

In this final chapter we wish to note a few of the implications of our findings for theories of personality development, for theories of schizophrenia, for therapy and prophylaxis of schizophrenia, and finally for future research in the area. Any thorough discussion of the theoretical implications would require an extremely lengthy dissertation; such an attempt would be out of place in this volume which is primarily concerned with reporting and analyzing our findings.

423

The impact of relating the family setting to the understanding of schizophrenia has widespread repercussions upon concepts of personality development and psychopathology; a few of these were considered in "The Relevance of Family Studies to Psychoanalytic Theory" and "Family Studies and a Theory of Schizophrenia." We have noted that a mature workable personality integration does not develop simply through nurturance of inborn directives and potentialities but requires positive direction and guidance in a suitable interpersonal environment. The positive molding forces have, in the past, been largely neglected because they are built into the mores of all societies and mediated to a large degree by the omnipresent family that has the task of primary enculturation of its offspring in every society. Man's biological make-up requires that he grow up in a family or a reasonable substitute for it, not simply for protection and nurturance during his immaturity but in order to assimilate the techniques he needs for adaptation and survival. It requires that he grow into and internalize the institutions and instrumentalities of structured social systems as well as identify with persons who themselves have assimilated the culture. He acquires characteristics through identification but also by reactions to parental objects and through finding reciprocal roles with them. His integration is guided, in part, by the dynamic structure of the family in which he grows up, which channels his drives and guides into proper gender and generation roles, and provides a space relatively free from role conflict in which the immature child can develop and feel secure. His appreciation of the worth and meaning of both social roles and institutions is affected by the manner in which his parents fill their roles, relate maritally, and behave in other institutional contexts. The value of being a man or woman, or of marriage as a way of gaining satisfaction and security, etc., depends on how the parents relate to each other as well as on the individual models they provide. Superego development derives from internalization of directives and superegos of two parents, and internalized conflict and splits in ego development can reflect efforts to relate to irreconcilable parental figures. The capacities to think clearly, to test reality, to have the verbal tools necessary for directing the self depend upon tutelage within the family and the consistencies and styles of the parents' ways of communicating. Indeed, trust in the usefulness of verbal communication as a means of problem solving and of fostering interpersonal cooperation depends largely upon how language is used within the family.

Without further elaboration, it becomes clear that numerous sources of deviant personality development open before us in addition to those deriving from arrested psychosexual development— and which, indeed, make such fixations more dynamically comprehensible than does a primary emphasis upon inborn predisposition or even upon the mother's ways of handling the child or of relating to him during a given psychosexual phase.

The concept that man could be free and without neuroses if rid of the delimitations and repressions required by society is, of course, a chimera that has actually caused grave harm. Without a social system and its directives and delimitations there can be no freedom, indeed no humans could develop into persons and probably could not even survive.

We trust that it has become clear that we do not consider that the usefulness of the orientation that has emerged is confined to schizophrenia or psychiatric illness alone. We can as an illustration briefly consider some aspects of the case of Dora, many of which Freud (1905) noted but did not clearly utilize in explaining the origins of her hysteria. What were the consequences of her father's disruption of the generation boundaries when he used Dora, first as something of a replacement for his wife, and then as a means of distracting, assuaging or "buying off" Mr. K., his mistress's husband? What of the failures of the parental coalition in which her father derogated and neglected his wife, and, at times, handed Dora over to the maternal chaperonage of Mrs. K., who further violated the generation boundaries by making Dora her confidante and roommate, and also by fostering the relationship between Dora and Mr. K.? What of the split feminine role model afforded Dora by a mother who is neglected as a wife and by Mrs. K. who is desirable as a mistress but not as a wife? The continuance of the oedipal strivings into incestuous desires surely did not depend upon constitutional factors as much as upon her mother's denigrated position, her father's seductiveness and being placed in a situation with the Ks. in which a semi-incestuous relationship to Mr. K. was condoned, and a homosexually toned "incestuous" relatedness to Mrs. K. abetted. Might not the betrayal by her father—her recognition that he was sacrificing her as he did his wife for his own gratification—lead to a renewed identification with her mother, with attendant feelings of worthlessness that led to suicidal preoccupations? The conflicts to which Dora was subjected were far more pervasive and disruptive than the conflict over Mr. K.'s desired and feared advances with their oedipal implications. Might not her use of illness and her specific symptoms have to do with her identification with her tubercular and luetic father? Had she not been taught by her father's example to dissimulate, to use illness as a pretext and as an escape when trapped and unable to resolve opposing motives? An examination of the parental coalition, generation boundaries, gender role models, parental styles of behaving and communicating contributes to an increased understanding of Dora's dilemma, her illness, and her choice of symptoms.

Indeed, some of the most telling and therapeutically useful contributions to personality development and psychopathology in recent decades have derived from paying attention to family configurations and styles of behavior, to habitual parental ways of interacting with a child rather than to the interactions during a single psychosexual phase, to the internalization by the offspring of parental ways of perceiving, thinking and communicating. The Johnson-Szurek (1952) hypothesis concerning the origins of antisocial behavior involves the lacunae in the parents' superegos and their unconscious directives to the child. Bruch's studies of obesity and anorexia relate the patient's food intake to the mother's childhood, the mother's emotional needs, and the family configuration (Bruch and Touraine, 1940); and further, to how the nurturant person's problems can confuse the child's physiological responses, a concept of the programing of physiological reactions through parent-child transactions that can also be applied to schizophrenia (Bruch and Palombo, 1961). The studies of the manic-depressive psychoses by Cohen et al. (1954) place considerable emphasis upon the family expectations that the patient recoup the family's lost prestige.

When Wynne and Singer (1963a, 1963b; Singer and Wynne, 1965a, 1965b) drew attention to the parents' amorphous or fragmented styles of thinking and communicating as an important factor in the production of schizophrenia in an offspring, or when Bateson et al. (1956) formulated their "double-bind" hypothesis, or when we noted how schizophrenic patients had been taught to misperceive, to be suspicious, etc., a new dimension was added to the study of psychopathology. The parents' styles of thinking, communicating, and behaving that create both an environment and also a type of teaching which the child both learns and reacts to becomes important. One might ask, for example, if obsessional neuroses may be a matter of being raised by obsessive parents who incidentally would be apt to use rigid bowel training, but who would also foster ambivalence, stubbornness, shame, undoing defenses, etc., in many other ways, as well as teach the use of undoing, isolation, and reaction formation as a means of handling anxiety. The Yurok Indians studied by Erikson (1950b) who are severely obsessive though never subjected to formalized bowel training would suggest such concepts.

Simply to indicate the scope of the expansion and reorganization of psychoanalytic theory and psychopathology that appears to be required, we shall briefly consider problems of sexual identity. Whether a person is a male or a female is probably the most important determinant of personality characteristics, and security of gender identity is of critical moment to harmonious personality development. Confusions of sexual identity are basic to most of the perversions, and thereby, if we accept Freud's dicta, contribute to the causation of the neuroses. We have already adequately emphasized the critical role of gender identity confusion in schizophrenia. Yet, the tendency to consider in theory though usually not in practice that homosexuality is biologically determined, and that confusions in sexual identity are a reflection of the innate bisexuality of all persons stultifies progress.

Re-examination of the Schreber case (Freud, 1911) in the light of his family background (Niederland, 1951, 1961, 1963; Macalpine and Hunter, 1955; White, 1963; Nydes, 1963) requires radical reassessment of the direct relating of paranoid trends to homosexuality, and of the simple attribution of Schreber's homosexual trends to an innate bisexuality.

It has become amply clear that biological sex provides only a directive to proper gender identity. Gender attribution and allocation by the parents from birth; the satisfaction of the parents with the child's biological gender; the initial identification of children of both sexes with the mother and how it is resolved; the model provided by the parent of the same sex as the patient for the child's identification; and the worth attributed to the same-sexed parent by the spouse who should be an early love object to the child; and the nature of the parents' marital relationship; the advantages or disadvantages of siblings of the opposite sex—all these and still other such factors enter into a person's acceptance, satisfaction, and security with his given sex. Consideration of the dynamic interplay of such intrafamilial influences seems essential for proper clarification of the multiplicity of psychopathological problems related to gender identity.

Various consequences of our studies for the understanding of schizophrenia have been noted in each chapter, and we do not wish to elaborate further here. The theories which have guided our investigations and also those that appear to us to result from them lead away from the conceptualization of schizophrenia as a clear-cut entity to consideration of an aberration of the developmental processes—a failure to achieve or maintain a workable integration with retreat into asociality and an inability to participate in the logic and meaning systems of the culture with attempts to resolve conflicts by altering the internalized version of the world without due consideration of reality testing (Chapter X). Such conceptualizations permit us to recognize what we actually observe rather than to confuse ourselves by attempting to force patients into categories into which they do not fit (even as schizophrenic patients become perplexed in seeking to perceive as their parents dictate). We would not only expect schizo-affective disorders, but also sociopathic-schizophrenic, psychosomatic-schizophrenic, addict-schizophrenic combinations, and schizophrenic decompensations from virtually all of the neuroses with failures of defensive mechanisms and defensive patterns of living. We should expect to encounter individuals who had never been capable of an integrated existence except under extremely sheltered conditions, and others who disorganized under conditions of extreme stress or when a lifelong pattern of security operations was suddenly undermined. The former might be termed "process" or "poor premorbid" schizophrenia and the latter "reactive," "schizophreniform" or "good premorbid" and, of course, some of the former will be virtually untreatable, and some of the latter will recover if given any sort of opportunity. We can still believe that the nature of the therapy and how early in life it is started can influence the life course of even the poorly integrated patients very appreciably, because we have ample evidence that some patients whom Rodnick and Garmezy (1957) classify as "poor premorbids" and whom Langfeldt (1953) would consider as true schizophrenics can "recover" under proper and therapeutic conditions which requires profound re-education in some very elementary adaptive techniques.

The findings and orientation would also lead to an expectation—or, at least, to a theoretical understanding—of the relationship between the prevalence of schizophrenia and social class, as found by Hollingshead and Redlich (1958), and confirmed by other prevalence studies. Family disorganization is more prevalent in the lower socioeconomic classes. Perhaps, equally pertinent is the increased alienation from cultural norms and directives in members of such families, their deficiencies in conceptualizing, and their apathy concerning the worth of meaningful relationships. Indeed, in our studies of control parents' ways of handling the Object Sorting Test, it became apparent that a large proportion of persons with less than twelve years of schooling had very limited conceptual capacities. Such persons not only have greater difficulty in guiding their own lives when they must be independent of their extended families, but may also have a greater tendency to fall back into the irrational and impulsive, or to disorganize when caught up in serious conflicts. A large segment of families in the lower socioeconomic levels have gradually sedimented out, created by persons who have declined because of personality disorganization and lack of essential social skills; and they tend to be self-perpetuating because they cannot provide the essentials for their children's integrated development. Other families, such as immigrant and some Negro families, have not yet had an opportunity to emerge from economic and socioeducational poverty. These two types of lower-class families need to be differentiated. Such considerations hold rather obvious implications for the understanding, treatment, and prevention of schizophrenia.

Although the question of whether schizophrenia is basically a genetic, biochemical, or environmental problem certainly has not yet been definitively settled, our findings and theory lean heavily toward the environmental. However, as parents convey both the genetic and basic cultural heritage, the genetic and environmental forces are not readily separated. It is possible that the poor family environments and also the disturbed ways of thinking and communicating noted in the parents are reflections of a genetically transmitted deficiency in the parents. Still, it appears to us that belief in a genetic or bio-chemical causation or predisposition to schizophrenia increasingly rests upon preconception and tradition, while evidence points to en-vironmental and social factors. One of the major reasons for belief in a genetic predisposition, the supposed high concordance rates in identical twins, appears to have been discredited or, at least, seriously challenged by the studies of Tienari (1963) and Kringlen (1964). Even if a clear-cut physiological or biochemical abnormality were found in schizophrenic patients, it might still depend upon faulty nur-turant care in childhood. The disturbed lactate-pyruvate ratio that Gottlieb and his coworkers (Beckett et al., 1963) have found in schizophrenic serum may be related to the maternal care the patients had received, for they find a similar abnormal ratio in the serum of monkeys Harlow had reared in isolation.

Although it is often held that it is sufficient to assume that both genetic and environmental influences are—or may be—significant, resolution of the problem has practical importance, and if not pos-sible, evaluation of the weight of the evidence is necessary. The direc-tion of future investigative work as well as the emphasis of thera-peutic efforts rests upon the resolution or careful evaluation of this problem. Although in investigating problems such as schizophrenia, it is worth backing long-shots and hunches, the bulk of research should follow where evidence leads. We believe that by now we pos-sess evidence that schizophrenia is related to failures of the family to fill its essential tasks and the outline of a plausible theory of how this transpires is presented in Chapter XX.

Some indications of how our studies have led to alterations in the therapy offered to schizophrenic patients can be noted in this volume, specifically in the chapters, "Interaction Between Hospital Staff and

Families" and "Psychiatric Hospitalization as a Family Experience." An article "Residential Treatment of Young Schizophrenics" (Fleck, 1962) describes other new therapeutic developments. In a broad sense, the findings of our investigations aid psychotherapy by elucidating the nature of the problems in patients' developments and through directing attention to areas previously overlooked. Here, we simply wish to note that uncovering and documenting the importance of the family in the etiology of schizophrenia does not *ipso facto* mean that conjoint family therapy is the treatment of choice. Although improving the family environment and the intrafamilial relationships can be very helpful, in some instances it appears almost essential that the patient become able to separate from his family and deal with his internalized family problems without continuing involvement in therapy together with his family.

An appreciation of the importance of the family in the genesis of schizophrenia leads, rather, to efforts to provide relationships with a different type of significant person and a lengthy experience in a therapeutic environment. The milieu seeks to foster the development of autonomy and responsibility for the self to replace the search for direction and motivation in the needs of others; to help direct growth and structuring of the personality by its consistency and values; to promote trust in the motives of others by an openness of communication; to provide for the patient's need to learn social skills and roles that he had not acquired in his family; and, critically, to enable him through a new relationship to a consistent person or persons to perceive, think, feel, and relate in new ways by learning through the experience that the parents' ways and edicts need no longer be accepted axiomatically as correct and necessary, and that dissent need not be destructive of either the other person or the relationship. Conjoint family sessions may be helpful as an adjunct to such goals, but they are not necessarily the proper way of achieving them. Clearly, we also do not go along with a current trend to discharge schizophrenic patients rapidly in order to offset regressive dependency upon the hospital and increased asocial withdrawal, but which in actuality often returns the patient to a pathogenic environment. We believe, rather, in the need for establishing hospital settings that can foster autonomy rather than dependency and withdrawal.

We have noted some of the consequences and implications of the studies of families of schizophrenic patients, indicating that they have opened paths for further investigations. We wish in closing this volume briefly to designate studies now in progress and others that we intend to pursue.

1a.   Comparisons of families of schizophrenic patients with families that have offspring with different types of psychopathology are essential to sharpen our understanding of what factors or influences predispose to schizophrenia or to other psychiatric illnesses. As noted in the Introduction, we have carried out a study of ten families of upper- and middle-class delinquents who were hospitalized in the Yale Psychiatric Institute. The analysis of the data is now in progress, and we believe it will help further to clarify the understanding of schizophrenic families through presenting certain similarities but also some very notable differences. We cannot here enter upon the extremely complicated matter of differentiating these two series of families, but we can note that in contrast to the disturbed communicative processes and irrationalities of the parents of schizophrenics, the parents of delinquents though seeming to communicate clearly often use language in the service of deception, and that they are interested in maintaining appearances rather than integrity or consistency, and are satisfied by what is said or professed rather than what is done. Somewhat in contrast to the Johnson-Szurek hypothesis, we have found that a number of the parents not only have superego lacunae which the children "act out" but set an example of "acting out" themselves. The finding that in the majority of our "delinquent" families a parent is in the advertising or public relations field, whereas none of the parents of the seventeen schizophrenics was so engaged, is probably not fortuitous.

1b.   The families of other types of patients must also be studied. As there appears to be a close resemblance between the mothers of patients with ulcerative colitis and a type of "schizophrenogenic" mother, a scrutiny of the family setting of ulcerative colitis patients would probably be rewarding. In a similar vein, as women with hyperthyroidism are apt to have similar traits and attitudes toward their children as mothers of male schizophrenics, an investigation of the children of hyperthyroid women might be revealing; indeed, a study of the incidence of schizophrenia in their children could be a relatively simple preliminary step.

2. A study of families with schizophrenic offspring from low socioeconomic levels is required. Not only is generalization to such families from our study hazardous, but a careful scrutiny of such families seems essential for epidemiologic purposes, to ascertain rather than conjecture about why the prevalence of schizophrenia is higher in the lower socioeconomic classes. We anticipate conducting such studies when our new clinical facilities supported by governmental funds are completed.

3. Comprehensive and global comparisons of series of families require intensive and extremely lengthy work. We wish to emphasize once again that serious errors can occur when assessments of families are made on the basis of only a few interviews. Painstaking work over a prolonged period of time is essential to supply the foundations in this field which eventually will permit more rapid judgments that are reasonably correct. Specific aspects of family structure and process can be compared only after discrete and testable hypotheses can be formulated. Poorly conceived experiments that test diffuse or highly conjectural hypotheses more often add confusion than settle critical issues. We believe that it is now possible to formulate testable hypotheses concerning parents of schizophrenic patients and the families they create—and to assess the findings appropriately in the larger frame of reference of essential family functions rather than to consider them tests of "causes" of schizophrenia. Research concerning the schizophrenic patient and his family can now move beyond the exploratory phase into such hypothesis testing.

a. Our first effort in this direction is recorded in the third section of this volume—a test of the hypothesis that parents of schizophrenic patients show, more commonly than controls, deficiencies in their capacities to categorize. The second effort was the testing in a quantifiable manner of Wynne and Singer's findings concerning the amorphous and fragmented styles of thinking and communicating of such parents. Both studies though yielding significant findings still lack control series of parents of other types of mental patients. The difficulties in obtaining proper controls, and indeed, in knowing *a priori* what must be controlled, presented serious problems, but taught a number of useful lessons for future studies.

b.   Currently a study is in progress testing the hypothesis that the meanings of words as used by parents of schizophrenic patients tend to deviate from the communicative norms. A word association test and the Semantic Differential (Osgood et al., 1957) are used to compare parents of schizophrenic patients, of nonschizophrenic psychiatric patients, and of normative controls matched for education and age.

c.   The hypothesis concerning the confused gender identities and faulty sexual role assumptions of parents of schizophrenic patients should also be amenable to experimental testing. Currently, a group of colleagues is seeking suitable ways of measuring objectively confusions in gender identity, reviewing existing tests and experimenting with new procedures.

d.   Another approach involves testing hypotheses concerning family interaction patterns under specific circumstances and assuming that conditions observed in a test situation typify habitual or continuing behavior. A number of investigators have presented families with some specific tasks to solve as a group, or observed their interaction under some very specific circumstances as a means of gaining samples of family behavior that can be compared with those of other families. We have presented families of schizophrenic patients, of delinquent patients, and of "normal" controls with a series of problems to solve and questions to answer as a group, recording the procedure, to study not only communication patterns but also parental coalitions, generation boundaries, and sex-linked roles in these families. Although the objective analysis of the fascinating data obtained presents difficult problems, they do not seem insurmountable. We hope that such techniques will be suited for testing specific hypotheses concerning parental interaction, generation boundaries, and gender roles.

4.   A major current objective concerns preparation of the way for longitudinal studies of families which can be expected later to have schizophrenic offspring. Retrospective studies such as we have carried out are always subject to the dangers of biased reconstruction. In long-term studies it is patently impossible to conceal an offspring's

diagnosis from the investigators. Intensive longitudinal studies are not possible unless means exist to select out families with a high risk of producing a schizophrenic offspring. In a random selection, some thirty to forty families could be expected to yield not more than one family that eventually had a schizophrenic offspring. The tests of the thought and communicative processes of parents, such as those reported in Part III of this volume, are being conducted, in part, to find a first step for a screening system. For example, families in which both parents have high scores on the Wild-Singer scoring of the Object Sorting Test can be scrutinized further. Other tests can be given the parents, their young adolescent children can be given projective tests, etc. Perhaps, one useful step will be to ascertain through study of old child guidance clinic records if certain behavioral disorders or configurations of problems or symptoms occur significantly more often in children who later become schizophrenic. It may also be feasible to use group projective tests to select out high school students who have a fairly high risk of becoming schizophrenic. Mixing high-risk families with control families would permit longitudinal studies which could test hypotheses, lead to new and more definitive knowledge concerning the development of schizophrenia, and have great importance for future prophylactic measures. However, as such studies must continue for fifteen or twenty years, careful preparation is essential.

5. Studies of siblings of schizophrenic patients and particularly identical twins both discordant and concordant for schizophrenia offer another useful approach, particularly when attention is directed toward differential factors in the siblings' development rather than simply to concordance rates. Identical twins provide the opportunity for making a reasonable comparison between the developments of two individuals because the number of variables is narrowed down by the common genetic inheritance and because the twins have been reared by the same parents in the same home at the same time. However, attention must be paid to the unique developmental problems of identical twins (Chapter XII). A study with such interests is now in progress at the National Institute of Mental Health (Pollin et al., 1965).

The study of adopted children who become schizophrenic also

holds considerable promise as a means of clarifying genetic issues as well as family dynamics, but such studies, particularly if data about the real parents are also sought, may present insurmountable problems, at least in the United States.

6.   Beyond systematic studies, the further clarification of the role of parental personalities, parental ways and styles of communicating, and of family structure and dynamics in the etiology of schizophrenia will continue to rest heavily upon clinical observation and the gradual accumulation of data gathered during the psychoanalytically oriented study of schizophrenic patients and their relatives. The demonstrations of the importance of the family in the understanding and treatment of the schizophrenic patient have greatly increased opportunities for pertinent observations, for an increasing number of social workers, sociologists, and psychiatrists are now focusing attention on patients' families. The study of the patient and how his illness arose in the ecological setting of his family, and the trend toward studying and treating disturbed families rather than only the designated patient will increasingly provide knowledge of the family that is needed for more specific studies such as the one in which we have been engaged.

Abraham, K. (1908), The Psycho-Sexual Differences Between Hysteria and Dementia Praecox. In *Selected Papers of Karl Abraham*. London: Hogarth Press, 1948.

—— (1916), The First Pregenital Phase of the Libido. In *Selected Papers of Karl Abraham*. London: Hogarth Press, 1948.

Abrahams, J. & Varon, E. (1953), *Maternal Dependency and Schizophrenia: Mothers and Daughters in a Therapeutic Group*. New York: Int. Univ. Press.

Ackerman, N. W. (1954a), The Diagnosis of Neurotic Marital Interaction. *Soc. Casew.*, 35:139-147.

—— (1954b), Interpersonal Disturbances in the Family: Some Unsolved Problems in Psychotherapy. *Psychiatry*, 17:359-368.

—— (1958a), Behavior Trends and Disturbances of the Contemporary Family. In *The Family In Contemporary Society*, ed. I. Galdston. New York: Int. Univ. Press.

—— (1958b), *The Psychodynamics of Family Life*. New York: Basic Books.

—— (1960), Family-focused Therapy of Schizophrenia. In *The Outpatient Treatment of Schizophrenia*, eds. S. Scher & H. Davis. New York: Grune & Stratton.

—— (1961), The Schizophrenic Patient and His Family Relationships: A Conceptual Basis for Family-focused Therapy of Schizophrenia. In *Mental Patients in Transition, Steps in Hospital-Community Rehabilitation*, eds. M. Greenblatt, D. Levinson, & G. Klerman. Springfield, Ill.: Thomas.

—— (1962), Adolescent Problems: A Symptom of Family Disorder. *Fam. Proc.*, 1:202-213.

—— & Behrens, M. (1956), A Study of Family Diagnosis. *Amer. J. Orthopsychiat.*, 26:66-78.

Alanen, Y. O. (1958), The Mothers of Schizophrenic Patients. *Acta Psychiat. Neurol. Scand.*, Suppl. 124.

—— (1960a), Some Thoughts on Schizophrenia and Ego Development in the Light of Family Investigations. *Arch. Gen. Psychiat.*, 3:650-656.

—— (1960b), Über die Familiensituation der Schizophrenie-Patienten. *Acta Psychother.*, 8:89-104.

Alexander, F. (1930), *The Psychoanalysis of the Total Personality: The Application of Freud's Theory of the Ego to the Neuroses.* New York: Nerv. & Ment. Dis. Publ. Co.

Ariès, P. (1962), *Centuries of Childhood: A Social History of Family Life.* New York: Knopf.

Arieti, S. (1955), *Interpretation of Schizophrenia.* New York: Brunner.

—— (1960), Recent Conceptions and Misconceptions of Schizophrenia. *Amer. J. Psychother.,* 14:3-21.

Baldamus, W. & Timms, N. (1955), The Problem Family: A Sociological Approach. *Brit. J. Sociol.,* 6:318-327.

Bateson, G. (1958), Schizophrenic Distortions of Communication. In *Psychotherapy of Chronic Schizophrenic Patients,* ed. C. A. Whitaker. Boston: Little, Brown.

—— (1960), Minimal Requirements for a Theory of Schizophrenia. *Arch. Gen. Psychiat.,* 2:477-491.

—— (1961a), The Biosocial Integration of Behavior in the Schizophrenic Family. In *Exploring the Base for Family Therapy,* eds. N. W. Ackerman, F. Beatman, & S. Sherman. New York: Family Service Assn. of Amer.

—— (1961b), The Challenge of Research in Family Diagnosis and Therapy, Summary of Panel Discussion: I. Formal Research in Family Structure. In *Exploring the Base for Family Therapy,* eds. N. W. Ackerman, F. Beatman, & S. Sherman. New York: Family Service Assn. of Amer.

——, Jackson, D., Haley, J., & Weakland, J. (1956), Toward a Theory of Schizophrenia. *Behav. Sci.,* 1:251-264.

Bauer, F. C. (1953), Folie à Trois: A Case Report. *Psychiat. Quart.,* 27:624-636.

Bauer, W. (1961), The Responsibility of the University Hospital in the Synthesis of Medical Science and Learning. *New Engl. J. Med.,* 265: 1292-1298.

Baxter, J. C. & Arthur, S. C. (1964), Conflict in Families of Schizophrenics as a Function of Premorbid Adjustment and Social Class. *Fam. Proc.,* 3:273-279.

—— —— Flood, C., & Hedgepeth, B. (1962), Conflict Patterns in the Families of Schizophrenics. *J. Nerv. Ment. Dis.,* 135:419-424.

—— & Becker, J. (1962), Anxiety and Avoidance Behavior in Schizophrenics in Response to Parental Figures. *J. Abnorm. Soc. Psychol.,* 64:432-437.

—— —— & Hooks, W. (1963), Defensive Style in the Families of Schizophrenics and Controls. *J. Abnorm. Soc. Psychol.,* 66:512-518.

Beck, S. J. (1960), Families of Schizophrenic and of Well Children: Method, Concepts, and Some Results. *Amer. J. Orthopsychiat.,* 30:247-262.

—— & Nunnally, J. C. (1953), Method of Social Work Research in Schizophrenia. *J. Psychiat. Soc. Work*, 22:123-128.

Beckett, P. G. S., Frohman, C. E., & Gottlieb, J. S. (1963), Schizophrenic-like Mechanisms in Monkeys. *Amer. J. Psychiat.*, 119:835-842.

—— Robinson, D. B., Frazier, S. H., Steinhilber, R. M., Duncan, G. M., Estes, H. R., Litin, E. M., Grattan, R. T., Lorton, W. L., Williams, G. E., & Johnson, A. M. (1956), Studies in Schizophrenia at the Mayo Clinic: 1. The Significance of Exogenous Traumata in the Genesis of Schizophrenia. *Psychiatry*, 19:137-148.

Bell, J. E. (1961), *Family Group Therapy*. Public Health Monograph 64.

Bell, N. (1962), Extended Family Relations of Disturbed and Well Families. *Fam. Proc.*, 1:175-193.

—— & Vogel, E. (1960), Toward a Framework for Functional Analysis of Family Behavior. Introduction to *A Modern Introduction to the Family*, eds. N. Bell & E. Vogel. Glencoe, Ill.: Free Press.

Beres, D. & Obers, S. J. (1952), The Effects of Extreme Deprivation in Infancy on Psychic Structure in Adolescence: A Study in Ego Development. *The Psychoanalytic Study of the Child*, 5:212-235. New York: Int. Univ. Press.

Binswanger, L. (1958a), Insanity as Life-Historical Phenomenon and as Mental Disease: The Case of Ilse. In *Existence: A New Dimension in Psychiatry and Psychology*, eds. R. May, E. Angel, & H. Ellenberger. New York: Basic Books.

—— (1958b), The Case of Ellen West. In *Existence: A New Dimension in Psychiatry and Psychology*, eds. R. May, E. Angel, & H. Ellenberger. New York: Basic Books.

Bion, W. R. (1954), Notes on the Theory of Schizophrenia. *Int. J. Psycho-Anal.*, 35:113-118.

—— (1959), *Experiences in Groups*. London: Tavistock Publ.

Bleuler, E. (1911), *Dementia Praecox or the Group of Schizophrenias*. New York: Int. Univ. Press, 1950.

—— (1930), Primäre und sekundäre Symptome der Schizophrenie. *Z. ges. Neurol. Psychiat.*, 124:607-646.

Bleuler, M. (1941), *Krankheitsverlauf, Persönlichkeit und Verwandtschaft Schizophrener und ihre gegenseitigen Beziehungen*. Leipzig: Thieme.

—— (1955), Research and Changes in Concepts in the Study of Schizophrenia, 1941-1950. *Bull. Isaac Ray Med. Library*, 3:1-132.

—— (1956), Aspects Secrets de la Psychiatrie. *L'Evol. Psychiat.*, 21:45-50.

Block, J., Patterson, V., Block, J., & Jackson, D. D. (1958), A Study of the Parents of Schizophrenic and Neurotic Children. *Psychiatry*, 21:387-397.

Blum, G. S. & Rosenzweig, S. (1944), The Incidence of Sibling and Parental Deaths in the Anamnesis of Female Schizophrenics. *J. Gen. Psychol.*, *31*:3-13.

Boisen, A. T. (1947), Onset in Acute Schizophrenia. *Psychiatry*, *10*:159-166.

Bonner, H. (1950), Sociological Aspects of Paranoia. *Amer. J. Sociol.*, *56*:255-262.

Boszormenyi-Nagy, I. (1962), The Concept of Schizophrenia from the Perspective of Family Treatment. *Fam. Proc.*, *1*:103-113.

Bott, E. (1955), Urban Families: Conjugal Roles and Social Networks. *Hum. Relat.*, *8*:345-384.

—— (1957), *Family and Social Network*. London: Tavistock Publ.

Bour, P. (1958), Schizophrénie et Dissociation Familiale. *L'Evol. Psychiat.*, *23*:85-104.

Bowen, M. (1957), Family Participation in Schizophrenia. Presented at meeting of Amer. Psychiat. Assn.

—— (1960), A Family Concept of Schizophrenia. Chapter 12 in *The Etiology of Schizophrenia*, ed. D. D. Jackson. New York: Basic Books.

—— (1961), The Family as the Unit of Study and Treatment: 1. Family Psychotherapy. *Amer. J. Orthopsychiat.*, *31*:40-60.

—— Dysinger, R. H., Brodey, W., & Basamania, B. (1957), Study and Treatment of Five Hospitalized Families Each with a Psychotic Member. Presented at Amer. Orthopsychiat. Assn. meeting.

—— —— & Basamania, B. (1959), The Role of the Father in Families with a Schizophrenic Patient. *Amer. J. Psychiat.*, *115*:117-120.

Brecher, S. (1956), The Rorschach Reaction Patterns of Maternally Overprotected and Maternally Rejected Schizophrenic Patients. *J. Nerv. Ment. Dis.*, *123*:41-52.

Brodey, W. (1959), Some Family Operations and Schizophrenia: A Study of Five Hospitalized Families Each with a Schizophrenic Member. *AMA Arch. Gen. Psychiat.*, *1*:379-402.

—— (1961), The Family as the Unit of Study and Treatment: 3. Image, Object and Narcissistic Relationships. *Amer. J. Orthopsychiat.*, *31*: 69-73.

Brody, E. B. (1956), Modification of Family Interaction Patterns by a Group Interview Technique. *Int. J. Group Psychother.*, *6*:38-47.

—— & Redlich, F. C., eds. (1952), *Psychotherapy with Schizophrenics*. New York: Int. Univ. Press.

Brody, J. P. (1958), Language in Schizophrenia. *Amer. J. Psychother.*, *12*:473-487.

Bross, R. B. (1957), The Schizophrenogenic Parents in Group Psychotherapy. *Congr. Rep. IInd Int. Congr. Psychiat.*, *Zurich*, *3*:469-474.

Brown, R. (1958), *Words and Things*. Glencoe, Ill.: Free Press.

Bruch, H. (1957), Weight Disturbances and Schizophrenic Development. *Congr. Rep. IInd Int. Congr. Psychiat.*, *Zurich*, *2*:190-193.

—— (1959), Studies in Schizophrenia. *Acta Psychiat. Neurol. Scand.*, Suppl. 130, Vol. *34*:5-48.

—— (1961a), Conceptual Confusion in Eating Disorders. *J. Nerv. Ment. Dis.*, *133*:46-54.

—— (1961b), Transformation of Oral Impulses in Eating Disorders: A Conceptual Approach. *Psychiat. Quart.*, *35*:458-481.

—— & Palombo, S. (1961), Conceptual Problems in Schizophrenia. *J. Nerv. Ment. Dis.*, *132*:114-117.

—— & Touraine, G. (1940), Obesity in Childhood: V. The Family Frame of Obese Children. *Psychosom. Med.*, 2:141-206.

Burgess, E. W. (1926), The Family as a Unit of Interacting Personalities. *Family*, 7:3-9.

Buell, B. (1953), *Classification of Disorganized Families for Use in Family Oriented Diagnosis and Treatment*. New York: Community Research Associates.

Burlingham, D. T. (1952), *Twins. A Study of Three Pairs of Identical Twins*. New York: Int. Univ. Press.

Burnham, D. L. (1956), Misperception of Other Persons in Schizophrenia: A Structural View of Restitution Processes, Reality Representation, and Perception. *Psychiatry*, *19*:283-303.

Cameron, N. (1959), The Paranoid Pseudo-community Revisited. *Amer. J. Sociol.*, *65*:52-58.

—— & Magaret, A. (1951), *Behavior Pathology*. Boston: Houghton Mifflin.

Cammer, L. & Tarzie, M. (1962), The Private Practitioner and the Psychiatric Referral. *Ment. Hosp.*, *13*:19-21.

Caputo, D. V. (1963), The Parents of the Schizophrenic. *Fam. Proc.*, 2:339-356.

Carr, A. (1963), Observations on Paranoia and Their Relationship to the Schreber Case. *Int. J. Psycho-Anal.*, *44*:195-200.

Carroll, E. J. (1960), Treatment of the Family as a Unit. *Penn. Med. J.*, *63*:57-62.

Carroll J. B. (1959), Language and Thought Studied Across Languages: A Report of the "Southwest Project." Presented at meeting of Amer. Psychol. Assn.

Caudill, W. (1958), *The Psychiatric Hospital as a Small Society*. Cambridge: Harvard Univ. Press.

—— & Stainbrook, E. (1954). Some Covert Effects of Communication Difficulties in a Psychiatric Hospital. *Psychiatry*, *17*:27-40.

Cheek, F. E. (1964), A Serendipitous Finding: Sex Roles and Schizophrenia. *J. Abnorm. Soc. Psychol.*, *69*:392-400.

Chein, I. (1956), The Family of the Addict. Presented at Conference on Drug Addiction, Bellevue Hospital, New York.

Chrzanowski, G. (1957), The Family Environment of Schizophrenic Patients. *Congr. Rep. IInd Int. Congr. Psychiat., Zurich,* 4:42-47.

Clausen, J. A. & Kohn, M. L. (1960), Social Relations and Schizophrenia. In *The Etiology of Schizophrenia,* ed. D. D. Jackson. New York: Basic Books.

Cohen, M. B., Baker, G., Cohen, R., Fromm-Reichmann, F., & Weigert, E. (1954), An Intensive Study of Twelve Cases of Manic-Depressive Psychosis. *Psychiatry,* 17:103-137.

Cronin, H. J. (1933), Analysis of Neuroses of Identical Twins. *Psychoanal. Rev.,* 20:375-387.

da Silva, G. (1963), The Role of the Father with Chronic Schizophrenic Patients: A Study in Group Therapy. *Canad. Psychiat. Assn. J.,* 8:190-203.

Delay, J., Deniker, P., & Green, A. (1957), Le milieu familial des schizophrènes: 1. Proposition du Problème. *L'Encéphale,* 46:189-232.

———— ———— ———— (1960), Le milieu familial des schizophrènes: 2. Méthode d'approache. *L'Encéphale,* 49:1-21.

———— ———— ———— (1962), Le milieu familial des schizophrènes: 3. Résultats et Hypothèses. *L'Encéphale,* 51:5-73.

Demarest, E. W. & Winestine, M. C. (1955), The Initial Phase of Concomitant Treatment of Twins. *The Psychoanalytic Study of the Child,* 10:336-352. New York: Int. Univ. Press.

Despert, J. L. (1942), Prophylactic Aspects of Schizophrenia in Childhood. *Nerv. Child,* 1:199-231.

———— (1951), Some Considerations Relating to the Genesis of Autistic Behavior in Children. *Amer. J. Orthopsychiat.,* 21:335-350.

Detre, T., Sayres, J., Norton, N., & Lewis, H. (1961), An Experimental Approach to the Treatment of the Acutely Ill Psychiatric Patient in the General Hospital. *Conn. Med.,* 25:613-619.

Devereux, G. (1949), The Social Structure of the Hospital as a Factor in Total Therapy. *Amer. J. Orthopsychiat.,* 19:492-500.

Devoto, A. (1960), *I Precedenti Psicologici dello Schizofrenico.* Florence: Leo S. Olschki.

Dicks, H. V. (1953), Clinical Studies in Marriage and the Family: A Symposium on Methods. I. Experiences with Marital Tensions Seen in the Psychological Clinic. *Brit. J. Med. Psychol.,* 26:181-196.

Dworin, J. & Wyant, O. (1957), Authoritarian Patterns in the Mothers of Schizophrenics. *J. Clin. Psychol.,* 13:332-338.

Dysinger, R. H. (1957), The "Action Dialogue" in an Intense Relationship: A Study of a Schizophrenic Girl and Her Mother. Presented at meeting of Amer. Psychiat. Assn.

Edwards, R. V. (1964), Some Schizophrenic Mechanisms. *Amer. J. Psychiat.*, *120*:1105-1107.

Ehrenwald, J. (1958), Neurotic Interaction and Patterns of Pseudo-Heredity in the Family. *Amer. J. Psychiat.*, *115*:134-142.

——— (1963a), Family Diagnosis and Mechanisms of Psychosocial Defense. *Fam. Proc.*, *2*:121-131.

——— (1963b), Family Dynamics and Communication Theory. *J. Communication*, *13*:191-198.

Eisenberg, L. (1956), The Autistic Child in Adolescence. *Amer. J. Psychiat.*, *112*:607-612.

——— (1957), The Fathers of Autistic Children. *Amer. J. Orthopsychiat.*, 27:715-724.

Eldred, D. M., Brooks, G. W., Deane, W. N., & Taylor, M. (1962), The Rehabilitation of the Mentally Ill—The Vermont Story. *Amer. J. Publ. Hlth.*, *52*:39-46.

Ellison, E. A. & Hamilton, D. M. (1949), The Hospital Treatment of Dementia Praecox: Part II. *Amer. J. Psychiat.*, *106*:454-461.

Elsasser, G. (1952), *Die Nachkommen geisteskranker Elternpaare.* Stuttgart: Thieme.

Endicott, T. (1958), Personal communication.

Erikson, E. H. (1946), Ego Development and Historical Change: Clinical Notes. *The Psychoanalytic Study of the Child*, *2*:359-396. New York: Int. Univ. Press.

——— (1950a), Growth and Crises of the "Healthy Personality." In *Symposium on the Healthy Personality*, Vol. 2: *Problems of Infancy and Childhood*, ed. M. J. E. Senn. New York: Josiah Macy, Jr., Foundation.

——— (1950b), *Childhood and Society.* New York: W. W. Norton.

——— (1956), The Problem of Ego Identity. *J. Amer. Psychoanal. Assn.*, *4*:56-121.

——— (1964), *Insight Into Responsibility.* New York: W. W. Norton.

Ernst, K. (1956), Geordnete Familienverhältnisse späterer Schizophrener im Lichte einer Nachuntersuchung. *Arch. Psychiat. Nervenheilkr.*, *194*:355-367.

Fairbairn, W. R. D. (1940), Schizoid Factors in the Personality. In *Psycho-Analytic Studies of the Personality.* London: Tavistock Publ., 1952.

——— (1944), Endopsychic Structure Considered in Terms of Object Relationships. *Int. J. Psycho-Anal.*, *25*:70-93.

——— (1952), *Psycho-Analytic Studies of the Personality.* London: Tavistock Publ.

Farina, A. (1960), Patterns of Dominance and Conflict in Parents of Schizo-
phrenic Patients. *J. Abnorm. Soc. Psychol.*, *61*:31-38.
——— & Dunham, R. (1963), Measurement of Family Relationships and
Their Effects. *Arch. Gen. Psychiat.*, *9*:64-73.
Faris, M. T. (1955), Casework with Relatives. *J. Psychiat. Soc. Work*,
24:108-112.
Faris, R. E. L. (1934), Cultural Isolation and the Schizophrenic Personality.
Amer. J. Sociol., *40*:155-164.
——— (1944), Ecological Factors in Human Behavior. In *Personality and
the Behavior Disorders*, Vol. II, ed. J. McV. Hunt. New York: Ronald
Press.
Federn, P. (1952), *Ego Psychology and the Psychoses*, ed. E. Weiss. New
York: Basic Books.
Ferreira, A. J. (1960), The Semantics and the Context of the Schizophren-
ic's Language. *Arch. Gen. Psychiat.*, *3*:128-138.
Fetterman, J. L. (1948), Better Doctor-Family Cooperation as an Aid to
the Mentally Ill Patient. *Med. Clin. No. Amer.*, *32*:631-640.
Fisher, S., Boyd, I., Walker, D., & Sheer, D. (1959), Parents of Schizo-
phrenics, Neurotics, and Normals. *Arch. Gen. Psychiat.*, *1*:149-166.
——— & Mendell, D. (1956), The Communication of Neurotic Patterns
Over Two and Three Generations. *Psychiatry*, *19*:41-46.
Fleck, S. (1953), Vigilance (Orienting Behavior), Conditional Reactions
and Adjustment Patterns in Schizophrenic and Compulsive Patients.
Ann. N.Y. Acad. Sci., *56*:342-379.
——— (1956), Nurses' Training in Mental Health Aspects of Public Health
Field Work. *Amer. J. Publ. Hlth.*, *46*:748-754.
——— (1960), Family Dynamics and Origin of Schizophrenia. *Psychosom.
Med.*, *22*:333-344.
——— (1962), Residential Treatment of Young Schizophrenics. *Conn.
Med.*, *26*:369-376.
——— (1963), Psychotherapy of Families of Hospitalized Patients. In
Current Psychiatric Therapies, Vol. III, ed. J. Masserman. New York:
Grune & Stratton.
Flugel, J. C. (1921), *The Psycho-Analytic Study of the Family*. London:
Hogarth Press.
——— (1947), *Man, Morals and Society: A Psychoanalytic Study*. New
York: Int. Univ. Press.
Foote, N. & Cottrell, L. (1955), *Identity and Interpersonal Competence:
A New Direction in Family Research*. Chicago: Univ. Chicago Press.
Foudraine, J. (1961), Schizophrenia and the Family: A Survey of the Liter-
ature 1956-1960 on the Etiology of Schizophrenia. *Acta Psychother.*,
9:82-110.

Frazee, H. E. (1953), Children Who Later Became Schizophrenic. *Smith Coll. Stud. Soc. Work, 23*:125-149.

Freeman, H. E. & Simmons, O. G. (1959), Mental Patients in the Community: Family Settings and Performance Levels. *Amer. Sociol. Rev., 23*:147-154.

Freeman, R. V. & Grayson, H. M. (1955), Maternal Attitudes in Schizophrenia. *J. Abnorm. Soc. Psychol., 50*:45-52.

Freeman, T., Cameron, J. L., & McGhie, A. (1958), *Chronic Schizophrenia*. New York: Int. Univ. Press.

Freud, S. (1905), Fragment of an Analysis of a Case of Hysteria. In *The Standard Edition of the Complete Psychological Works of Sigmund Freud, 7*:112-122. London: Hogarth Press, 1953.

—— (1906), My Views on the Part Played by Sexuality in the Aetiology of the Neuroses. In *The Standard Edition of the Complete Psychological Works of Sigmund Freud, 7*:271-279. London: Hogarth Press, 1953.

—— (1911), Psycho-Analytic Notes on an Autobiographical Account of a Case of Paranoia (Dementia Paranoides). In *The Standard Edition of the Complete Psychological Works of Sigmund Freud, 12*:3-82. London: Hogarth Press, 1958.

—— (1913), Totem and Taboo. In *The Standard Edition of the Complete Psychological Works of Sigmund Freud, 13*:1-161. London: Hogarth Press, 1955.

—— (1916-1917), *A General Introduction to Psychoanalysis*. New York: Boni and Liveright.

—— (1921), Group Psychology and the Analysis of the Ego. In *The Standard Edition of the Complete Psychological Works of Sigmund Freud, 18*:67-143. London: Hogarth Press, 1955.

—— (1922), Some Neurotic Mechanisms in Jealousy, Paranoia and Homosexuality. In *The Standard Edition of the Complete Psychological Works of Sigmund Freud, 18*:221-232. London: Hogarth Press, 1955.

—— (1923), The Ego and the Id. In *The Standard Edition of the Complete Psychological Works of Sigmund Freud, 19*:3-66. London: Hogarth Press, 1961.

—— (1924a), Neurosis and Psychosis. In *The Standard Edition of the Complete Psychological Works of Sigmund Freud, 19*:149-153. London: Hogarth Press, 1961.

—— (1924b), The Dissolution of the Oedipus Complex. In *The Standard Edition of the Complete Psychological Works of Sigmund Freud, 19*:173-179. London: Hogarth Press, 1961.

—— (1933), *New Introductory Lectures on Psychoanalysis*. New York: W. W. Norton.

Freyhan, F. A. (1951), Study of a Schizophrenic Family, *Delaware Med. J.*, *23*:213-217.

Fromm-Reichmann, F. (1939), Transference Problems in Schizophrenics. *Psychoanal. Quart.*, *8*:412-426.

—— (1940), Notes on the Mother Rôle in the Family Group. *Bull. Menninger Clin.*, *4*:132-145.

—— (1948), Notes on the Development of Treatment of Schizophrenics by Psychoanalytic Psychotherapy. *Psychiatry*, *11*:263-273.

—— (1950), *Principles of Intensive Psychotherapy*. Chicago: Univ. Chicago Press.

Frumkin, R. M. (1954), Social Factors in Schizophrenia. *Sociol. Soc. Res.*, *38*:383-386.

Fry, W. F. & Heersema, P. (1963), Conjoint Family Therapy: A New Dimension in Psychotherapy. *Topic. Prob. Psychother.*, *5*:147-153.

Fujinawa, A. (1960), Die Untersuchungen über die Familienverhältnisse der Schizophrenen. *Psychiat. et Neurol. Japonica* (Tokyo), *62*:1375.

Galvin, J. (1956), Mothers of Schizophrenics. *J. Nerv. Ment. Dis.*, *123*:568-570.

Garmezy, N., Clarke, A., & Stockner, C. (1961), Child-rearing Attitudes of Mothers and Fathers as Reported by Schizophrenic and Normal Control Patients. *J. Abnorm. Soc. Psychol.*, *63*:176-182.

—— Farina, A., & Rodnick, E. (1960), The Structured Situational Test: A Method for Studying Family Interaction in Schizophrenia. *Amer. J. Orthopsychiat.*, *30*:445-452.

Gerard, D. L. & Houston, L. G. (1953), Family Setting and the Social Ecology of Schizophrenia. *Psychiat. Quart.*, *27*:90-101.

—— & Siegel, J. (1950), The Family Background of Schizophrenia. *Psychiat. Quart.*, *24*:47-73.

Giffin, M., Johnson, A. M., & Litin, E. M. (1954), Antisocial Acting Out. 2. Specific Factors Determining Antisocial Acting Out. *Amer. J. Orthopsychiat.*, *24*:668-684.

Gjessing, R. (1953), Beiträge zur Somatologie der periodischen Katatonie. *Arch. Psychiat. Nervenheilkr.*, *191*:191-326.

Glueck, B. C. (1957), *Final Report: Research Project for the Study and Treatment of Persons Convicted of Crimes Involving Sexual Aberrations, June, 1952–June, 1955*. New York State Department of Mental Hygiene.

Goldberg, E. M. (1953), Experiences with Families of Young Men with Duodenal Ulcer and "Normal" Control Families: Some Problems of Approach and Method. *Brit. J. Med. Psychol.*, *26*:204-214.

Goldfarb, W. (1961), The Mutual Impact of Mother and Child in Childhood Schizophrenia. *Amer. J. Orthopsychiat.*, *31*:738-747.

Goldstein, A. P. & Carr, A. C. (1956), The Attitudes of Mothers of Male
    Catatonic and Paranoid Schizophrenics Toward Child Behavior. *J.
    Cons. Psychol.*, 20:190.
Gralnick, A. (1960), In-patient Psychoanalytic Psychotherapy of Schizo-
    phrenia. In *Psychoanalysis and Human Values*, ed. J. Masserman. New
    York: Grune & Stratton.
Greenberg, H. P. (1956), *Folie à Deux:* An Historical and Clinical Study.
    Unpublished thesis written as Registrar at Guy's Hospital, London.
Greenblatt, M., Levinson, D., & Williams, R. H. (1957), *The Patient and
    the Mental Hospital.* Glencoe, Ill.: Free Press.
Grof, S. & Dytrych, Z. (1963), K Otázce Vlivu Rodinného Prostředí Na
    Vznik a Vývoj Schizofrenie. *Ceskoslovenská Psychiatrie*, 59:340-354.
Grotjahn, M. (1960), *Psychoanalysis and the Family Neurosis.* New York:
    W. W. Norton.
Group for the Advancement of Psychiatry, Committee on the Family
    (1954), *Integration and Conflict in Family Behavior.* Report No. 27.

Hajdu-Gimes, L. (1940), Contributions to the Etiology of Schizophrenia.
    Psychoanal. Rev., 27:421-438.
Haley, J. (1959a), The Family of the Schizophrenic: A Model System.
    J. Nerv. Ment. Dis., 129:357-374.
——— (1959b), An Interactional Description of Schizophrenia. *Psychia-
    try*, 22:321-332.
——— (1960), Observation of the Family of the Schizophrenic. *Amer. J.
    Orthopsychiat.*, 30:460-467.
——— (1962), Family Experiments: A New Type of Experimentation.
    Fam. Proc., 1:265-293.
Hampson, J. L., Hampson, J. G., & Money, J. (1955), The Syndrome of
    Gonadal Agenesis (Ovarian Agenesis) and Male Chromosomal Pat-
    tern in Girls and Women: Psychologic Studies. *Bull. Johns Hopkins
    Hosp.*, 97:207-226.
Handel, G. & Hess, D. (1956), The Family as an Emotional Organization.
    Marriage and Family Living, 18:99-101.
Hartmann, H. (1934-1935), Psychiatric Studies of Twins. In *Essays on Ego
    Psychology.* New York: Int. Univ. Press, 1964.
——— (1939), *Ego Psychology and the Problem of Adaptation.* New
    York: Int. Univ. Press, 1958.
——— (1944), Psychoanalysis and Sociology. In *Psychoanalysis Today*,
    ed. S. Lorand. New York: Int. Univ. Press.
——— (1950), The Application of Psychoanalytic Concepts to Social Sci-
    ence. *Psychoanal. Quart.*, 19:385-392.
——— (1953), The Metapsychology of Schizophrenia. In *The Psychoana-
    lytic Study of the Child*, 8:177-197. New York: Int. Univ. Press.

———— Kris, E., & Loewenstein, R. M. (1951), Some Psychoanalytic Comments on "Culture and Personality." In *Psychoanalysis and Culture*, ed. G. B. Wilbur & W. Muensterberger. New York: Int. Univ. Press.

Hawkes, R. & Albert, R. (1962), Some Psychological Dimensions of Mental Illness in the Family. *Psychiat. Quart. Suppl.*, *36*:195-208.

Hayward, M. L. (1960), Schizophrenia and the Double Bind. *Psychiat. Quart.*, *34*:89-91.

Hendricks, R. C. (1944), Schizophrenia in Three Brothers. *U.S. Naval Med. Bull.*, *42*:1097-1101.

Hilgard, J. & Newman, M. (1963a), Early Parental Deprivation as a Functional Factor in the Etiology in Schizophrenia and Alcoholism. *Amer. J. Orthopsychiat.*, *33*:409-420.

———— ———— (1963b), Parental Loss by Death in Childhood as an Etiological Factor Among Schizophrenic and Alcoholic Patients Compared with a Non-Patient Community Sample. *J. Nerv. Ment. Dis.*, *137*: 14-28.

Hill, L. B. (1955), *Psychotherapeutic Intervention in Schizophrenia*. Chicago: Univ. Chicago Press.

Hill, R. (1954), Marriage and Family Research: A Critical Evaluation. *Eugenics Quart.*, *1*:58-63.

———— Mark, J., & Wirths, C. S. (1953), *Eddyville's Families: Study of Personal and Family Adjustment Subsequent to the Rapid Urbanization of a Southern Town*. Chapel Hill, North Carolina: Institute for Research in Social Science.

Hobson, J. A. (1964), Identical Twins Discordant for Schizophrenia. *J. Nerv. Ment. Dis.*, *138*:432-442.

Hoch, P. & Polatin, P. (1949), Pseudoneurotic Forms of Schizophrenia. *Psychiat. Quart.*, *23*:248-276.

Hollingshead, A. & Redlich, F. (1958), *Social Class and Mental Illness*. New York: Wiley.

Holzberg, J. (1960), The Historical Traditions of the State Hospitals as a Force of Resistance to the Team. *Amer. J. Orthopsychiat.*, *30*:87-94.

Hotchkiss, G. D., Carmen, L, Ogilby, A., & Wiesenfeld, S. (1955), Mothers of Young Male Single Schizophrenic Patients as Visitors in a Mental Hospital. *J. Nerv. Ment. Dis.*, *121*:452-462.

Houston, P. E., Cohen, B. D., & Senf, R. (1955), Shifting of Set and Goal Orientation in Schizophrenia. *J. Ment. Sci.*, *101*:344-350.

Hubbard, J. P. (1953), Observation of the Family in the Home. *J. Med. Educ.*, *28*:26-30.

Inwood, E. R. (1952), Therapeutic Interviewing of Hostile Relatives. *Amer. J. Psychiat.*, *109*:455-458.

———— (1953), The Problem of the Hostile Relative. *U.S. Armed Forces Med. J.*, *4*:1734-1747.

Jackson, D. D. (1954), Some Factors Influencing the Oedipus Complex. *Psychoanal. Quart.*, *23*:566-581.

—— (1957a), A Note on the Importance of Trauma in the Genesis of Schizophrenia. *Psychiatry*, *20*:181-184.

—— (1957b), The Question of Family Homeostasis. *Psychiat. Quart.* Suppl., *31*:79-90.

—— (1958), The Family and Sexuality. In *The Psychotherapy of Chronic Schizophrenic Patients*, ed. C. Whitaker. Boston: Little, Brown.

—— (1959), Family Interaction, Family Homeostasis, and Some Implications for Conjoint Family Psychotherapy. In *Individual and Familial Dynamics*, ed. J. Masserman. New York: Grune & Stratton.

——, Ed. (1960), *The Etiology of Schizophrenia*. New York: Basic Books.

—— (1961), Family Therapy in the Family of the Schizophrenic. In *Contemporary Psychotherapies*, ed. M. Stein. Glencoe, Ill.: Free Press.

—— Block J., Block J., & Patterson, V. (1958), Psychiatrists' Conceptions of the Schizophrenogenic Parent. *Arch. Neurol. Psychiat.*, *79*: 448-459.

—— & Haley, J. (1963), Transference Revisited. *J. Nerv. Ment. Dis.*, *137*:363-371.

—— Riskin, J., & Satir, V. (1961), A Method of Analysis of a Family Interview. *Arch. Gen. Psychiat.*, *5*:321-339.

—— & Satir, V. (1961), A Review of Psychiatric Developments in Family Diagnosis and Therapy. In *Exploring the Base for Family Therapy*, eds. N. W. Ackerman, F. Beatman, & S. Sherman. New York: Family Service Assn. of Amer.

—— & Weakland, J. (1959), Schizophrenic Symptoms and Family Interaction. *Arch. Gen. Psychiat.*, *1*:618-621.

—— —— (1961), Conjoint Family Therapy: Some Considerations on Theory, Technique and Results. *Psychiatry*, Suppl., *24*:30-45.

Jensen, T. (1952), Measuring Family Solidarity. *Amer. Sociol. Rev.*, *17*: 727-733.

Johanson, E. (1958), A Study of Schizophrenia in the Male. *Acta Psychiat. Neurol. Scand.*, Suppl. 125.

Johansson, A. (1956), Family Dynamics in Schizophrenia in the Light of Psychotherapy. Presented at meeting of Finnish Neuropsychiatric Society.

Johnson, A. M., Giffin, M. E., Watson, J., & Beckett, P. G. S. (1956), Studies in Schizophrenia at the Mayo Clinic: II. Observations on Ego Functions in Schizophrenia. *Psychiatry*, *19*:143-148.

—— & Szurek, S. A. (1952), The Genesis of Antisocial Acting Out in Children and Adults. *Psychoanal. Quart.*, *21*:323-343.

———— ———— (1954), Etiology of Antisocial Behavior in Delinquents and Psychopaths. *J. Amer. Med. Assn.*, *154*:814-817.

Jones, D. (1964), Binds and Unbinds. *Fam. Proc.*, *3*:323-331.

Jones, M. (1953), *The Therapeutic Community: A New Treatment Method in Psychiatry*. New York: Basic Books.

Joseph, E. D. (1959), An Unusual Fantasy in a Twin with an Inquiry into the Nature of Fantasy. *Psychoanal. Quart.*, *28*:189-206.

Jung, C. G. (1909), *The Psychology of Dementia Praecox*. New York: J. Nerv. Ment. Dis. Publ. Co.

Kahn, S. & Prestwood, A. R. (1954), Group Therapy of Parents as an Adjunct to the Treatment of Schizophrenic Patients. *Psychiatry*, *17*:177-185.

Kahne, M. J. (1959), Bureaucratic Structure and Interpersonal Experience in Mental Hospitals. *Psychiatry*, *22*:363-375.

Kallmann, F. J. (1946), The Genetic Theory of Schizophrenia: An Analysis of 691 Schizophrenic Twin Index Families. *Amer. J. Psychiat.*, *103*:309-322.

———— (1953), *Heredity in Health and Mental Disorder: Principles of Psychiatric Genetics in Light of Comparative Twin Studies*. New York: W. W. Norton.

———— & Bondy, E. (1952), Applicability of the Twin Study Method in the Analysis of Variations in Mate Selection and Marital Adjustment. *Amer. J. Hum. Genet.*, *4*:209-222.

Kammerer, T., Cahn, R., & Nevers, J. (1957), Etude des mères de schizophrènes. *Congr. Rep. IInd Int. Congr. Psychiat.*, Zurich, *3*:93-96.

Kant, I. (1783), *Prolegomena to Any Future Metaphysic*. London: Macmillan, 1915.

Karon, B. & Rosberg, J. (1958), Study of the Mother-Child Relationship in a Case of Paranoid Schizophrenia. *Amer. J. Psychother.*, *12*:522-533.

Karpf, M. J. (1922), The Demoralized Family. *J. Soc. Forces*, *1*:417-420.

Karpman, B. (1953), Psychodynamics in a Fraternal Twinship Relation. *Psychoanal. Rev.*, *40*:243-267.

Kasanin, J., Knight, E., & Sage, P. (1934), The Parent-Child Relationship in Schizophrenia: I. Over-protection-rejection. *J. Nerv. Ment. Dis.*, *79*:249-263.

———— & Rosen, Z. (1933), Clinical Variables in Schizoid Personalities. *Arch. Neurol. Psychiat.*, *30*:538-566.

Katan, M. (1954), The Non-Psychotic Part of the Personality in Schizophrenia. *Int. J. Psycho-Anal.*, *35*:119-128.

Kempler, W., Iverson, R., & Beisser, A. (1962), The Adult Schizophrenic Patient and His Siblings. *Fam. Proc.*, *1*:224-235.

Kennell, J. H. (1961a), Experience with Medical School Family Study: I. A Description of the General Plan. *J. Med. Educ.*, *36*:1649-1655.

—— (1961b), Experience with Medical School Family Study: III. Student Experience and Learning. *J. Med. Educ.*, *36*:1663-1675.

Kent, E. (1949), A Study of Maladjusted Twins. *Smith Coll. Stud. Soc. Work*, *19*:63-77.

Khan, M. M. R. (1960a), Regression and Integration in the Analytic Setting. *Int. J. Psycho-Anal.*, *41*:130-146.

—— (1960b), Clinical Aspects of the Schizoid Personality: Affects and Technique. *Int. J. Psycho-Anal.*, *41*:430-437.

—— (1962), The Role of Polymorph-Perverse Body Experiences and Object Relations in Ego Integration. *Brit. J. Med. Psychol.*, *35*:245-261.

Kisker, K. P. (1960), *Der Erlebniswandel des Schizophrenen: Ein psychopathologischer Beitrag zur Psychonomie schizophrener Grundsituationen.* Berlin: Springer.

—— (1962), Schizophrenie und Familie. *Nervenarzt, 33*:13-21.

—— & Strötzel, L. (1961a), Zur vergleichenden Situationsanalyse beginnender Schizophrenien und erlebnisreaktiver Fehlentwicklungen bei Jugendlichen. *Arch. Psychiat. Nervenheilkr., 202*:1-30.

—— —— (1961b), Soziologisch-psychologische Voraussetzungen und methodische Probleme einer psychiatrischen Familienforschung. *Fortschr. Neurol. Psychiat., 29*:477-499.

Kizu, M. (1960), A Parental Study on Schizophrenia Through Rorschach Test. *J. Osaka Med. Coll.* (Osaka, Japan), *20*:1362.

Klein, D. C. & Lindemann, E. (1961), Preventive Intervention in Individual and Family Crisis Situations. In *Prevention of Mental Disorders in Children*, ed. G. Caplan. New York: Basic Books.

Klein, M. (1946), Notes on Some Schizoid Mechanisms. *Int. J. Psycho-Anal.*, *27*:99-110.

Kluckhohn, F. (1952), The American Family: Past and Present and American Women. In *Patterns for Modern Living*. Chicago: Delphian Society.

—— & Strodtbeck, F. (1957), *Variants in Value Orientations*. Evanston, Ill.: Row, Peterson.

Knight, R. P. (1953), Borderline States. *Bull. Menninger Clin., 17*:1-12.

Knöpfel, H. K. & Redlich, F. (1952-53), Psychiatrische Ausbildung in USA. *Psyche*, *7*:67-79.

Kohn, M. L. & Clausen, J. A. (1955), Social Isolation and Schizophrenia. *Amer. Sociol. Rev., 20*:265-273.

—— —— (1956), Parental Authority Behavior and Schizophrenia. *Amer. J. Orthopsychiat., 26*:297-313.

Kosaka, H. (1960a), A Study on the Family Relationship of Schizophrenics, I. *Iryo, 14*:259-271.

——— (1960b), A Study on the Family Relationship of Schizophrenics, II. *Iryo, 14*:354-360.

Kraepelin, E. (1899), Zur Diagnose und Prognose der Dementia Praecox. *Allg. Z. Psychiat., 56*:254.

Kringlen, E. (1964), Schizophrenia in Male Monozygotic Twins. *Acta Psychiat. Neurol. Scand.*, Suppl. 178.

Kronhausen, E. & Kronhausen, P. (1957), The Therapeutic Family: A Family Life Approach to the Rehabilitation of the Emotionally Disturbed. *Congr. Rep. IInd Int. Congr. Psychiat., Zurich, 3*:75-79.

Laing, R. D. (1962), *The Self and Others: Further Studies in Sanity and Madness.* London: Tavistock Publ.

Lampron, E. (1933), Children of Schizophrenic Parents: Present Mental and Social Status of 186 Cases. *Ment. Hyg., 17*:82-91.

Lane, E. & Albee, G. (1964), Early Childhood Intellectual Differences Between Schizophrenic Adults and Their Siblings. *J. Abnorm. Soc. Psychol., 68*:193-195.

Lane, R. C. & Singer, J. L. (1959), Familial Attitudes in Paranoid Schizophrenics and Normals from Two Socioeconomic Classes. *J. Abnorm. Soc. Psychol., 59*:328-339.

Langfeldt, S. (1953), Some Points Regarding the Symptomatology and Diagnosis of Schizophrenia. *Acta Psychiat. Neurol. Scand.*, Suppl. 80.

Langworthy, O. R. (1933), Development of Behavior Patterns and Myelinization of the Nervous System in the Human Fetus. *Contributions to Embryology*, No. 443. Washington, D.C.: Carnegie Institute.

Lennard, H. L., Beaulieu, M. R., & Embrey, N. G. (1965), Interaction in Families with a Schizophrenic Child. *Arch. Gen. Psychiat., 12*:166-183.

Lichtenberg, J. D. & Ping-nie, P. (1960), The Prognostic and Therapeutic Significance of the Husband-Wife Relationship for Hospitalized Schizophrenic Women. *Psychiatry, 23*:209-213.

Lidz, R. W. & Lidz, T. (1950), Eine Interpretation der Grundideen der amerikanischen Psychiatrie. *Nervenarzt, 21*:490-494.

Lidz, T. (1939), A Study of the Effect of Right Frontal Lobectomy on Intelligence and Temperament. *J. Neurol. Psychiat., 2*:211-222.

——— (1942), The Amnestic Syndrome. *Arch. Neurol. Psychiat., 47*:588-605.

——— (1949), The Analysis of a Prefrontal Lobe Syndrome and Its Theoretic Implications. *Arch. Neurol. Psychiat., 62*:1-26.

——— (1963a), *The Family and Human Adaptation.* New York: Int. Univ. Press.

——— (1963b), Family Organization and Personality Structure. In *The Family and Human Adaptation.* New York: Int. Univ. Press.

—— (1963c), The Family, Language, and Ego Functions. In *The Family and Human Adaptation*. New York: Int. Univ. Press.

—— Carter, J., Lewis, B., & Surratt, C. (1952), Effects of ACTH and Cortisone on Mood and Mentation. *Psychosom. Med., 14*:363-377.

—— & Fleck, S. (1960), Schizophrenia, Human Integration, and the Role of the Family. The *The Etiology of Schizophrenia,* ed. D. D. Jackson. New York: Basic Books.

—— Gay, J., & Tietze, C. (1942), Intelligence in Cerebral Deficit States and Schizophrenia Measured by Kohs Block Test. *Arch. Neurol. Psychiat., 48*:568-582.

—— & Kahn, R. (1946), Toxicity of Quinacrine (Atabrine) for the Central Nervous System: III. An Experimental Study of Human Subjects. *Arch. Neurol. Psychiat., 56*:284-299.

—— Miller, J., Padget, P., & Stedem, A. (1949), Muscular Atrophy and Pseudologia Fantastica Associated with Islet Cell Adenoma of the Pancreas. *Arch. Neurol. Psychiat., 62*:304-313.

Limentani, D. (1956), Symbiotic Identification in Schizophrenia. *Psychiatry, 19*:231-236.

Lindemann, E. (1950), Modifications in the Course of Ulcerative Colitis in Relationship to Changes in Life Situations and Reaction Patterns. In *Life Stress and Bodily Disease*. New York: Williams & Wilkins.

Linn, E. L. (1959), Drug Therapy, Milieu Change and Release from a Mental Hospital. AMA Arch. Neurol. Psychiat., *81*:785-794.

Locke, H. J., Sabagh, G., & Thomas, M. (1955), Primary Communication, Empathy and Family Unity. Presented at Amer. Sociol. Soc. meeting.

Lomas, P. (1961), Family Role and Identity Formation. *Int. J. Psycho-Anal., 42*:371-380.

Lovibond, S. H. (1953), The Object Sorting Test and Conceptual Thinking in Schizophrenia. *Aust. J. Psychol., 5*:52-70.

Lu, Y. C. (1962), Contradictory Parental Expectations in Schizophrenia. *Arch. Gen. Psychiat., 6*:219-234.

Lyketsos, G. (1957), Histories of Symbiotic Relationship Pattern in Schizophrenia. *Congr. Rep. IInd Int. Congr. Psychiat., Zurich, 3*:189-191.

—— (1959), On the Formation of Mother-Daughter Symbiotic Relationship Patterns in Schizophrenia. *Psychiatry, 22*:161-166.

Macalpine, I. & Hunter, R. A. (1953), The Schreber Case: A Contribution to Schizophrenia, Hypochondria, and Psychosomatic Symptom-Formation. *Psychoanal. Quart., 22*:328-371.

McConaghy, N. (1959), The Use of an Object Sorting Test in Elucidating the Hereditary Factor in Schizophrenia. *J. Neurol. Neurosurg. Psychiat., 22*:243-245.

McGhie, A. (1961), A Comparative Study of the Mother-Child Relationship in Schizophrenia: I. The Interview. *Brit. J. Med. Psychol.*, *34*:195-208.

McKeown, J. E. (1950), The Behavior of Parents of Schizophrenic, Neurotic, and Normal Children. *Amer. J. Sociol.*, *56*:175-179.

Main, T. (1951), *Five Year Report of the Cassel Hospital.* London: Hodge & Chilver.

Mangus, A. R. (1952), Family Impacts on Mental Health. *Marriage and Family Living, 14*:1-6.

Mark, J. D. (1953), The Attitudes of Mothers of Male Schizophrenics Toward Child Behavior. *J. Abnorm. Soc. Psychol.*, *48*:185-189.

Matte-Blanco, I. (1957), A Study of Schizophrenic Thinking: Its Expression in Terms of Symbolic Logic and Its Representation in Terms of Multi-dimensional Space. *Congr. Rep. IInd Int. Congr. Psychiat.*, *Zurich, 1*:254-259.

Mead, G. H. (1934), *Mind, Self and Society.* Chicago: Univ. Chicago Press.

Mendell, D. & Fisher, S. (1956), An Approach to Neurotic Behavior in Terms of a Three Generation Family Model. *J. Nerv. Ment. Dis.*, *123*:171-180.

Meyer, A. (1906), Fundamental Concepts of Dementia Praecox. *Brit. Med. J.*, *2*:757-760.

—— (1910), The Dynamic Interpretation of Dementia Praecox. *Amer. J. Psychol.*, *21*:385-402.

Meyer-Gross, W., et al. (1955), *Clinical Psychiatry.* London: Cassel.

Meyers, D. & Goldfarb, W. (1961), Studies of Perplexity in Mothers of Schizophrenic Children. *Amer. J. Orthopsychiat.*, *31*:551-564.

Meyers, J. & Roberts, B. (1959), *Family and Class Dynamics in Mental Illness.* New York: Wiley.

Meyerson, A. (1940), The Total Push Method Schema for Recording Certain Important Attitudes in Chronic Schizophrenia. *Amer. J. Psychiat.*, *96*:935-943.

Midelfort, C. F. (1957), *The Family in Psychotherapy.* New York: McGraw-Hill.

Milici, P. & Von Salzen, C. (1938), Situational Schizophrenia. *Psychiat. Quart., 12*:650-668.

Miller, N. & Dollard, J. (1941), *Social Learning and Imitation.* New Haven: Yale Univ. Press.

Modell, A. H. (1956), Some Recent Psychoanalytic Theories of Schizophrenia. *Psychoanal. Rev.*, *43*:181-194.

Mohr, J. (1956), Research in a Medical Setting. *Soc. Work, 1*:70-77.

Morris, G. O. & Wynne, L. C. (1965), Schizophrenic Offspring and Parental Styles of Communication: A Predictive Study Using Excerpts of Family Therapy Recordings. *Psychiatry*, 28:19-44.

Muller, H. J. (1925), Mental Traits and Heredity. *J. Hered.*, 16:443-448.

—— (1949), Progress and Prospects in Human Genetics. *Amer. J. Hum. Genet.*, 1:1-18.

Murphy, B. W. (1952), The Genesis of Schizoid Personality: A Study of Two Cases Developing Schizophrenia. *Psychiat. Quart.*, 26:450-461.

Nakajima, G. (1960), A Study of Schizophrenics and the Intrafamilial Relationships. *J. Nagoya Med. Coll.* (Nagoya, Japan), 81:73.

Newell, H. & Lidz, T. (1946), The Toxicity of Atabrine to the Central Nervous System: I. Toxic Psychoses. II. Convulsions. *Amer. J. Psychiat.*, 102:805-818.

Niederland, W. G. (1951), Three Notes on the Schreber Case. *Psychoanal. Quart.*, 20:579-591.

—— (1959), Schreber: Father and Son. *Psychoanal. Quart.*, 28:151-169.

—— (1960), Schreber's Father. *J. Amer. Psychoanal. Assn.*, 8:492-499.

—— (1963), Further Data and Memorabilia Pertaining to the Schreber Case. *Int. J. Psycho-Anal.*, 44:201-207.

Nielsen, C. (1954), The Childhood of Schizophrenics. *Acta Psychiat. Neurol. Scand.*, 29:281-289.

Nuffield, E. (1954), The Schizogenic Mother. *Med. J. Australia*, 2:283-286.

Nydes, J. (1963), Schreber, Parricide, and Paranoid-Masochism. *Int. J. Psycho-Anal.*, 44:208-212.

Odenwald, R. P. (1957), The Father's Role in the Development of Schizophrenia. *Congr. Rep. IInd Int. Congr. Psychiat.*, Zurich, 3:462-469.

Oltman, J. E., McGarry, J. J., & Friedman, S. (1952), Parental Deprivation and "Broken Home" in Dementia Praecox and Other Mental Disorders. *Amer. J. Psychiat.*, 108:685-693.

O'Neal, P. & Robins, L. (1958), Childhood Patterns Predictive of Adult Schizophrenia: A 30-Year Follow-up Study. *Amer. J. Psychiat.*, 115:385-391.

Opler, M. K. (1957), Schizophrenia and Culture. *Sci. Amer.*, 197:103-110.

—— (1959), The Cultural Backgrounds of Mental Health. Introduction to *Culture and Mental Health*, ed. M. Opler. New York: Macmillan.

Orr, D. (1941), A Psychoanalytic Study of a Fraternal Twin. *Psychoanal. Quart.*, 10:284-296.

Osborn, L. A. (1945), Five Psychotic Sisters. *J. Nerv. Ment. Dis.*, 101:158-165.

Osgood, C., Suci, G., & Tannenbaum, P. (1957), *The Measurement of Meaning*. Urbana, Ill.: Univ. Illinois Press.

Parsons, T. (1953), The Superego and the Theory of Social System. In *Working Papers in the Theory of Action,* eds. T. Parsons, R. Bales, & E. Shils. Glencoe, Ill.: Free Press.

———— (1954), The Incest Taboo in Relation to Social Structure and the Socialization of the Child. *Brit. J. Sociol.,* 5:101-117.

———— (1958), Social Structure and the Development of Personality: Freud's Contribution to the Integration of Psychology and Sociology. *Psychiatry,* 21:321-340.

———— & Bales, R. (1955), *Family, Socialization and Interaction Process.* Glencoe, Ill.: Free Press.

———— & Fox, R. (1952), Illness, Therapy, and the Modern Urban American Family. *J. Soc. Issues,* 8:31-44.

Paul, J. R. (1950), Preventive Medicine at Yale University School of Medicine, 1940-1949. *Yale J. Biol. Med.,* 22:199-211.

Peabody, F. W. (1927), Care of the Patient. *J. Amer. Med. Assn.,* 88:877-882.

Penrose, L. S. (1945), Survey of Cases of Familial Mental Illness. *Dig. Neurol. Psychiat.,* 13:644.

Ping-nie, P. (1960), The Use of Patient-Family-Doctor Interviews to Facilitate the Schizophrenic Patient's Return to the Community. *Psychiatry,* 23:199-207.

Plank, R. (1953), The Family Constellation of a Group of Schizophrenic Patients. *Amer. J. Orthopsychiat.,* 23:817-825.

Pollak, O. (1957), Some Conceptual Steps Toward a Theoretical Framework for Studying Family Situations and Child Development. *Children,* 4:169-173.

Pollin, W., Stabenau, J., & Tupin, J. (1965), Family Studies with Identical Twins Discordant for Schizophrenia. *Psychiatry,* 28:60-78.

Pollock, H. M. & Malzberg, B. (1940), Hereditary and Environmental Factors in the Causation of Manic-Depressive Psychoses and Dementia Praecox. *Amer. J. Psychiat.,* 96:1227-1243.

———— ———— & Fuller, R. G. (1939), *Heredity and Environmental Factors in the Causation of Manic-Depressive Psychoses and Dementia Praecox.* Utica, N.Y.: State Hospitals Press.

Prout, C. T. & White, M. A. (1950), A Controlled Study of Personality Relationships in Mothers of Schizophrenic Male Patients. *Amer. J. Psychiat.,* 107:251-256.

———— ———— (1956), The Schizophrenic's Sibling. *J. Nerv. Ment. Dis.,* 123:162-170.

Querido, A. (1956), Early Diagnosis and Treatment Services. In *The Elements of a Community Mental Health Program.* New York: Milbank Memorial Fund.

Rapaport, D., Gill, M., & Schafer, R. (1945), *Diagnostic Psychological Testing*, Vol. I. Chicago: Year Book Publishers.

Redlich, F. C. (1952), The Concept of Schizophrenia and Its Implication for Therapy. In *Psychotherapy with Schizophrenics*, ed. E. B. Brody & F. C. Redlich. New York: Int. Univ. Press.

Reichard, S. & Tillman, C. (1950), Patterns of Parent-Child Relationships in Schizophrenia. *Psychiatry*, *13*:247-257.

Rhinehart, J. (1961), Genesis of Overt Incest. *Comprehen. Psychiat.*, *2*:338-349.

Richardson, H. B. (1945), *Patients Have Families*. New York: Commonwealth Fund.

Rioch, D. (1961), The Sense and the Noise. *Psychiatry*, Suppl. to Vol. 24, No. 2, pp. 7-18.

Riskin, J. (1963), Methodology for Studying Family Interaction. *Arch. Gen. Psychiat.*, *8*:343-348.

Roberts, A. L. (1940), Three Schizophrenic Brothers. *Med. Bull. Vet. Admin.*, *16*:278-279.

Roberts, B. H. & Myers, J. K. (1955), Schizophrenia in the Youngest Male Child of the Lower Middle Class. *Amer. J. Psychiat.*, *112*:129-134.

Rodnick, E. & Garmezy, N. (1957), An Experimental Approach to the Study of Motivation in Schizophrenia. In *Nebraska Symposium on Motivation*, ed. M. R. Jones. Lincoln, Nebraska: Univ. Nebraska Press.

Rosanoff, A. J., Handy, L. M., Plesset, I., & Brush, S. (1934), The Etiology of So-Called Schizophrenic Psychoses: With Special Reference to Their Occurrence in Twins. *Amer. J. Psychiat.*, *91*:247-286.

Rose, J. A. (1952), The Relation of the Family to the Hospital. *Med. Clin. No. Amer.*, *36*:1551-1554.

Rosen, J. N. (1947), The Treatment of Schizophrenic Psychosis by Direct Analytic Therapy. *Psychiat. Quart.*, *21*:3-25.

―――― (1948), In panel on Theory and Treatment of Schizophrenia. Summary in *Bull. Amer. Psychoanal. Assn.*, *4*:15.

―――― (1953), *Direct Analysis: Selected Papers*. New York: Grune & Stratton.

―――― (1963), *The Concept of Early Maternal Environment in Direct Psychoanalysis*. Doylestown, Penna.: Doylestown Foundation.

Rosenbaum, C. P. (1961), Patient-Family Similarities in Schizophrenia. *Arch. Gen. Psychiat.*, *5*:120-126.

Rosenfeld, H. (1947), Analysis of a Schizophrenic State with Depersonalisation. *Int. J. Psycho-Anal.*, *28*:130-139.

―――― (1952), Notes on the Psycho-Analysis of the Super-Ego Conflict of an Acute Schizophrenic Patient. *Int. J. Psycho-Anal.*, *33*:111-131.

―――― (1954), Considerations Regarding the Psycho-Analytic Approach to Acute and Chronic Schizophrenia. *Int. J. Psycho-Anal.*, *35*:135-140.

Rosenthal, D. (1959), Some Factors Associated with Concordance and Discordance with Respect to Schizophrenia in Monozygotic Twins. *J. Nerv. Ment. Dis.*, *129*:1-10.

—— (1960), Confusion of Identity and the Frequency of Schizophrenia in Twins. *Arch. Gen. Psychiat.*, *3*:297-304.

Rubenstein, C. R. & Lasswell, H. D. *Psychiatric Treatment as a Political Process.* To be Published.

Rud, F. (1951), The Social Psychopathology of the Schizophrenic States. *J. Clin. Exp. Psychopath.*, *12*:67-78.

Ryckoff, I., Day, J., & Wynne, L. C. (1959), Maintenance of Stereotyped Roles in the Families of Schizophrenics. *Arch. Gen. Psychiat.*, *1*:109-114.

Sampson, H., Messinger, S., & Towne, R. D. (1961a), Two Types of Schizophrenic Crises in Women. *Bull. Menninger Clin.*, *25*:296-306.

—— —— —— (1961b), The Mental Hospital and Marital Family Ties. *Soc. Prob.*, *9*:141-155.

Sanua, V. D. (1961), Socio-cultural Factors in Families of Schizophrenics: A Review of the Literature. *Psychiatry*, *24*:246-265.

—— (1962), Comparison of Jewish and Protestant Paranoid and Catatonic Patients. *Dis. Nerv. Sys.*, *23*:320-328.

—— (1963), The Socio-Cultural Aspects of Schizophrenia: A Comparison of Protestant and Jewish Schizophrenics. *Int. J. Soc. Psychiat.*, *9*:27-36.

Satir, V. (1963), Schizophrenia and Family Therapy. In *Social Work Practice, 1963.* New York: Columbia Univ. Press.

—— (1964), *Conjoint Family Therapy.* Palo Alto: Science and Behavior Books.

Schachtel, E. (1959), The Development of Focal Attention and the Emergence of Reality. In *Metamorphosis: On the Development of Affect, Perception, Attention and Memory.* New York: Basic Books.

Schafer, R. (1949), Psychological Tests in Clinical Research. *J. Consult. Psychol.*, *13*:328-334.

Schaffer, L., Wynne, L., Day, J., Ryckoff, I., & Halperin, A. (1962), On the Nature and Sources of the Psychiatrist's Experience with the Family of the Schizophrenic. *Psychiatry*, *25*:32-45.

Scher, J. M. (1957), Indirection: A Communicative Basis for a Theory of Schizophrenia. *Congr. Rep. IInd Int. Congr. Psychiat.*, *Zurich*, *3*:69-74.

Schlegel, W. S. (1955), *Beiträge zur Sexualforschung.* Stuttgart: Enke.

—— (1957), *Körper und Seele: Eine Konstitutionslehre für Ärzte, Juristen, Pädagogen und Theologen.* Stuttgart: Enke.

Schulz, B. (1940a), Kinder schizophrener Elternpaare. *Z. Neurol. Psychiat.*, *168*:332-381.

—— (1940b), Kinder von Elternpaaren mit einem schizophrenen und einem affektivpsychotischen Partner. *Z. Neurol. Psychiat.*, *170*:441-514.

Searles, H. F. (1958), Positive Feelings in the Relationship Between the Schizophrenic and His Mother. *Int. J. Psycho-Anal.*, *39*:569-586.

—— (1959), The Effort to Drive the Other Person Crazy: An Element in the Aetiology and Psychotherapy of Schizophrenia. *Brit. J. Med. Psychol.*, *32*:1-18.

Semrad, E. V., Menzer, D., Mann, J., & Standish, C. (1952), A Study of the Doctor-Patient Relationship in Psychotherapy of Psychotic Patients. *Psychiatry*, *15*:377-384.

Senf, R., Huston, P. E., & Cohen, B. (1955), Thinking Deficit in Schizophrenia and Changes with Amytal. *J. Abnorm. Soc. Psychol.*, *50*:383-387.

Shapiro, D. S. (1957), Perceptions of Significant Family and Environmental Relationships in Aggressive and Withdrawn Children. *J. Consult. Psychol.*, *21*:381-385.

Shepherd, I. L. & Guthrie, G. M. (1959), Attitudes of Mothers of Schizophrenic Patients. *J. Clin. Psychol.*, *15*:212-215.

Shugart, G. (1957), Casework with Parents of Psychotic Children. *Soc. Casew.*, *38*:8-15.

Silverman, L. H. & Silverman, D. K. (1962), Ego Impairment in Schizophrenia as Reflected in the Object Sorting Test. *J. Abnorm. Soc. Psychol.*, *64*:381-385.

Simmons, L. W. & Wolff, H. G. (1954), *Social Science in Medicine*. New York: Russell Sage Foundation.

Singer, M. T. (1963), Personality Measurements in the Aged. In *Human Aging*, ed. J. Birren, R. Butler, S. Greenhouse, L. Sokoloff, & M. Yarrow. Bethesda, Md.: Public Health Service Publ. #986.

—— & Wynne, L. (1963), Differentiating Characteristics of the Parents of Childhood Schizophrenics, Childhood Neurotics and Young Adult Schizophrenics. *Amer. J. Psychiat.*, *120*:234-243.

—— —— (1965a), Thought Disorder and Family Relations of Schizophrenics: III. Methodology Using Projective Techniques. *Arch. Gen. Psychiat.*, *12*:187-200.

—— —— (1965b), Thought Disorder and Family Relations of Schizophrenics: IV. Results and Implications. *Arch. Gen. Psychiat.*, *12*:201-212.

Sivadon, P. & Mises, R. (1954), Le Milieu Familial du Schizophrène (Reflections sur un Cas Clinique). *L'Evol. Psychiat.*, *19*:147-157.

Slater, E. (1953), *Psychotic and Neurotic Illness in Twins*. London: H. M. Stationery Office.

Solomon, H. C. (1958), The American Psychiatric Association in Relation to American Psychiatry. *Amer. J. Psychiat., 115*:1-9.

Solomon, R. & Bliss, E. L. (1956), Simultaneous Occurrence of Schizophrenia in Identical Twins. *Amer. J. Psychiat., 112*:912-915.

Sonne, J. C., Speck, R. V., & Jungreis, J. (1962), The Absent-Member Maneuver as a Resistance in Family Therapy of Schizophrenia. *Fam. Proc., 1*:44-62.

Southard, S. (1957), *The Family and Mental Illness*. Philadelphia: Westminster Press.

Spiegel, J. P. (1954), New Perspectives in the Study of the Family. *Marriage and Family Living, 16*:4-12.

—— (1957), The Resolution of Role Conflict Within the Family. *Psychiatry, 20*:1-16.

—— (1958), Homeostatic Mechanisms Within the Family. In *The Family in Contemporary Society*, ed. I. Galdston. New York: Int. Univ. Press.

—— & Bell, N. W. (1959), The Family of the Psychiatric Patient. In *American Handbook of Psychiatry*, ed. S. Arieti. New York: Basic Books.

—— & Kluckhohn, F. (Chairmen) Committee on the Family, Group for the Advancement of Psychiatry (1954), *Integration and Conflict in Family Behavior*. Report 27. Topeka, Kansas: Group for the Advancement of Psychiatry.

Spitz, R. A. (1937), Familienneurose und neurotische Familie. *Int. Z. Psychoanal., 23*:548-560.

Stabenau, J. R., Tupin, J., Werner, H., & Pollin, W. (1965), Comparative Study of Families of Schizophrenics, Delinquents, and Normals. *Psychiatry, 28*:45-59.

Stanton, A. H. (1961), Milieu Therapy and the Development of Insight. *Psychiatry*, Suppl. to Vol. 24, No. 2, pp. 19-29.

—— & Schwartz, M. S. (1954), *The Mental Hospital: A Study of Institutional Participation in Psychiatric Illness and Treatment*. New York: Basic Books.

Stierlin, H. (1959), The Adaptation to the "Stronger" Person's Reality: Some Aspects of the Symbolic Relationship of the Schizophrenic. *Psychiatry, 22*:143-152.

—— (1963a), Treatment Dilemmas with Psychotic and Sociopathic Patients. *Brit. J. Med. Psychol., 36*:75-84.

—— (1963b), Familie und Schizophrenie. *Nervenarzt, 34*:495-500.

Strauss, A. & Sabshin, M. (1961), Large State Mental Hospitals. *Arch. Gen. Psychiat., 5*:565-577.

Sullivan, H. S. (1925-1926), Peculiarity of Thought in Schizophrenia. *Amer. J. Psychiat., 82*:21-86.

——— (1940), Conceptions of Modern Psychiatry: Therapeutic Conceptions. *Psychiatry, 3*:87-117.

——— (1946-1947), *The Interpersonal Theory of Psychiatry*, ed. H. Perry & M. Gawel. New York: W. W. Norton, 1953.

Suzuki, K. (1962), The Difference in Mother-Child Relationship Between Schizophrenics and Neurotics Can Be Measured Using Interpersonal Check List by Leavy. *Psychiat. et Neurol. Japonica* (Tokyo), *64*:1103.

Szalita-Pemow, A. (1951), Remarks on Pathogenesis and Treatment of Schizophrenia. *Psychiatry, 14*:295-300.

Szasz, T. (1957), A Contribution to the Psychology of Schizophrenia. *AMA Arch. Neurol. Psychiat.*, 77:420-436.

Szurek, S. A. (1952), Some Lessons from Efforts at Psychotherapy with Parents. *Amer. J. Psychiat.*, 109:296-302.

Tafuse, H. (1960), A Familial Study on Schizophrenia: An Investigation of Parent-Child Relationship Chiefly Through Rorschach's Test. *Psychiat. et Neurol. Japonica* (Tokyo), *62*:737.

Tennant, M. A. (1954), Psychiatric Social Work in a Private Mental Hospital. *J. Psychiat. Soc. Work*, 23:234-241.

Terry, G. C. & Rennie, T. A. C. (1938), *Analysis of Parergasia*. Nerv. Ment. Dis. Monogr. No. 64.

Thorne, F. (1957), Epidemiological Studies of Chronic Frustration-Hostility-Aggression States. *Amer. J. Psychiat.*, 113:717-721.

Tienari, P. (1963), Psychiatric Illness in Identical Twins. *Acta Psychiat. Neurol. Scand.*, Suppl. 171.

Tietze, T. (1949), A Study of Mothers of Schizophrenic Patients. *Psychiatry, 12*:55-65.

Toman, W. (1961), *Family Constellation*. New York: Springer.

Towne, R. D. & Afterman, J. (1955), Psychosis in Males Related to Parenthood. *Bull. Menninger Clin.*, 19:19-26.

——— Sampson, H., & Messinger, S. (1961), Schizophrenia and the Marital Family: Identification Crises. *J. Nerv. Ment. Dis.*, 133:423-429.

Tudor, G. E. (1952), A Sociopsychiatric Nursing Approach to Intervention in a Problem of Mutual Withdrawal on a Mental Hospital Ward. *Psychiatry, 15*:193-217.

Vogel, E. & Bell, N. (1960), The Emotionally Disturbed Child as the Family Scapegoat. In *A Modern Introduction to the Family*, ed. N. Bell & E. Vogel. Glencoe, Ill.: Free Press.

Vygotsky, L. D. (1934), Thought in Schizophrenia, tr. J. Kasanin. *Arch. Neurol. Psychiat.*, 31:1063-1077.

Wahl, C. W. (1954), Some Antecedent Factors in the Family Histories of

392 Schizophrenics. *Amer. J. Psychiat.*, *110*:668-676.

——— (1956), Some Antecedent Factors in the Family Histories of 568 Male Schizophrenics of the United States Navy. *Amer. J. Psychiat.*, *113*:201-210.

Warner, S. L., Fleming, B., & Bullock, S. (1962), The Philadelphia Program for Home Psychiatric Evaluations, Precare and Involuntary Hospitalization. *Amer. J. Publ. Hlth.*, *52*:29-38.

Weakland, J. H. (1960), The "Double-Bind" Hypothesis of Schizophrenia and Three-Party Interaction. Chapter 13 in *The Etiology of Schizophrenia*, ed. D. D. Jackson. New York: Basic Books.

——— (1962), Family Therapy as a Research Arena. *Fam. Proc.*, *1*:63-68.

——— & Fry, W. (1962), Letters of Mothers of Schizophrenics. *Amer. J. Orthopsychiat.*, *32*:604-623.

——— & Jackson, D. D. (1958), Patient and Therapist Observations on the Circumstances of a Schizophrenic Episode. *AMA Arch. Neurol. Psychiat.*, *79*:554-574.

Weatherly, J. & Deabler, H. L. (1954), Schizophrenia in Identical Twins One of Whom was Lobotomized. *J. Nerv. Ment. Dis.*, *120*:262-267.

Weblin, J. (1962), Communication and Schizophrenic Behavior. *Fam. Proc.*, *1*:5-14.

Wedge, B. & Fry, C. (1955), Schizophrenic Reactions As Developmental Crises. Presented at meeting of Amer. Psychiat. Assn.

Weinberg, S. K. (1955), *Incest Behavior*. New York: Citadel Press.

Weiss, V. W. & Munroe, R. R. (1959), A Framework for Understanding Family Dynamics. Parts I & II. *Soc. Casewk.*, *40*:3-9, 80-87.

White, R. (1963), The Schreber Case Reconsidered in the Light of Psychosocial Concepts. *Int. J. Psycho-Anal.*, *44*:213-221.

Whorf, B. (1956), *Language, Thought and Reality: Selected Writings of Benjamin Lee Whorf*, ed. J. Carroll. New York: M.I.T. Press and Wiley.

Willi, J. (1962), Die Schizophrenie in ihrer Auswirkung auf die Eltern: Untersuchung der Eltern von 15 jugendlichen Schizophrenen. *Schweiz. Arch. Neurol., Neurochir. Psychiat.*, *89*:426-463.

Winnicott, D. W. (1956), Primary Maternal Preoccupation. In *Collected Papers*. London: Tavistock Publ., 1958.

——— (1960), The Theory of the Parent-Infant Relationship. *Int. J. Psycho-Anal.*, *41*:585-595.

Wood, E. C., Rakusin, J., & Morse, E. (1960), Interpersonal Aspects of Psychiatric Hospitalization: I. The Admission. *Arch. Gen. Psychiat.*, *3*:632-641.

——— ——— ——— (1962), Interpersonal Aspects of Psychiatric Hospitalization: II. Some Correlations Between the Admission Circumstances and the Hospital Treatment Experience. *Arch. Gen. Psychiat.*, 6:55-61.

—— —— —— & Singer, R. (1962), Interpersonal Aspects of Psychiatric Hospitalization: III. The Follow-Up Survey. *Arch. Gen. Psychiat.*, 6:62-71.

Wynne, L. C., Day, J., Hirsch, S., & Ryckoff, I. (1957), The Family Relations of a Set of Monozygotic Quadruplet Schizophrenics. *Congr. Rep. IInd Int. Congr. Psychiat., Zurich*, 2:43-49.

—— Ryckoff, I., Day, J., & Hirsch, S. (1958), Pseudo-Mutuality in the Family Relations of Schizophrenics. *Psychiatry*, 21:205-220.

—— & Singer, M. T. (1963a), Thought Disorder and Family Relations of Schizophrenics: I. A Research Strategy. *Arch. Gen. Psychiat.*, 9:191-198.

—— —— (1963b), Thought Disorder and Family Relations of Schizophrenics: II. A Classification of Forms of Thinking. *Arch. Gen. Psychiat.*, 9:199-206.

Zelditch, M. (1955), Role Differentiation in the Nuclear Family: A Comparative Study. In *Family, Socialization and Interaction Process*, ed. T. Parsons & R. Bales. Glencoe, Ill.: Free Press.

Name Index

Abraham, K., 16, 99, 437
Abrahams, J., 119, 262, 290, 437
Ackerman, N. W., 15, 134, 147, 289, 437
Afterman, J., 461
Alanen, Y. O., 14, 26, 262, 290, 303, 315, 333, 397, 437
Albee, G., 452
Albert, R., 448
Alexander, F., 438
Aries, P., 438
Arieti, S., 438
Arthur, S. C., 438

Baker, G., 426, 442
Baldamus, W., 438
Bales, R., 15, 102, 104, 134, 135, 147, 224, 269, 353, 367, 456
Basamania, B., 440
Bateson, G., 14, 180, 333, 352, 427, 438
Bauer, F. C., 438
Bauer, W., 272, 438
Baxter, J. C., 438
Beaulieu, M. R., 452
Beck, S. J., 438-439
Becker, J., 438
Beckett, P. G. S., 430, 439, 449
Behrens, M., 437
Beisser, A., 450
Bell, J. E., 439
Bell, N., 439, 460, 461
Bently, 353
Beres, D., 439
Binswanger, L., 439
Bion, W. R., 439
Bleuler, E., 170, 439
Bleuler, M., 75, 439
Bliss, E. L., 206, 460
Block, J. & J., 439, 449
Blum, G. S., 439

Boisen, A. T., 440
Bondy, E., 205, 450
Bonner, H., 440
Boszormenyi-Nagy, I., 440
Bott, E., 96, 147, 440
Bour, P., 440
Bowen, M., 14, 180, 440
Boyd, I., 444
Brecher, S., 440
Brodey, W., 440
Brody, E. B., 99, 119, 120, 440
Brody, J. P., 440
Brooks, G. W., 286, 443
Bross, R. B., 440
Brown, R., 373, 440
Bruch, H., 351, 352, 421, 426, 440-441
Brush, S., 457
Buell, B., 134, 441
Bullock, S., 462
Burgess, E. W., 441
Burlingham, D. T., 441
Burnham, D. L., 441

Cahn, R., 450
Cameron, J. L., 99, 445
Cameron, N., 163, 441
Cammer, L., 441
Caputo, D. V., 441
Carmen, L., 448
Carr, A., 441, 447
Carroll, E. J., 441
Carroll, J. B., 441
Carter, J., 453
Caudill, W., 119, 272, 441
Cheek, F. E., 441
Chein, I., 441
Chrzanowski, G., 442
Clarke, A., 446
Clausen, J. A., 338, 339, 442, 451

465

Subject Index

Problems relating to the organization of this study are indexed under: *Study*.
The specific families on which the study is based are indexed by name under:
Families in this study.

MONOGRAPH SERIES ON SCHIZOPHRENIA

No. 1—DEMENTIA PRAECOX OR THE GROUP OF SCHIZOPHRENIAS
By EUGEN BLEULER
Translated by Joseph Zinkin
Foreword by Nolan D. C. Lewis

No. 2—SYMBOLIC REALIZATION
A New Method of Psychotherapy Applied to a Case of Schizophrenia
By M. A. SECHEHAYE

No. 3—PSYCHOTHERAPY WITH SCHIZOPHRENICS
Edited by EUGENE B. BRODY and FREDRICK C. REDLICH
Foreword by Robert P. Knight

No. 4—A WAY TO THE SOUL OF THE MENTALLY ILL
By GERTRUD SCHWING
Translated by Rudolf Ekstein and Bernard H. Hall
Foreword by Frieda Fromm-Reichmann

No. 5—THE NONHUMAN ENVIRONMENT
In Normal Development and in Schizophrenia
By HAROLD F. SEARLES

No. 6—THE EXPERIENCE OF REALITY IN CHILDHOOD SCHIZOPHRENIA
By AUSTIN M. DES LAURIERS